# Noyes'
# ORAL HISTOLOGY
# AND EMBRYOLOGY

## With Laboratory Directions

*Eighth Edition, Edited and Revised*

BY

### ISAAC SCHOUR, B.S., D.D.S., M.S., Ph.D., Sc.D.

*Professor of Histology and Head of Department and Dean, University of Illinois, College of Dentistry.*

*With 345 Illustrations on 295 Figures and 21 Plates, 12 in Color*

## LEA & FEBIGER

PHILADELPHIA 1960

611.314
N 954

*Eighth Edition*

---

Copyright © 1960 by Lea & Febiger
All Rights Reserved.

---

*First Edition, 1912*

*Second Edition, 1915*

*Third Edition, 1921*

*Fourth Edition, 1929*

*Fifth Edition, 1938*

*Sixth Edition, 1948*

*Seventh Edition, 1953*

Library of Congress Catalog Card Number: 60–11022

Printed in the United States of America

To my Father

# Dr. Edmund Noyes

Whose long and active professional career was devoted,
without personal ambition for selfish advancement, to
the good of the Dental Profession, and whose
unselfishness and sacrifice have made
possible all that I have done
or may do.

FREDERICK B. NOYES

# Preface to the Eighth Edition

THE exhausting of seven editions and the necessity of reprinting each edition indicate that the book has been of assistance to students of Oral Histology. In preparing the eighth edition, the original plan of Dr. Frederick B. Noyes, now retired, to keep the book a simple and straightforward statement of current conceptions of the structure and functions of the tissues has been followed. Three colored plates and 40 new figures and illustrations were added to replace old illustrations and to demonstrate new findings. Six tables were prepared to increase the clarity of the text.

Special effort was placed on stimulating the student to think in biologic terms, to focus his attention to the total functional masticatory apparatus and to recognize the intimate interdependence between the oral cavity and the rest of the body. With this in mind chapters were added on the histology of the temporomandibular joint and on experimental dental histology.

A text book should be used as an aid in acquiring knowledge and never accepted as an authority. It is an inventory of our knowledge of today and a base line for further investigations. The function of a text is so well stated by Patten in the first paragraph of the preface to the student for his text book, *Embryology of the Pig,* that it is quoted with the change of one word.

"You and I are to start out together to explore some of the regions of histology (embryology). Still vivid memories of the erratic progress of my own first expeditions of that kind have led me to offer my services to you. Perhaps I can help you to avoid some of the difficulties I encountered and lead you to points of interest by routes less devious than you might otherwise find. But it is your own expedition. I am merely a guide. I can show you the passes to understand but you must climb them. I can lead you to worthwhile things but you yourself must unearth them and carry them away."

When you read a positive statement in this book please remember that it is made after many years of study of the tissues, and all available facts, but tomorrow facts may be developed that will make it necessary to change our views. It is very easy to misinterpret what is seen through a microscope. In fact, in learning to use a microscope one must learn to interpret the meaning just as a baby learns to interpret direct ocular impressions. The repetition of a thousand mistaken observations does not establish a fact. Probably no field of histology offers the difficulties of interpretation and technique that are encountered in the study of the oral tissues. It should stimulate the interest of the dental student to realize that in Oral Histology you arrive on the frontier of the known very soon.

Current trends in oral histology, as in general histology and anatomy, show an increasing shift from the purely morphologic description toward the physiologic and experimental methods of analysis. Today oral histology is inseparable from histophysiology and closely interdependent with other biologic fields such as nutrition and endocrines.

In this edition, therefore, brief consideration was given to findings that have been made possible by electron microscopy, histochemistry, and other recent developments in biologic and physical methods. It is interesting that, while these developments have led us to a molecular level of observation, the new findings for the most part represent additions to rather than substitutions for current knowledge.

Histophysiologic remarks and clinical considerations have been added in a number of chapters. These seemed to be appropriate in view of the growing tendency to bring the dental student in contact with the patient even in his freshman year. This approach facilitates the early integration of what the student learns in basic science with what he observes in the patient. In order to motivate the student to apply his histologic knowledge to clinical correlation a laboratory exercise is included on the determination of the age of the patient on the basis of the gross and microscopic analysis of extracted teeth. Recent advances in the field of dental caries have been considered in terms of new emphasis on the organic components of the enamel, on its permeability and on the nature of the membranes covering the enamel and its outer layer. Attention has also been given to the biology of the pulp and its response to physical and chemical irritants as related to cavity preparation and filling materials.

The oral histologist is equally interested in oral embryology. In the past decades dentists have sometimes taken the view that such studies were only of academic interest. But this attitude has changed with the recognition, for example, of the fact that tooth development is a life-long process and does not stop except when the tooth is extracted or the patient has completed his life span. It is true that enamel is completed early in life and is lifeless thereafter. But it is abraded throughout life. The dentin grows continuously through secondary dentin formulation; cementum increases in thickness throughout life; and the aveolar bone grows as long as the tooth functions. Not only in dental growth continuous, but eruption and attrition are life-long processes in dental development. The life history of the tooth begins before birth but it continues to unfold even in old age. For this reason, many everyday clinical conditions that present themselves can be more readily understood in terms of normal or abnormal development.

The influence of diet, calcium metabolism, the endocrines and systemic disease on the growing dental structures is the object of continuous experimental and histologic investigation. The calcification of the enamel and the dentin is being used as an index of the developmental pattern of the child. The neonatal ring which is the biologic birth certificate permanently recorded in the deciduous tooth is an interesting example of what oral histology can offer to dental and medical science. As each problem has become clarified, it has influenced and broadened the practice of dentistry.

As long as oral diagnosis is practiced prior to treatment and treatment is based on understanding of normal development and normal histologic structure, oral histology will remain an essential part of the practice of dentistry. Oral histology is still a young science. The last word in this field has not been written. Discovery continues every day, and oral histology will continue to contribute significantly to the establishment of those biologic principles that form the basis of intelligent dental practice.

The student is urged to use the bibliography. The references at the end of the chapters are made to broaden the student's view of the subject. I hope that some will find the volume a help along a road that they will continue to follow and enrich by research.

I wish to acknowledge my special indebtedness to Dr. Harry Sicher, Professor of Anatomy and Histology, School of Dentistry, Loyola University, and Dr. James Gagnon, Associate Professor of Oral Histology and Anatomy, University of Illinois, College of Dentistry, who have generously contributed to this revision of the text. I am also grateful to Drs. Verda Elizabeth James and Roy Gillette and a number of other active teachers in Oral Histology too numerous to mention who provided valuable critical and constructive suggestions. Mr. William Winn prepared new photographs and photomicrographs of human material which replace the photographs of animal specimens.

The effort has been made to give credit for material when obtained from other authors and for illustrations from sources other than the University of Illinois College of Dentistry.

I. S.

Chicago, Illinois

# Contents

# Oral Histology and Embryology

## Introduction

THE development in knowledge of the cell has had a most profound effect upon the entire practice of medicine; in fact, the progress of modern medicine has dated from the studies of cell biology, the germ theory of disease being only one of the phases of this development. In terms of the cell theory the functions of the body are but the manifest expression of the activities of millions of intimately interdependent and correlated centers of activity. If these centers or cells perform their function correctly, the functions of the body are normal, but if they fail to perform their office or work abnormally, the functions of the body are perverted. In the last analysis, then, all physiology is cell physiology, all pathology cell pathology. To modern medicine, histology, or the cell structure of the organs and tissues of the body, together with cell physiology, is the rational foundation of all practice. This is as true for the dentist as for the physician in regard to the soft tissues of the mouth and teeth that he is called upon to treat.

All tissues are made up of two structural elements—cells and intercellular substances. The cells give the vital characteristics, the intercellular substances the physical character. The cells are the active living elements, the intercellular substances are formed materials produced by the activity of the cells, and more or less dependent upon them to maintain their quality but they possess no vital properties. They surround and support the cells, and the physical characteristics are given by them. An understanding of the relation of cells and intercellular substances in the structure and function of tissues is absolutely fundamental to the study of oral histology, and should be acquired in a thorough study of general histology before the subject is undertaken.

It is important that we focus our biologic thinking in dentistry on the total functional masticatory apparatus with its related parts and its high interdependence with the rest of the body lest we become tooth-minded rather than patient-oriented. For the sake of thorough analysis we may find it necessary to study component parts separately, but it is essential that we devote equal effort in the synthesis and integration of these parts. The functional tooth is much more than the hard structure revealed upon its extraction but a living organ. Cowdry has rightly pointed out that what marks the maturity of dentistry is not so much the improvement of dental instruments and techniques but rather the increased understanding of the interdependence of the teeth and oral cavity and the rest of the body.

# CHAPTER 1

# Introduction to Embryology

**Definition.**—Embryology is the science of anatomical and functional development and may be best understood when studied on a comparative basis. Human embryology, in particular, must be based on comparative embryology, not only because of the biogenetic relationships but also because of the great difficulty in procuring early human embryos. In embryology it is found that the individual in his physical development passes through stages which correspond to the development of the species to which he belongs; in other words, ontogeny recapitulates phylogeny.

**History.**—Although it is one of the most recently developed biological sciences, embryology presents a very interesting history. With the advent of the microscope, some students advocated the doctrine of preformation, which stated that the adult organism was present in miniature form in the egg or spermatozoön. They thus arrived at the conclusion that the entire race must have been preformed in the ovary of Mother Eve. Wolff (1759) carefully observed the early stages of the chick embryo and found that the chick did not arise through preformation, but that its organs developed gradually by infolding and differentiation from unorganized tissue. This observation was incorporated in the doctrine of *epigenesis*. Wolff's findings were later supported by the work of Von Baer (1827), the father of modern embryology, who discovered the mammalian ovum and established the law that all embryos come from the three germ layers. The founding of modern human embryology is accredited to Wilhelm His, who published his "Anatomy of Human Embryos" in 1880. The more recent advances in embryology have been made possible to a considerable extent by the use of the experimental method.

## PROLIFERATION AND DIFFERENTIATION OF THE THREE PRIMARY GERM LAYERS

Since our interest naturally centers on man, it is best to emphasize those principles and facts of vertebrate embryology which bear most closely to human development. Following the fertilization of the ovum there is a process of *multiplication of cells* (proliferation) upon which another process is soon superimposed—that of *differentiation*. There is a mutual relationship between structural and functional differentiation. The latter is only foreshadowed in the early stages and becomes more evident in later development.

2 (17)

**Law of Differential Growth.**—As proliferative growth progresses, certain areas are found to be more irregular than others, and correspond to various locations and rates of activity. According to a geometric law, the volume of a sphere increases as the cube of the diameter while the surface of a sphere increases as the square of the diameter. This law is universal and its significance can be easily observed in biology. As an organism grows it must maintain a proper proportion between its surface exposure and its mass, or it will not be able to live. In the case of a unicellular organism, growth soon becomes definitely limited and life continues only by cell division. In the case of the growing embryo, the proper proportion between

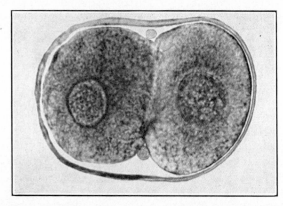

Fig. 1.—Photomicrograph of the 2-celled stage of the human zygote. × 500.
(Reproduced by the courtesy of Drs. Hertig and Rock.)

surface area and mass is maintained by the formation of surface irregularities. These are principally projections and invaginations and are brought about by certain areas growing more rapidly than others. This is called the *law of differential growth* and is a fundamental factor in development and organogenesis.

**Cleavage.**—Soon after fertilization the ovum undergoes a succession of rapid mitoses. This process is termed cleavage (Figs. 1 and 2).

**Morula and Blastocyst.**—The cells formed during cleavage are called *blastomeres*, which soon begin to rearrange themselves in order to differentiate into various groups and layers. At first the cells form a solid mass called the *morula* (because of its resemblance to a small mulberry) (Fig. 2). This stage is of short duration. In the next stage, called blastocyst, the blastomeres draw apart to form a central cavity called the segmentation cavity or *blastocoele* (Fig. 3). At this stage a mass of cells, the inner cell mass, is eccentrically attached to the inner aspect of the outer flattened cells which are called the trophoblast (Fig. 3).

**Amniotic Cavity.**—Particularly in mammals, another cavity soon appears between the cells of the inner cell mass and the trophoblast. This is the

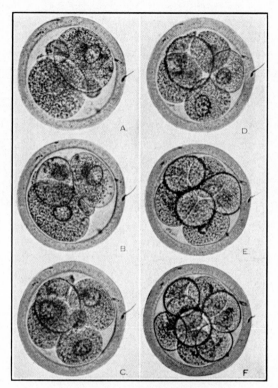

FIG. 2.—Photographs of living eggs of the macaque monkey. A—two-cell stage;
B—three-cell stage; C—four-cell stage; D—five-cell stage; E—six-cell stage; F—eight-
cell stage. (After Lewis and Hartman, 1933.) By courtesy of the Carnegie Institution
of Washington. × c. 200.

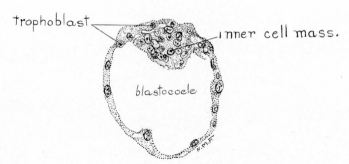

FIG. 3.—The blastodermic vesicle of the pig. (After Corner, from Patten:
Embryology of the Pig.)

amniotic cavity. The cells of the inner cell mass, which form the roof of the *blastocele,* migrate along its wall and form the primitive yolk sac. At this stage, then, the embryo consists of a two-cell layer thick plate of cells between the amniotic cavity and the primitive yolk sac. The cells forming the floor of the amniotic cavity constitute the primitive ectoderm, while the cells forming the roof of the yolk sac are the primitive endoderm (Fig. 4).

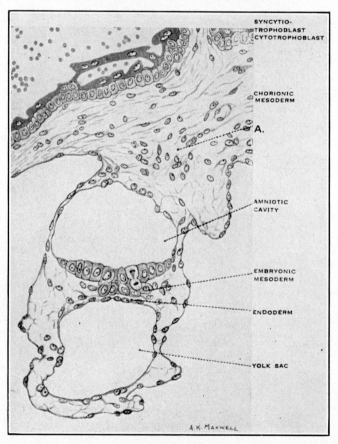

Fig. 4.—A transverse section through the posterior part of an embryo showing the primitive streak and early development of the intra-embryonic mesoderm.

*A,* mesodermal condensation in connecting stalk.  × c. 200.  (Hamilton, Boyd and Mossman's Human Embryology, courtesy of W. Heffer and Sons Ltd., England.)

*Primitive Streak.*—At one area of the ectoderm at the posterior edge of the embryonic disc, rapid proliferation of cells occurs. This area of the embryo is referred to as the primitive streak. It elongates by the backward growth of its posterior end along the axis of the future embryo. By proliferating cells in front of itself it furnishes material for the embryo anterior to it. From the sides of the primitive streak between the ectoderm and entoderm, cells proliferate laterally and form the middle germ layer—the *meso-derm* (Fig. 4). The *head process* is also formed from the anterior end of the primitive streak, and the ectoderm in this region begins to thicken to form the *neural plate*, which is the anlage of the nervous system (Fig. 5). Beneath this anlage there is another area of rapid cell proliferation, the cells of which form a cylindric rod or chord and constitute the *notochord*. The latter is the primitive vertebral column, and assumes its position between the ner-

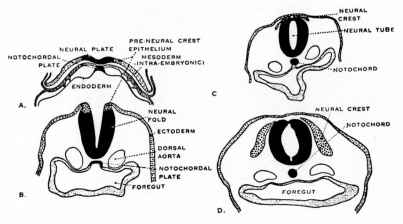

FIG. 5.—Transverse sections of four early human embryos to show origin of neural crest. Based on: A—Heuser pre-somite; B—Payne 7-somite; C—Corner 10-somite; and D—Heuser 14-somite embryos. (Hamilton, Boyd and Mossman's Human Embryology, courtesy of W. Heffer and Sons, Ltd., England.)

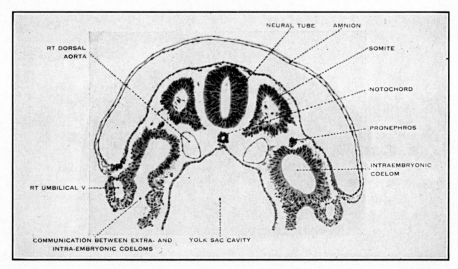

FIG. 6.—A drawing of a transverse section of a 14-somite human embryo at the level of the 8th somite showing the relationships of the structures. On the left side of the figure the intra-embryonic cœlom is in communication with the extra-embryonic cœlom (after Heuser, 1930). × c.140.

vous and digestive systems. The streak is used up in the production of the embryo. The formation of germ layers and primitive streak is called gastrulation.

*Mesoderm.*—The mesodermal cells grow out laterally from the sides of the *primitive streak* between the ectoderm and endoderm. Next to the midline they form into plates, which later constitute the dorsal mesoderm and organize into *somites* (Fig. 6). Lateral to this region the *mesodermal plates* narrow down and form the *intermediate mesoderm* or *nephrotomic plates*, which will give rise to the *nephric tubules*. Toward the distal end the mesodermal folds split into two layers with a space between them. The layer next to the ectoderm will form the *somatic mesoderm* and the layer next to the entoderm will form the *splanchnic mesoderm*. The space between the two mesodermic layers is the cœlomic or body cavity. During later development the somatic mesoderm is closely associated with the ectoderm and the two together form the *somatopleure*. Likewise the splanchnic mesoderm, together with the entoderm, form the *splanchnopleure*.

*Mesenchyme.*—The mesoderm of the head is derived from cells which migrate from the mesothelium lying posteriorly. These nonepithelial cells of mesodermal origin are designated as mesenchyme. The mesenchymatous tissue which fills the spaces between the ectodermal and endodermal epithelium and surrounds the medullary tube, notochord and blood vessels is also derived from the splanchnic and somatic layers of mesoderm and the somites. This mesenchyme gives rise to the various connective tissues, involuntary muscle and blood tissue, and plays an important part in the development of the skeleton.

**Summary.**—We have followed the development from the fertilized ovum through cleavage and the *morula*, *blastula* and *gastrula* periods to the formation of the three germ layers. In connection with the gastrula or gastrulation period we traced the differentiation of the *primitive streak* and the *mesoderm*, and the anlage of the nervous system and the notochord. The three primary germ layers make it convenient to subdivide organs according to the germ layer derivation of their principal tissues. Experimental embryology, however, has shown that the contributions of these germ layers are less specific than was formerly believed (Fig. 7).

The structural differentiation during and subsequent to the gastrula stage appears to be based on a tubular plan. We first have, externally, the ectodermal tube which covers the entire body and, internally, the endodermal tube which constitutes the digestive and later also the respiratory tracts. In addition we have the neural and chordal tubes and the lateral tubular body cavities of mesodermic origin. We find here an aggregate structure which is fundamentally similar to the body plan of the human adult.

In the development of the vertebrate type there arise specific characteristics. According to Minot these are:

1. The pharynx and pharyngeal structures.

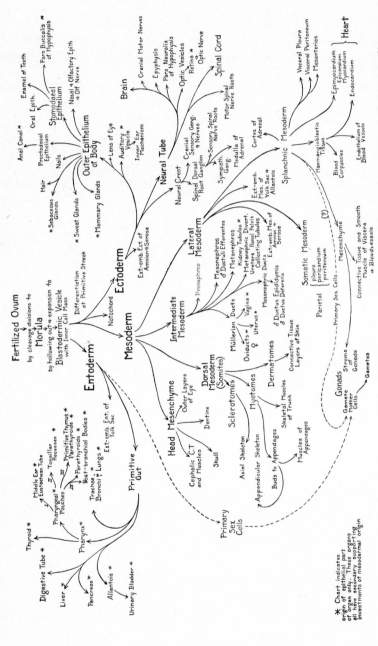

FIG. 7.—Chart showing the derivation of the various structures of the body by progressive differentiation and divergent specialization. Note especially how the origin of all the organs can be traced back to the three primary germ layers, ectoderm, entoderm, and mesoderm. The starred structures retain their epithelial characters and consist also of considerable supporting tissue of mesodermal origin. (After Patten: Embryology of the Pig.)

2. The notochord.

3. The tubular central nervous system.

4. The limbs.

5. The position of the mouth ventral to the nervous system.

6. The division of the cœlom into a dorsal segmented part and a ventral unsegmented part.

## THE NERVOUS SYSTEM

During the advanced stages of gastrulation there arises a thickening of the ectoderm anterior to the region of the primitive streak. This thickening is called the *neural* or *medullary plate* and forms the anlage of the nervous system. The cells of the lateral margins of the plate grow more rapidly than the central portion and form two ridges. The *neural groove* develops between them and grows deeper until the ridges bend over and fuse, converting the neural groove into the *neural tube* (Fig. 8). As the tube is being formed it loses its connection with the overlying ectoderm and comes to lie below the surface. The nervous system is thus afforded greater protection.

The neural tube will become the *spinal cord*, but at its anterior end it enlarges into three vesicles, which represent the primary divisions of the brain, the fore-brain, the mid-brain and the hind-brain. Soon the fore-brain subdivides into the telen- and diencephalon, and the hind-brain divides into the meten- and myelencephalon. All of these cavities of the neural tube become the *ventricular system*. The structures of the spinal cord and brain develop from the thickened walls of the canal and the *brain vesicles*.

Unequal growth causes the anterior part of the brain to fold over ventrally and produce the three primary *brain flexures*. The first *primary vesicle* assumes a position at right angles to the second, and thus forms the *cephalic flexure*. The *pontine flexure* is in the region of the hind-brain. The curvature at the junction of the brain and the spinal cord is called the *cervical flexure*.

## THE CŒLOM

The cœlom is the primitive body cavity (Fig. 8). It arises as a space in the lateral mesoderm and is lined by *mesothelium*, which later forms lining of the *serous membranes*. At first it is made up of two bilaterally symmetrical chambers, the inner walls of which surround and support the entodermal tube. These inner walls are composed of *splanchnic mesoderm* and tend to meet dorsal and ventral to the digestive tract. They form the *dorsal* and *ventral mesenteries*. The latter disappear in the posterior part and thus an unpaired body cavity is formed ventral to the gut.

The anterior portion of the cœlom subdivides and becomes the left and right *pleural cavities*, with the *pericardial cavity* between them.

PLATE I

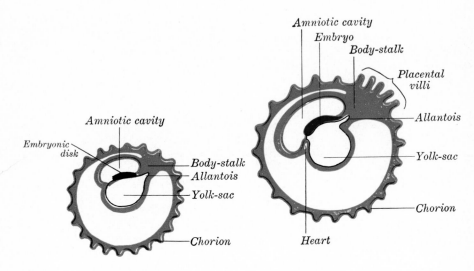

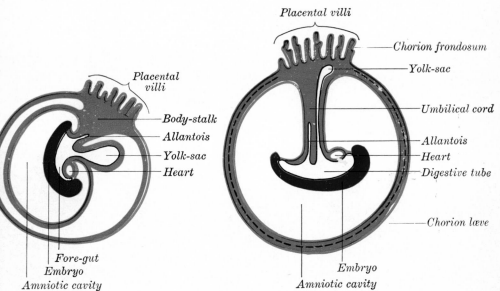

Successive stages in the development of the yolk sac and digestive tube
(Gray's Anatomy.)

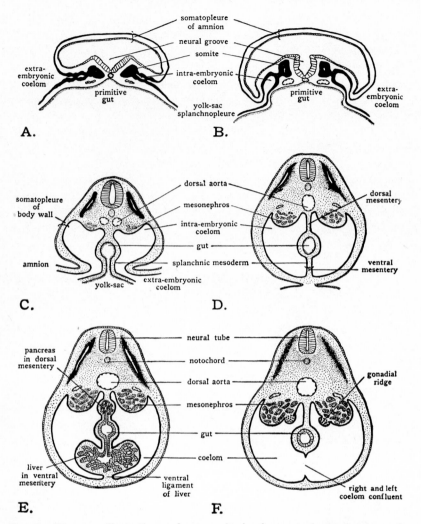

FIG. 8.—Diagrams illustrating early stages in development of neural tube, cœlom and digestive tube. (From Patten, Human Embryology, 1946, Courtesy of The Blakiston Company.)

## THE RESPIRATORY SYSTEM

In the 4-mm. embryo there develops immediately behind the pharyngeal pouches in the floor of the pharynx a ventral median outgrowth called the *laryngo-tracheal groove* which becomes tubular. The anterior part of this tube develops into the *larynx* and the posterior part into the *trachea*. As the latter elongates, its caudal end enlarges and bifurcates to form the *lung buds*.

## THE UROGENITAL SYSTEM

The urinary and genital systems are closely associated in their development and arise from the intermediate mesoderm or *nephrotomic* plates. The cells in this area differentiate into tubules and ducts which develop cranio-caudally into the successive *pronephros, mesonephros,* and *metanephros.* As these tubules expand they occupy more space and project ventrally into the cœlom, forming the longitudinal urogenital fold on each side of the dorsal mesentery. This fold is later subdivided into a lateral portion for the further development of the urinary system, and a medial portion or *genital fold* for the development of the genital system.

## THE DIGESTIVE TRACT

During gastrulation the embryo elongates, and the *archenteron,* which is the primitive digestive tract, becomes a tube. In the ensuing development of this tube, certain areas grow more rapidly than others, with the resulting formation of folds and flexures. This is especially true of the embryos of

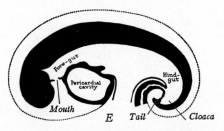

Fig. 9.—Sagittal section of human embryo at twenty-two somites stage. (Arey, *Developmental Anatomy,* 1954, Courtesy W. B. Saunders Co.)

higher vertebrates, which must develop within a limited space, such as the egg shell or uterine cavity. Among the first and largest folds to be developed are those of the head and of the tail. The entodermal tube is naturally affected by this folding process. That part which is included in the head fold is the *fore-gut.* The part included in the tail is the *hind-gut.* The *mid-gut* is the part which is at first continuous with the *yolk sac* (Plate I and Fig. 9).

The fore-gut gives rise to the epithelial lining of the pharynx, esophagus, stomach and also to the epithelium of its outgrowths, the tongue, the pharyngeal pouches, the respiratory tract, the liver and the pancreas. The mid-gut gives rise to the epithelial lining of part of the intestine. The hind-gut gives rise to the epithelial lining of the cœcal appendages, the colon, the rectum, the cloaca, the urinary bladder and the allantois.

## THE PHARYNX

During the third week the blind end of the fore-gut flattens dorsoventrally and extends laterally to form the pharyngeal cavity, which is soon characterized by a series of paired lateral outgrowths called *branchial* or *gill pouches.*

# PLATE II

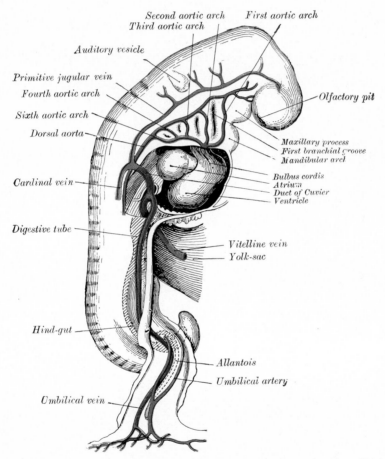

Second aortic arch
Third aortic arch
First aortic arch
Auditory vesicle
Primitive jugular vein
Fourth aortic arch
Sixth aortic arch
Dorsal aorta
Cardinal vein
Digestive tube
Hind-gut
Umbilical vein
Olfactory pit
Maxillary process
First branchial groove
Mandibular arch
Bulbus cordis
Atrium
Duct of Cuvier
Ventricle
Vitelline vein
Yolk-sac
Allantois
Umbilical artery

Profile view of a human embryo estimated at twenty-one days old.  (After His.)
Showing branchial arches and relation to blood vessels.

These are five in number and, with the exception of the fifth, which is rudimentary, are significant because they take part in the formation of the face and the jaws, and give rise to important structures.

The pouches develop first as grooves in the entoderm that extend toward the ectoderm, which likewise deepens in the corresponding areas in the form of *visceral furrows* or *grooves*. Where the ectoderm and entoderm meet they form plates which may break through and thus establish communications between the pharyngeal cavity and the exterior. These openings are called

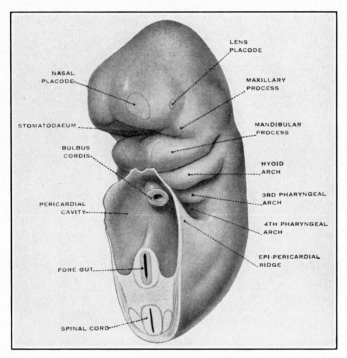

FIG. 10.—A drawing of the left ventro-lateral aspect of head end of a 6 mm. human embryo (after Streeter, 1922). × c.19.

*branchial* or *gill clefts* and are separated by mesenchymal thickenings of the lateral wall of the pharynx, which meet and fuse in the mid-ventral line with the corresponding thickenings of the opposite side. By this process *arches* are formed around the pharynx which are known as *branchial arches*. In addition to the blood vessels or *aortic arches*, nerves and muscular and skeletal tissue soon develop in the mesenchymal core of the branchial arches. The first arch is called the *mandibular*, the second, the *hyoid*, and the third, the *thyro-hyoid arch* (Plate II, Fig. 10).

The *pharyngeal pouches*, by means of small dorsal and large ventral outgrowths, differentiate into a series of organs. The *tympanic cavity* of the middle ear and the *Eustachian tube* develop from the first pouch. From the walls of the second pouch develops the *palatine tonsil*, and from the wall of the third and fourth pouches develop the *thymus* and the *parathyroid glands*.

In the floor of the pharynx, there arise from the first branchial arch two lateral prominences and a median protuberance which represent the first anlage of the body of the tongue. From the copula of the second and third arches arises the base of the tongue. After fusion the boundary is still marked by the terminal sulcus. At the midline and from this boundary, a median diverticulum grows down in the form of a stalk and terminates in the *thyroid anlage*. This stalk, which is the *thyroglossal duct*, soon atrophies and a blind pit at the back of the tongue persists as the *foramen cecum* and marks the former outlet of the duct.

## BIBLIOGRAPHY

AREY, L. B.: Developmental Anatomy, Philadelphia, Sixth Ed., W. B. Saunders Company, 1954.

BREMER, J. L., and WEATHERFORD, H. L.: A Textbook of Histology Arranged Upon an Embryological Basis, New York, The Blakiston Co., 1944.

HAMILTON, W. J., BOYD J. D., and MOSSMAN, H. W.: Human Embryology (Prenatal development of form and function), Second Edition, Baltimore, Md., The Williams & Wilkins Company, 1952.

KEIBEL, F., and MALL, F. P.: Manual of Human Embryology, Philadelphia and London, J. B. Lippincott Company, 1912.

LILLIE, F. R.: The Development of the Chick, New York, H. Holt & Co., 1913.

PATTEN, B. M.: Human Embryology, New York, The Blakiston Company, 1946.

————: The Embryology of the Pig, New York, The Blakiston Co., 1931.

SHUMWAY, W.: Vertebrate Embryology, New York, John Wiley & Sons, 1942.

# CHAPTER 2

# Prenatal Development of the Face and Oral Cavity

THOUGH the face of man has certain characteristics which are distinctive the basic development is the same in all mammals.

**Stomodeum.**—The embryonic gut is at first a blind tube lined with entodermal cells, closed to the outside. As the size of the brain increases, flexion occurs, folding the mid- and fore-brain over the cephalic end of the fore-gut (Fig. 10). Soon the fore-gut grows in the cephalic and ventral

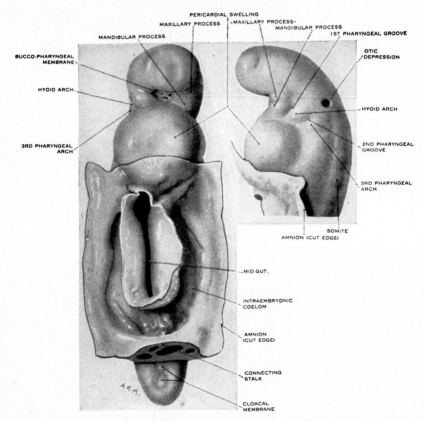

FIG. 11.—The ventral aspect of the reconstruction of a 20-somite human embryo of about 26 days. Modified from Davis (1923). (Hamilton, Boyd and Mossman's Human Embryology, 1952, Courtesy of W. Heffer and Sons, Ltd., England).

directions, and a corresponding ectodermal depression called the stomodeum develops to meet the entodermal outgrowth. As the ecto- and entodermal layers approximate the *oral plate* or *bucco-pharyngeal membrane* is formed. During the third week the oral plate ruptures and the fore-gut communicates with the stomodeum or primitive oral cavity (Fig. 11). A similar process in the posterior part of the hind-gut produces the *cloacal* membrane, and at about the ninth week the anal opening.

## EARLY DEVELOPMENT OF THE FACE

The face is developed from *two anlagen*, the *frontal process* and the *mandibular arch*. In the three-weeks human embryo, the anterior part of the fore-brain bulges forward and ventrally, in the manner of a thickened curtain of tissue, extending from beneath the fore-brain and over the anterior

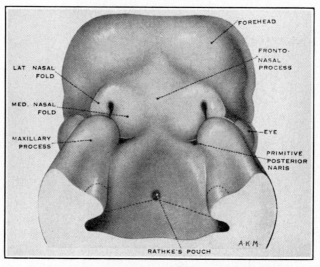

Fig. 12.—A drawing of the roof of the stomodeum of a 12 mm. human embryo to show the development of the primitive anterior and posterior nares by the approximation of the maxillary processes to the lateral and medial nasal folds. The mandibular processes have been removed. The previous site of attachment of the buccopharyngeal membrane is represented by the interrupted line. The maxillary palatal processes are just appearing. (Hamilton, Boyd and Mossman's Human Embryology, courtesy of W. Heffer and Sons, Ltd., England.)

opening of the stomodeum. This dependent structure is known as the *fronto-nasal process* and forms the upper anterior boundary of the primitive oral cavity.

At the same time the mandibular arch extends ventrally and forms the lateral inferior portion of the stomodeum. Above this arch on either side at the dorsal lateral angle the *maxillary buds* appear as bilateral swellings (Figs. 12 to 14). These gradually extend forward along the base of the

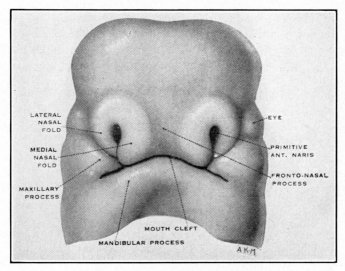

Fig. 13.—A drawing of the ventral aspect of the face of a 10 mm. human embryo. (Hamilton, Boyd and Mossman's Human Embryology, courtesy of W. Heffer and Sons Ltd., England.)

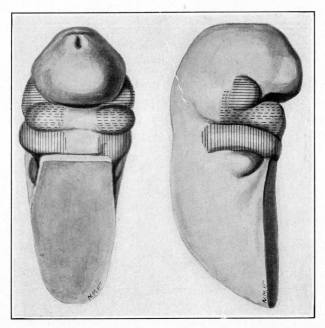

Fig. 14.—Model of head and neck of a 3-mm. human embryo. (Embryo Hal 2 of the first anatomical institute.) Front view and view from the right. Horizontal lines, maxillary process; dotted horizontal, mandibular arch; vertical lines, second visceral arch. (× 80.) (After Sicher and Tandler, Fig. 236, *a*, *b*.)

fore-brain.  They assist in defining the oral cavity laterally and form the anlage of the upper jaw.  The stomodeum is now bounded above by the floor of the fore-brain, anteriorly by the fronto-nasal process, below by the mandibular process and on each side by the maxillary processes.  As the halves of the mandibular arch increase in size ventrally they are at first separated by a central depression which upon fusion of the lateral segments disappears (Figs. 12 to 15).

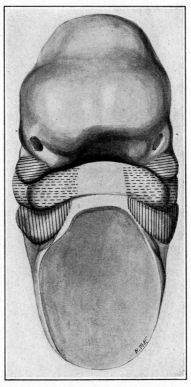

Fig. 15.—Model of head and neck of a 9-mm. human embryo.  (Embryo DL of the first anatomical institute.)  Front view.  Horizontal lines, maxillary process; dotted horizontal, mandibular arch; vertical lines, second visceral arch.  ($\times$ 30.)  (After Sicher and Tandler, Fig. 240.)

**The Nasal Pits.**—The differentiation at this time of the olfactory sense organs contributes to the development of the upper part of the face.  The *olfactory placodes* which develop the sense of smell, arise laterally from the ectoderm at the outer and lower portion of the fore-brain.  With the growth of the fronto-nasal process they assume a position at either side of this structure.  At the end of the fourth week *in utero* the tissue about the olfactory placodes grows more rapidly, producing depressions at these sites, *the nasal fossæ*.  Continued unequal growth produces a swelling or bud-like projection at the distal rim of each olfactory fossa, the *lateral nasal fold* and a similar enlargement may be observed along the mesial rim, which is formed by the lateral portion of the fronto-nasal process. This is sometimes referred to as the *medial nasal fold*. There is growth in both of these areas with the lateral nasal processes extending anteriorly until they meet and fuse with the medial nasal process, converting the nasal fossæ into the *nasal sacs* (Figs. 13, 15 and 16).

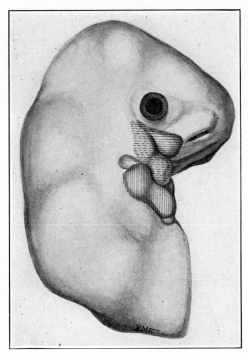

FIG. 16.—Model of head and neck of a 9-mm. human embryo. (Embryo DL of the first anatomical institute.) View from the right. Horizontal lines, maxillary process; dotted horizontal, mandibular arch; vertical lines, second visceral arch. (× 30.) (After Sicher and Tandler.)

Separation of the nostril from the oral cavity is attained in this way. Because of unequal growth between the rim and floor of the nasal pit, these structures are deepened until in 15-mm. embryos the base is separated from the oral cavity by a thin membrane, the *bucco-nasal membrane*. This separation of the oral cavity from the primitive nostril is soon terminated by the rupture of the membrane, thus establishing communication by means of the newly-formed passages known as the *primitive posterior nares* (*Fig. 12*).

**The Upper Jaw.**—In the formation of the nostrils and primitive choanæ the direction of growth of the fronto-nasal process, which carries the median nasal foldings upon its lateral borders, is predominantly downward. Thus,

3

when the medial growth of the lateral nasal processes has brought them forward, and fusion has occurred, the frontal process has extended below the rim of the nostril and developed a rounded globe of tissue descriptively termed the *globular process*. Between these paired structures growth is less rapid, resulting in a central depression (Figs. 17 and 18). The maxillary

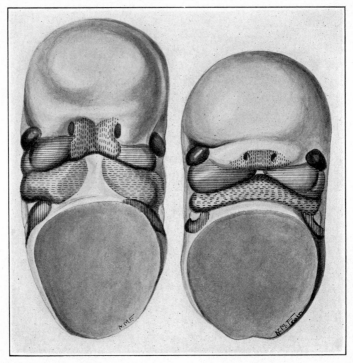

FIG. 17                    FIG. 18

FIG. 17.—Model of head and neck of a 9.2-mm. human embryo. (Embryo-H of the first anatomical institute.) Front view. Horizontal lines, maxillary process: dotted horizontal, mandibular arch; vertical lines, second visceral arch; dotted vertical, mesial nasal process. (× 20). (After Sicher and Tandler, Fig. 242.)

FIG. 18.—Model of head and neck of a 14.5-mm. human embryo. (Embryo S of the first anatomical institute.) Front view. Horizontal lines; maxillary process. Dotted horizontal; mandibular arch. Vertical lines; second visceral arch. Dotted vertical; mesial nasal process. (× 15.) (After Sicher and Tandler, Fig. 243.)

processes are extended at the same time along the inferior rim of the nostril. Together with the globular processes they form the upper jaw (Fig. 18). In this way the maxillary processes contribute the lateral halves of the upper jaw, while the right and left globular processes supply the medial (premaxillary) portion, including the philtrum of the upper lip and the central and lateral incisor part of the upper dental arch. The depression between the globular processes disappears gradually. The lateral nasal processes are at first separated from the maxillary buds by the *naso-lacrimal grooves* (Fig. 20).

"**Hare-lip**".—Failure of union of the median nasal and the lateral nasal process results in the deformity called hare or cleft lip. This defect may occur in all manner of degree and combination, causing the diverse deformities known to clinical oral surgery.

**Completion of Upper Jaw.**—The maxillary and globular processes form the complete arch of the upper jaw. The original cubical space or stomodeum is enclosed, leaving only the slit between the maxillary and mandibular arches which is to form the oral cavity. The space is one chamber with

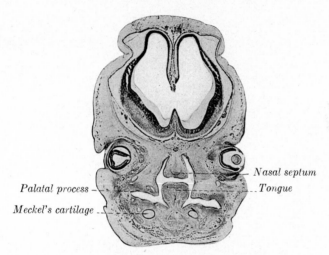

*Palatal process*

*Meckel's cartilage*

*Nasal septum*

*Tongue*

Fig. 19.—Transverse section of a 21-mm. human embryo. (Embryo H 405, Department of Anatomy, University of Chicago.) Early development of the palatal processes with the tongue between them. *ns*, Nasal septum; *t*, tongue: *Mc*. Meckel's cartilage; *pp*, palatal process. ( × 12.)

the superior-anterior part separated by a partition, the nasal septum, extending backward and downward from the sagittal portion of the frontonasal process. On either side of the septum the nasal cavities open through the primitive choanæ. The time of this development in the human embryo may be placed at about the fourth week *in utero*.

**The Lips.**—The maxillary and globular processes mentioned above together form the upper lip. At the same time the junction between the maxillary and the mandibular processes develop the angles of the mouth. The anterior superficial margin of the mandibular process contributes to the lower lip.

**The Cheeks and Oral Vestibule.**—Almost simultaneously with the fusion of the components of the lips a groove develops in each globular segment and extends distally along the maxillary portion. This depression, which eventually divides the tissue into an external and internal fold, is accomplished by a downgrowth of epithelium into the mesoderm, *the lip furrow band*. The subsequent growth on either side of this depression, the invasion of the deepest layer of the lip furrow band into the underlying tissue and the degeneration of the most superficial overlying epithelium develops *the oral vestibule*, separating the lips from the alveolar process (Fig. 38). A similar development of lip furrow band and vestibule along the free margin of the mandibular process differentiates the lower lip and alveolar process. At the midplane there is a deepening of the lip furrow band which proceeds less rapidly, making a division of the vestibule at the mid-line by a fold of tissue, the *frenum labii superioris*. This structure extends from the inner aspect of the lip to the alveolar process.

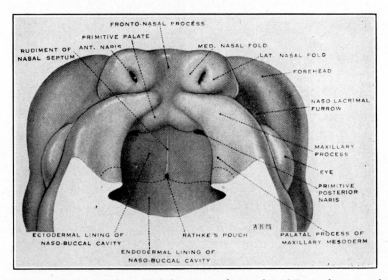

Fig. 20.—A drawing of the roof of the stomatodæum of a 13.5 mm. human embryo. A distinct palatal process from the maxillary mesoderm is now present. This will later meet its fellow of the opposite side and fuse with it and with the down growing nasal septum. The latter is now seen as a ridge in the roof of the primitive nasal cavity portion of the stomatodæum. The previous site of attachment of the buccopharyngeal membrane is show by the interrupted line. (Hamilton, Boyd and Mossman's Human Embryology, courtesy of W. Haffer and Sons, Ltd., England.)

Likewise, though in a less pronounced fashion, a sagittal fold of tissue, the *frenum labii inferioris*, unites the lower lip with the medial portion of the lower alveolar process.

While separation of the lip from the alveolar process is being accomplished anteriorly, growth at the side of the face distal to the angle of the mouth contributes to the formation of the cheeks. The continued development of the lip furrow band extends the vestibule into the buccal segments separating the lateral portions of upper and lower alveolar processes from the cheek.

**The Tongue.**—The body of the tongue arises from the fusion of bilateral swelling of the first branchial arch with *the tuberculum impar*. The base of the tongue is supplied by the anterior portion of an elevated structure developed at the medial extremity of the second and third branchial arches, *the copula*. The musculature of the tongue, in contrast to the double origin of the mucosa is a unit arising from post-branchial myotomes migrating cephalad to the region of the first and second branchial arches, and advancing further with the development of the tongue. The fungiform, filiform and circumvallate papillæ appear at ten to thirteen weeks *in utero* in the order mentioned. Taste buds may be distinguished in the fungiform papillæ at about the thirteenth week and at a somewhat later date in the circumvallate papillæ.

**The Salivary Glands.**—At about the fifth week in embryos of 8 mm. the ectoderm at the angle between the mandibular and maxillary portions of the first branchial arch develops an invaginated shelf-like projection which is the anlage of the *parotid gland*. This structure is eventually separated from the surface epithelium, and with growth and development of the adjacent parts, shifts its relative position until it comes to lie in the body of the cheek beneath the zygoma and just anterior to and below the ear.

A similar mechanism isolates a portion of the ectoderm in the sublingual sulcus forming the antecendent of the *submaxillary glands*. Likewise another location anteriorly gives rise to the *sublingual glands*. Mucin cells are differentiated by the sixteenth week, but complete development and function of these glands is not attained until after birth.

**The Separation of Oral and Nasal Cavities.**—The oral and nasal cavities are separated during the third month by the development of horizontal ingrowths from the three parts of the maxilla (Fig. 21). Union begins near the anterior extremity of the palatal processes of the maxillæ where they meet the palatal extension of the premaxilla. The above fusion continues distally. The anterior termination is the tuft of tissue designated after fusion as the *palatal papilla*. From this point posteriorly the palatal shelves join each other, forming the median raphé of the palate. The posterior extremity, when complete, forms the soft palate and uvula. In this way the oral cavity is separated from the nasal space, and the soft palate and uvula create the boundary between the oro- and naso-pharynx.

As the palatal shelves join in the mid-line, they also unite with the overlying nasal septum, thus completing the separation of right and left nasal cavities (Fig. 22). At the same time the communication between the oral and nasal cavities is being pushed backward, so that the permanent choanæ extend into the pharynx.

**Cleft Palate.**—A lack of union of the palatal shelves causes the malformation known as cleft palate. This deformity is then a later development than is hare-lip, either may occur without the other, though they are often found together. If the cleft palate combines with the "hare-lip," then the defect turns laterally and can be followed between the canine and incisor.

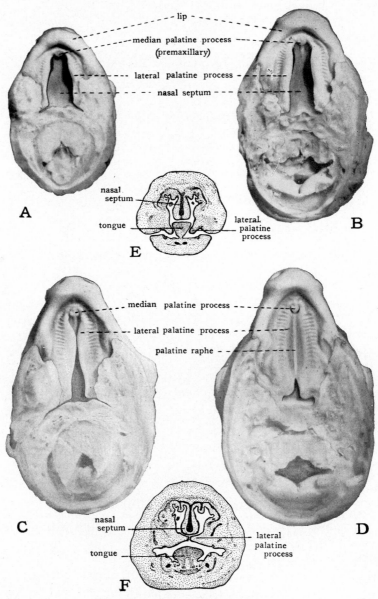

FIG. 21.—Photograph of dissections of pig embryos made to expose the roof of the mouth and show the development of the palate. *A*, 20.5 mm.; *B*, 25 mm.; *C*, 26.5 mm.; *D*, 29.5 mm. The diagrams of transverse sections are set in to show the relations before (*E*) and after (*F*) the retraction of the tongue from between the palatine processes. (× 5.) (After Patten: Embryology of the Pig.)

**The Naso-palatine Ducts.**—As the anterior portions of the palatal shelves approximate the lateral aspects of the premaxilla, the primitive choanæ are reduced to tubular structures, the *naso-palatine ducts.* The ducts rarely remain patent after fusion and open into the mouth at either side of the palatal papilla. If growth of the inferior portion of the palatal processes is rapid, and that of the palatal papilla slow, the two ducts may be united, opening through a common duct at the posterior end of the palatal papilla.

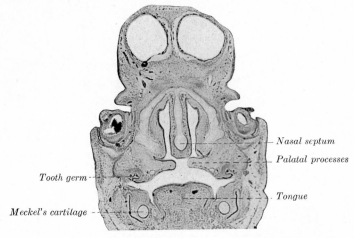

FIG. 22.—Transverse section of a 27.8-mm. human embryo. (Embryo H 91 of the Department of Anatomy, University of Chicago.) Inward and horizontal extension of the palatal processes with the tongue below them. *ns*, Nasal septum; *t*, tongue; *tg.*, tooth germ; *Mc*, Meckel's cartilage; *pp*, palatal processes. (× 12.)

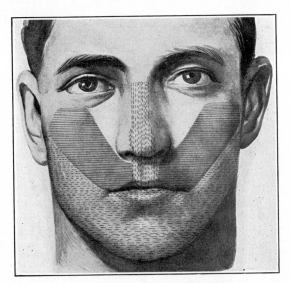

FIG. 23.—The contributions of the various facial processes to the formation of the adult face. Horizontal lines, maxillary process; dotted horizontal, mandibular arch; dotted vertical, mesial nasal process. (After Sicher and Tandler, Fig. 264.)

The epithelial lining of the naso-palatine ducts varies from that character-istic of the nasal cavity in their superior portion, to that of the oral cavity at their inferior extremity. Glands of mucous type are found in the upper two-thirds of their course. By the time of birth, regions of degeneration have usually interrupted the continuity of the ducts, but their course may easily be reconstructed in sections of tissue from this area taken from a new-born infant.

Not infrequently one of the ducts, and rarely both, remain patent after birth. Residual isolated portions of the ducts lined with epithelium con-taining mucous glands may give rise to cysts, *nasopalatine duct cysts*.

The early development of the face is thus characterized by the growth of the various facial processes concomitant with the differentiation of the sense organs of the nasal and oral cavities (Fig. 23).

## LATER FACE DEVELOPMENT

A discussion of the later stages of face development will aid in an under-standing of the normal processes leading to the formation of face indi-viduality. In addition there are certain facial abnormalities in the adult, and some jaw anomalies and malocclusions that may be associated with arrested facial development during various fetal stages. Retzius has pre-pared a number of figures that are very helpful in this study and that re-present characteristic stages of normal development.

**Eighteen-mm. Embryo.**—Retzius' figure of an 18-mm. human embryo, about fifty days old, shows in the front view a clear delineation of the out-standing parts of the future face. Its height is greater than its width. The nasal septum is formed, and two oblique and parallel grooves extend from the angle of the nose. One runs below the orbit and is called the suborbital groove. The other runs toward the angle of the mouth and is called the naso-labial groove. The globular processes are still visible. The eyes are wide apart and directed laterally. The ears are at a level below that of the mouth cleft. The latter is exceptionally wide, and is bounded above by the upper lip which is still notched (Fig. 24).

The profile view shows a pug nose, a shallow groove above it, and a re-cession of the lower jaw.

**Twenty-five-mm. Embryo.**—Retzius' figure of a 25-mm. human embryo (about eight weeks only) presents in the front view a face which is low and broad and almost square in outline. The nose is also low and broad and is separated from the forehead by the deep supranasal groove. Another groove runs above the orbit and is called the supraorbital groove. The eyes are still wide apart, but to a lesser degree than before. The ears are at about the level of the mouth cleft, which is still very wide (Fig. 25).

The profile view shows the pug nose, the deep supranasal groove, the prominently projecting forehead and a pronounced recession of the lower jaw.

**Forty-two-and-a-half-mm. Embryo.**—In Retzius' figure of a 42.5-mm. embryo, about nine to ten weeks old, the face is broad, but narrows down toward the chin. The nose is still broad and its external nares are closed by epithelial plugs. The supranasal groove is deeper than before. The eyes are less widely apart and are now closed by the lids. The mouth cleft is somewhat smaller, and its position is relatively higher than before. This is probably due to the more advanced development of the lower jaw (Fig. 26).

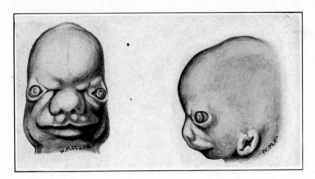

Fig. 24.—Head of an embryo of 18 mm.; front and profile view. (After Retzius, Plate XVI, Figs. 3 and 4.)

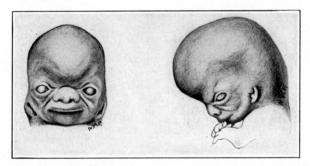

Fig. 25.—Head of a fetus of 25 mm.; front and profile view. (After Retzius, Plate XVI, Figs. 5 and 6.)

The profile view presents a pronounced development of the forehead region and a deep depression at the root of the nose. The lower jaw is decidedly prognathic.

**One Hundred and Seventeen-mm. Embryo.**—In Retzius' 117-mm. embryo (fourth month), the face tapers toward the chin. The nose is relatively higher and the eyes and auricles approach their adult position. The profile shows a semblance to adult symmetry, except for the relatively retarded development of the lower jaw, which is now micrognathic (Fig. 27). The apparent migration of the eyes to the front of the face and toward the midline is caused by differential growth. The tissue between the eyes and the

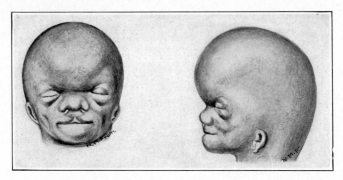

FIG. 26.—Head of a fetus of 42.5 mm.; front and profile view.  (After Retzius, Plate XVI, Figs. 8 and 9.)

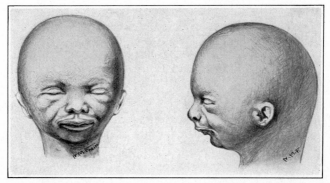

FIG. 27.—Head of a fetus of 117 mm.; front and profile view.  (After Retzius, Plate XVIII, Figs. 9 and 19.)

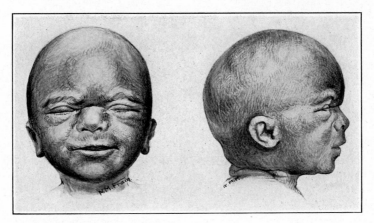

FIG. 28.—Head of a fetus of 206 mm.; front and profile view.  (After Retzius, Plate XXII, Figs. 3 and 4.)

corresponding tissue of the entire upper face grow at a slower rate than do the lateral areas.

**Later Changes.**—After the fifth month the lower jaw and lip grow faster than the upper, until shortly before birth the proper antero-posterior relationship between upper and lower jaw is reached (Fig. 28). If, however, there is an arrest in the normal course of the development, the fetal condition may persist in the adult as a permanent micrognathia.

TABLE 1.—DETERMINATION OF THE AGE OF EMBRYOS, RELATIONS OF AGE, SIZE AND WEIGHT IN THE HUMAN EMBRYO.

| Age of Embryo | Crown-Rump Length (MM.) | Crown-Heel Length (MM.) | Weight in Grams |
|---|---|---|---|
| One week | 0.1* | — | |
| Two weeks | 0.2* | — | |
| Three weeks | 2.0 | — | |
| Four weeks | 5.0 | — | .02 |
| Five weeks | 8.0 | — | |
| Six weeks | 12.0 | — | |
| Seven weeks | 17.0 | 19.0 | |
| Two lunar months | 23.0 | 30.0 | 1 |
| Three lunar months | 56 0 | 73.0 | 14 |
| Four lunar months | 112.0 | 157.0 | 105 |
| Five lunar months | 160.0 | 239.0 | 310 |
| Six lunar months | 203.0 | 296.0 | 640 |
| Seven lunar months | 242.0 | 355.0 | 1080 |
| Eight lunar months | 277.0 | 409.0 | 1670 |
| Nine lunar months | 313.0 | 458.0 | 2400 |
| Full term (38 weeks) | 350.0 | 500.0 | 3300 |

*Total length of embryonic disc.
(Arey, L. B.: Developmental Anatomy, 1954, p. 105, Courtesy of W. B. Saunders Co.)

## BIBLIOGRAPHY

AREY, L. B.: Developmental Anatomy, Sixth Ed., Philadelphia, W. B. Saunders Company, 1954.

KEIBEL, F., and MALL, F. P.: Manual of Human Embryology, Philadelphia and London, J. B. Lippincott Company, 1912.

RABKIN, SAMUEL: Variation in Structural Morphogenesis of the Face and Jaws, Jour. Dent. Res., *31*, 535, 1952.

RETZIUS, G.: Zur Kenntniss der Entwicklung der Körperform des Menschen während der fetalen Lebensstufen, Biologische Untersuchungen, Neue Folge XI, Stockholm-Jena, 1904.

SICHER, H.: Oral Anatomy, 2nd Ed., St. Louis, C. V. Mosby Co., 1952.

# CHAPTER 3

# Introduction to the Teeth

## FUNCTIONS OF THE TEETH

THE main function of the teeth is that of mastication. They are divided into different classes especially designated to best perform this function. Man has, therefore, a heterodont dentition, that is, teeth of different shapes; incisors to cut and saw the food; canines and premolars to seize and tear the food; and molars to grind or comminute the food. The teeth also aid in the production of sound and speech and add to the esthetic harmony of the face.

In must be pointed out that the tooth is more than an organ of mastication. During the development of its enamel and dentin the tooth is also a biologic recorder of health and disease, especially of alterations in mineral metabolism. The incremental layer of enamel and dentin reflect metabolic fluctuations just as the growth rings of the tree reflect its life history (weather, nutrition, etc.).

## THE DENTITIONS

Man is diphyodont, possessing two sets of teeth. The first set, composed of ten teeth in each arch, is lost by the twelfth year and is therefore called the deciduous or temporary set. Histogenetically, the deciduous teeth arise directly from the oral epithelium. The teeth that succeed them or are added to them are called the permanent teeth, since they are intended to last for the remaining life span. They number 16 in each arch and are bilaterally symmetrical. With the exception of the molars, which have the same origin as the deciduous teeth, the permanent teeth arise through the budding of the dental lamina of the deciduous teeth.

**Chronology.**—The chronology and development of both dentitions are given in Table 2 and Plate III. Further studies in chronology of tooth development are indicated. Recently Kraus reported that initial calcification in the deciduous central incisors may begin as early as twelve weeks.

## GROSS ANATOMY OF THE TEETH

Anatomically, the teeth are divided into the crown and the root (Fig. 29). The root is embedded within the alveolar process of the jaw and supports

( 44 )

the crown in its masticatory function. The anatomical crown is covered by enamel, the anatomical root by cementum. Clinically, that portion of the tooth that is exposed to the oral fluids, is called the functional crown. In young individuals the functional crown is smaller than the anatomical crown, while in the aged it may be greater than the anatomical crown and include a part of the anatomical root.

TABLE 2.—CHRONOLOGY OF THE HUMAN DENTITION. (SLIGHTLY MODIFIED AFTER LOGAN AND KRONFELD.)

| | | Tooth. | First evidence of calcification. | Crown completed. | Eruption. | Root completed |
|---|---|---|---|---|---|---|
| Deciduous dentition | Upper jaw | Central incisor | 3–4 mos. *in utero* | 4 mos. | 7½ mos. | 1½–2 yrs. |
| | | Lateral incisor | 4½ mos. *in utero* | 5 mos. | 8 mos. | 1½–2 yrs. |
| | | Canine | 5¼ mos. *in utero* | 9 mos. | 16–20 mos. | 2½–3 yrs. |
| | | First molar | 5 mos. *in utero* | 6 mos. | 12–16 mos. | 2–2½ yrs |
| | | Second molar | 6 mos. *in utero* | 10–12 mos. | 20–30 mos. | 3 yrs. |
| | Lower jaw | Central incisor | 4½ mos. *in utero* | 4 mos. | 6½ mos. | 1½–2 yrs |
| | | Lateral incisor | 4½ mos. *in utero* | 4¼ mos. | 7 mos. | 1½–2 yrs |
| | | Canine | 5 mos. *in utero* | 9 mos. | 16–20 mos. | 2½–3 yrs |
| | | First molar | 5 mos. *in utero* | 6 mos. | 12–16 mos. | 2–2½ yrs |
| | | Second molar | 6 mos. *in utero* | 10–12 mos. | 20–30 mos. | 3 yrs |
| Permanent dentition | Upper jaw | Central incisor | 3–4 mos. | 4– 5 yrs. | 7– 8 yrs. | 10 yrs |
| | | Lateral incisor | 10 mos. | 4– 5 yrs. | 8– 9 yrs. | 11 yrs |
| | | Canine | 4–5 mos. | 6– 7 yrs. | 11–12 yrs. | 13–15 yrs. |
| | | First premolar | 1½–1¾ yrs. | 5– 6 yrs. | 10–11 yrs. | 12–13 yrs. |
| | | Second premolar | 2–2¼ yrs. | 6– 7 yrs. | 10–12 yrs. | 12–14 yrs. |
| | | First molar | At birth | 2½– 3 yrs. | 6– 7 yrs. | 9–10 yrs. |
| | | Second molar | 2½–3 yrs. | 7– 8 yrs. | 12–13 yrs. | 14–16 yrs. |
| | | Third molar | 7–9 yrs. | 12–16 yrs. | 17–21 yrs. | 18–25 yrs. |
| | Lower jaw | Central incisor | 3–4 mos. | 4– 5 yrs. | 6– 7 yrs. | 9 yrs. |
| | | Lateral incisor | 3–4 mos. | 4– 5 yrs. | 7– 8 yrs. | 10 yrs. |
| | | Canine | 4–5 mos. | 6– 7 yrs. | 9–10 yrs. | 12–14 yrs. |
| | | First premolar | 1¾– 2 yrs. | 5– 6 yrs. | 10–12 yrs. | 12–13 yrs. |
| | | Second premolar | 2¼–2½ yrs. | 6– 7 yrs. | 11–12 yrs. | 13–14 yrs. |
| | | First molar | At birth | 2½– 3 yrs. | 6– 7 yrs. | 9–10 yrs. |
| | | Second molar | 2½– 3 yrs. | 7– 8 yrs. | 11–13 yrs. | 14–15 yrs. |
| | | Third molar | 8–10 yrs. | 12–16 yrs. | 17–21 yrs. | 18–25 yrs. |

## THE DENTAL TISSUES

**The Tissues of the Tooth.**—The tooth proper is composed of four tissues, three calcified and one soft tissue (Figs. 29 to 31, Table 2).

1. *Enamel.*—The hard outer covering of the anatomical crown of the tooth. It is epithelial in origin, while all the other dental tissues are mesenchymal in origin.

2. *Dentin.*—The main bulk of the tooth.

3. *Cementum.*—The outer covering of the root.

4. *Pulp.*—The soft connective tissue within the central cavity of the dentin. It lies within a wide pulp chamber in the crown and a narrow pulp canal in the root, and communicates with the periodontal membrane through a small opening at the apex of the root—the apical foramen. Because of its position within the tooth, the pulp has been termed the endodontal organ.

# PLATE III

### Development of

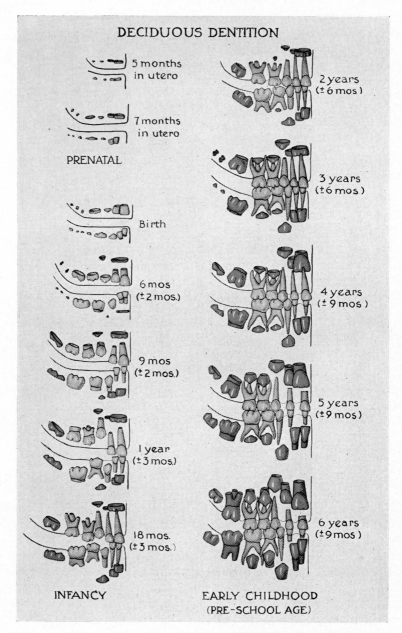

DECIDUOUS DENTITION

5 months in utero

7 months in utero

PRENATAL

Birth

6 mos (±2 mos.)

9 mos (±2 mos.)

1 year (±3 mos.)

18 mos. (±3 mos.)

INFANCY

2 years (±6 mos.)

3 years (±6 mos.)

4 years (±9 mos.)

5 years (±9 mos.)

6 years (±9 mos.)

EARLY CHILDHOOD
(PRE-SCHOOL AGE)

Schour and Massler, University of Illinois, College of Dentistry, distributed by
the American Dental Association.

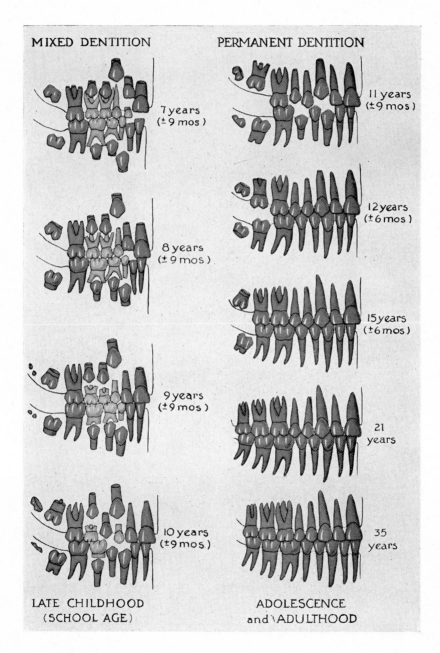

MIXED DENTITION
PERMANENT DENTITION

7 years (±9 mos)

11 years (±9 mos)

8 years (±9 mos)

12 years (±6 mos)

9 years (±9 mos)

15 years (±6 mos)

21 years

10 years (±9 mos)

35 years

LATE CHILDHOOD
(SCHOOL AGE)

ADOLESCENCE
and ADULTHOOD

**The Supporting Tissues.**—The teeth are rendered functional by the implantation of their roots in a socket of bone known as the alveolus (Fig. 29). The implantation is not ankylosed, but the tooth is instead allowed slight movement by the attachment of the cementum of the root to the walls of the alveolus and surrounding soft tissue by means of the fibers of the periodontal ligament (Fig. 29). This type of implantation is termed

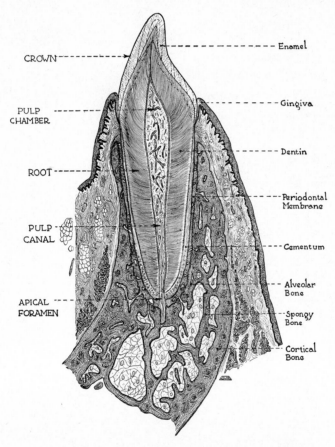

CROWN

PULP CHAMBER

ROOT

PULP CANAL

APICAL FORAMEN

Enamel

Gingiva

Dentin

Periodontal Membrane

Cementum

Alveolar Bone

Spongy Bone

Cortical Bone

Fig. 29.—Diagrammatic representation of the dental tissues.

gomphosis. In addition, the gingiva clothes the alveolar process and borders the teeth (Fig. 29).

Thus the dental tissues consist of:

    *A. Tooth Tissues.*
        1. Enamel.
        2. Dentin.
        3. Cementum.
        4. Pulp.

4

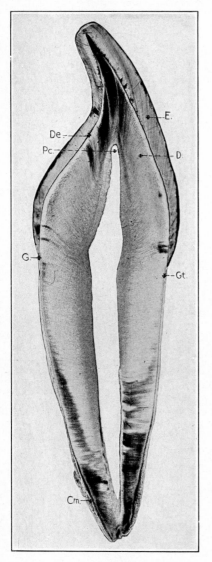
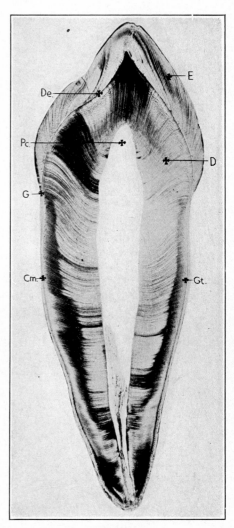

| Fig. 30 | Fig. 31 |

Fig. 30.—Ground section of an incisor. *E*, Enamel; *Cm*, cementum; *D*, dentin; *Pc*, pulp chamber; *De*, dentino-enamel junction; *G*, cemento-enamel junction; *Gt*, dentino-cemental junction (*See* Fig. 97).

Fig. 31.—Ground section of a canine. *E*, Enamel; *Cm*. cementum; *D*, dentin; *Pc*, pulp chamber; *De*, dentino-enamel junction; *G*, cemento-enamel junction; *Gt*, granular layer of Tomes.

B. *Supporting Tissues* (*Periodontium*).
 1. Cementum.
 2. Periodontal ligament.
 3. Alveolar bone.
 4. Gingiva.

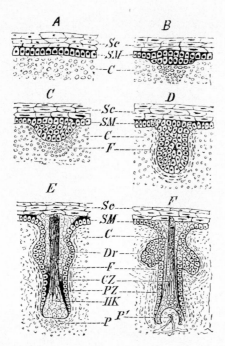

Fig. 32.—Development of the hair: *Sc*, stratum corneum; *SM*, stratum malpighii, *C*, derma; *Dr*, sebaceous gland; *F*, follicles; *CZ*, central, *PZ*, peripheral zone of hair germ; *HK*, hair knob; *P*, beginning the formation of the hair papilla; P¹, same in a later stage of development when it has become vascular. (Wiedersheim, *Comparative Anatomy of Vertebrates.*)

## THE DEVELOPMENT OF THE TOOTH

In embryology so many things are going on at the same time, and the changes are so rapid, that it is difficult to obtain a clear idea of the process from a written description. A comprehensive moving picture, such as has been made of the growth of plants and the opening of flowers, has not yet been made of the development of the tooth, but it is important to visualize the process in a similar way. The present description is intended to correlate in an elementary fashion some of the most important facts, and relates specifically to the condition in the human species, except as otherwise noted.

The teeth, like the nails and hair, are cutaneous appendages which consist of highly specialized and differentiated cells and intercellular substances. Phylogenetically, they are derived from the placoid scales of the selachians.

The tooth as a living functional organ arises in a harmonious and sequential manner through the following developmental stages:

I. Growth.
    (*a*) Initiation.
    (*b*) Proliferation (cell-division).
    (*c*) Histo- or Cyto-differentiation.
    (*d*) Morpho-differentiation (outline of size and shape of tooth).
    (*e*) Apposition (additive extra-cellular growth).

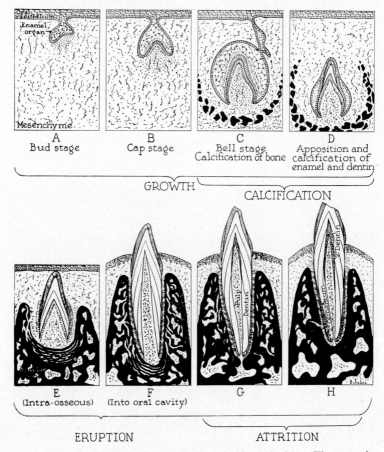

Fig. 33.—Diagram of life cycle of a human deciduous incisor. The normal resorption of the root is not indicated. Enamel and bone are drawn in black. (Slightly modified after Schour and Massler from Maximow and Bloom).

  II. Calcification.
  III. Eruption.
  IV. Attrition.

In the tooth we thus have three instead of the usual one or two developmental processes that go into the formation of an organ. The liver grows, bone grows and calcifies, but the tooth must not only grow and calcify, but must also erupt before it can carry out its masticatory function. Thus, the life cycle of the tooth is complex (Figs. 33 and 34).

There are five successive and distinct phenomena in the growth of the teeth. Immediately after initiation there is a very rapid proliferative growth of the cells from the ectodermal and mesodermal layers of the oral mucosa. This is characterized by vigorous metabolic activity and a marked increase

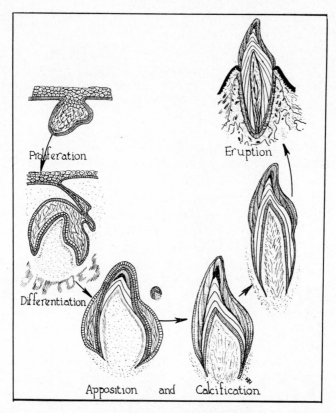

Proliferation

Eruption

Differentiation

Apposition and Calcification

FIG. 34.—The life-cycle of the tooth.

in size (the bud, cap and bell stages of the enamel organ). The next stages of the growth process are those of histo- and morpho-differentiation, when the formative cells acquire their functional specialization and the varied morphological forms and differences in size of deciduous and permanent teeth (incisor, canine, premolar and molar) are established. These stages and processes overlap considerably and often occur at the same time. They result in the formation of the *tooth germ*, a cell aggregate which is composed of three parts, and whose function it is to form the dental tissues (Fig. 33).

1. *The enamel organ*, an epithelial derivative which will form the enamel and perform additional functions (p. 62).

Because of the essential role of this structure in tooth formation the term *odontogenic epithelial organ* or *odontogenic organ* is more appropriate and will be used as synonymous with the "enamel organ."

2. *The dental papilla,* a mesenchymal derivative which will form the dentin and pulp.

3. *The dental sac,* also a mesenchymal derivative which will form the cementum, the periodontal ligament and the alveolar bone.

TABLE 3.—A CLASSIFICATION OF THE HISTOPHYSIOLOGIC AND CHEMICAL CHARACTERISTICS OF THE DENTAL TISSUES

| *Tissues* | *Enamel* | *Dentin* | *Pulp* | *Cementum* | *Periodontal Ligament* | *Alveolar Bone* | *Gingiva* |
|---|---|---|---|---|---|---|---|
| Origin | Ecto-dermal | Mesodermal | | | | | Ecto- and mesodermal |
| Degree of calcification | 97% | 70% | Uncalcified | 66% | Uncalcified | 66% | Uncalcified |
| Function | Resistant to wear | Elastic strength | Formation and vitality of dentin | Support | | | Investment and protection |
| Anatomic classification | Propriodontal (unique to the tooth) | | Endodontal | Periodontal | | | |
| Regenerative capacity | Nil | Restricted | Limited | Good | | | |
| Disease | Enamel caries | Dentin caries | Pulpitis | Periodontitis Periodontosis | | | Gingivitis Gingivosis |
| Special field of dentistry | Restorative dentistry | | Endodontia | Periodontia | | | |

The fifth and last phase of growth is one of a quantitative addition of extra-cellular material to the morphological outline established at the fourth phase. This is termed appositional growth, and is characterized by the regularity and rhythmicity of the deposition of new material, periods of activity and rest alternating at definite time intervals, and by the fact that the material is of itself incapable of further growth.

The appositional stage is accompanied by the processes of calcification and eruption, which proceed in a harmonious and rhythmic manner, following each other or occurring concomitantly.

Though the tooth is primarily derived from the ectodermal epithelium of the oral cavity, it develops within the jaw from the ectodermal and mesodermal tissues. In order to function, the tooth finally erupts into the oral cavity (Fig. 34).

The tooth, in a broad sense, is a living cooperative and highly interdependent organ. The supporting and investing tissues are just as essential as the tooth tissues proper, since they maintain the tooth in position and render it functional.

## CLASSIFICATION OF DENTAL TISSUES

The dental tissues may be classified according to their origin, the degree of calcification, function, anatomic position and clinical significance (Table 3). These tissues naturally have direct bearing on clinical problems of oral diagnosis and treatment.

### BIBLIOGRAPHY

Kraus, B. S.: Calicification of the Human Deciduous Teeth, J.A.D.A., **59**, 1128–1136, December, 1959.

Schour, I., and Massler, M.: Studies in Tooth Development, The Growth Pattern of the Human Teeth. Part I. J.A.D.A., *27*, 1778–1793, November, 1940; Part II. 1918–1931, December, 1940.

Schour, I.: Recent Advances in Oral Histology. Int. Dent. J., *2*, (1), Sept. 1951.

# CHAPTER 4

# The Development of the Tooth Germ

## STAGES IN PROLIFERATION AND DIFFERENTIATION

**Dental Lamina.**—During the sixth week of embryonic life (thirty-fourth to thirty-eighth day) there arises an epithelial thickening near the free margin of the jaws, which is continuous and runs arch-like along the ridge of the jaw (Fig. 35). It is the anlage of the ectodermal portion of the tooth,

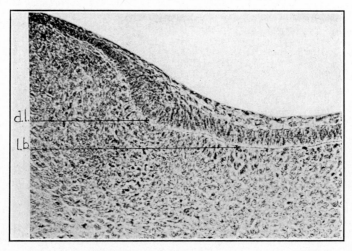

Fig. 35.—Transverse section of a 21-mm. human embryo. (Embryo H 405, Department of Anatomy. University of Chicago.) Early differentiation of dental lamina, *d.l.*, and vestibular lamina, *l.b.* in the region of the future lower first deciduous molar. (About × 350.)

the future odontogenic organ, and is called the dental lamina. Histologically, it consists of superficial squamous cells and a basal layer of columnar cells that belong to the stratum germinativum. The dental lamina is separated from the mesoderm by a distinct basement membrane. Many mitotic figures are seen in the early stages.

**Vestibular Lamina.**—Shortly after the appearance of the dental lamina there arises between it and the future region of the lips and cheeks another, less prominent, epithelial thickening. This thickening is, therefore, parallel and labial or buccal to the dental lamina, and represents the vestibular lamina (Fig. 36). This splits and forms the vestibular groove which will

( 56 )

become the vestibule of the mouth. The epithelium of the labial wall of this groove will give rise to the inner surface of the lips and cheeks, and the epithelium of its inner wall will give rise to the gingiva and the labial surface of the alveolar ridge.

**Formation of the Odontogenic Organ.**—Bud Stage.—The dental lamina proliferates at ten points, corresponding to the 10 primary teeth of each jaw. The resultant buds increase in size, become bulbous at their deep ends and constitute the first stage of the odontogenic organ. The proliferating epithelium *bud* consists of a basal layer of low columnar cells continuous with the basal layer of the oral epithelium, and a central mass of larger polyhedral cells (Fig. 36). The oral surface consists of flattened cells

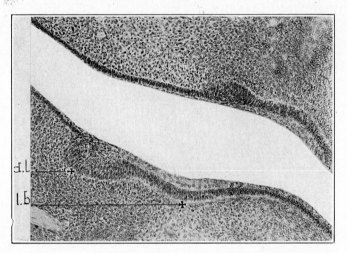

Fig. 36.—Transverse section of a 21-mm. human embryo. (Embryo H 405, Department of Anatomy, University of Chicago.) Bud-like proliferation of dental lamina to form tooth germ of lower deciduous incisor. *dl*. Dental lamina; *lb*, vestibular lamina, or labial alveolar sulcus. (× 200.)

which are rich in glycogen. The latter does not stain in routine sections and gives these cells an empty appearance. Mitotic activity is evident in both the epithelium and subjacent connective tissue.

**Cap Stage.**—The epithelial bud becomes invaginated and the underlying mesoderm shows a corresponding condensation, the mesenchymal dental papilla (Figs. 37 and 38). In this stage the odontogenic organ contains an *outer* and *inner layer of enamel epithelium*. The inner layer, which later will differentiate into the ameloblasts or enamel-forming cells, is concave toward the mesenchyme. Its cells are highly columnar and show many mitotic figures.

The cells of the outer layer are shorter and are somewhat cuboidal in shape. Enclosed by the inner and outer layer is a central mass of cells which begin to separate and arrange themselves in a network called the

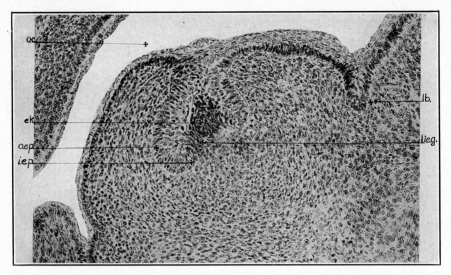

FIG. 37.—Transverse section of a 27.8-mm. human embryo. (Embryo H 91, Department of Anatomy, University of Chicago.) Differentiation of enamel organ and enamel knot of lower second deciduous molar. *ek*, Enamel knot; *lieg*, lingual enamel groove; *iep*, inner layer of enamel epithelium; *oc*, oral cavity; *lb*, lip furrow band; *oep*, outer layer of enamel epithalium. (× 320.)

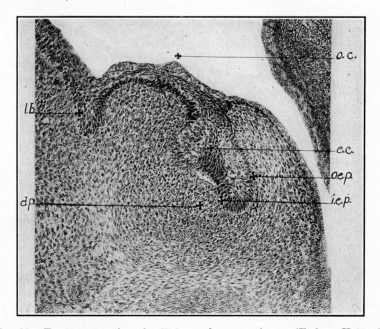

FIG. 38.—Transverse section of a 27.8-mm. human embryo. (Embryo H 91 of the Department of Anatomy, University of Chicago.) Differentiation of enamel organ and enamel cord of the lower second deciduous molar. *dp*, Dental papilla; *ec*, enamel cord; *iep*, inner layer of enamel epithelium; *lb*, lip furrow band; *oc*, oral cavity; *oep*, outer layer of enamel epithelium. (× 210.)

stellate reticulum or enamel pulp (Figs. 38 and 39). The enlarged intercellular spaces are filled with a mucoid fluid rich in albumin, resulting in a protective consistency for the ameloblast. The underlying dental papilla shows further cellular condensation and vascularization.

**Bell Stage.**—With further proliferation of the odontogenic organ and increased depth of its concave surface, the bell stage is reached. This stage is characterized by the final *differentiation* of the cells of the tooth germ preparatory to the appositional stage, which is concerned with the formation of the enamel and dentin. Figure 39 shows the tooth germ at this stage. The odontogenic organ consists of:

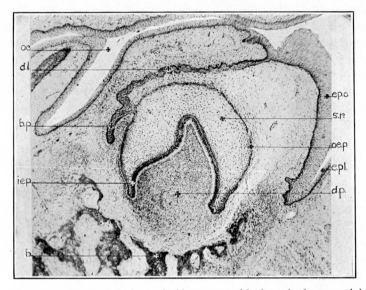

FIG. 39.—Sagittal section of a lower deciduous central incisor of a four-month human embryo. *b*, Bone of mandible; *epo*, epithelium of oral cavity; *bp*, bud for permanent tooth; *iep*, inner enamel epithelium; *dl*, dental lamina; *oc*, oral cavity; *dp*, dental papilla; *oep*, outer enamel epithelium; *epl*, epithelium of lip; *sr*, stellate reticulum. (× 80.)

1. The cuboidal outer enamel epithelium which lines the convex surface of the odontogenic organ.

2. The tall columnar inner enamel epithelium, which is confined to the invaginated concavity of the odontogenic organ.

3. The star-shaped cells of the stellate reticulum, enclosed by the enamel epithelia.

4. The low squamous cells of the stratum intermedium lying between the inner enamel epithelium and the stellate reticulum.

**Formation of the Dental Papilla.**—The mesenchyme which is enclosed by the enamel organ is called the dental papilla and is the primordium of the the dentin and pulp. This underlying mesenchymal tissue becomes condensed during the cap stage of the formation of the enamel organ. The condensation is so marked that it is easily distinguished from the looser tissue from which it arose (Fig. 38). Blood vessels become more numerous. During the differentiating bell stage of the enamel organ, the mesenchymal cells which face the inner enamel epithelium become larger and assume a columnar form so that they resemble high columnar epithelium (Fig. 40). They now are called odontoblasts. These cells will be discussed in greater detail in the chapter on dentin formation. The boundary between the enamel organ and dental papilla represents the future dentino-enamel junction.

**Formation of the Dental Sac.**—As soon as the dental papilla and enamel organ take on their full form, differentiation of the surrounding mesoderm occurs and fibrous tissue begins to form around the outer surface of the enamel organ and the base of the dental papilla (Fig. 39). The fibers assume a parallel arrangement and extend coronally. The connective tissue cells of the dental sac will differentiate into cementoblasts, fibroblasts and osteoblasts; and form cementum, periodontal membrane and alveolar bone, respectively (Fig. 44).

## CYTOLOGY OF THE ODONTOGENIC ORGAN

**Outer Odontogenic Epithelium.**—This epithelium which originally had a columnar shape similar to the basal layer of the oral epithelium becomes flattened (Fig. 40). It later folds into epithelial ridges to allow richer blood supply.

**Stellate Reticulum.**—The cells of the stellate reticulum (or enamel pulp) constitute the type of stratified squamous epithelium in which the intercellular bridges reach an especially high development and elongation. Intercellular substances which show metachromasia and contain phosphatase accumulate between the cell bodies and push them aside. The cells assume a stellate appearance, and a cellular network arises which resembles embryonic connective tissue or mesenchyme (Fig. 40). That this reticulum is of epithelial origin is indicated by the presence of desmosomes and intracellular tonofibrils. The cells show a central apparatus, a Golgi network and many mitochondria which indicate energetic metabolic activity. Vital dyes are not stored. The stellate reticulum is avascular but vascularization has been observed in the enamel organ of the molar of the rat. The ground substance is Schiff-positive and strongly metachromatic. It has a rich mucopolysaccharide content of what appears to be chondroitin sulphate.

The stellate reticulum serves as a medium for transportation of nutrients and in all probability performs a nutritional as well as a mechanical function. It appears to protect and to support the tooth germ and begins to disappear when the formation of dentin and enamel starts. From then on the shape of the crown is maintained by the hard dental tissues themselves.

**Stratum Intermedium.**—This layer intervenes between the enamel pulp and the inner enamel epithelium. It consists of several layers of flat, round cells, which are joined in a syncytium and show a gradual transition into the stellate reticulum. Distinct intercellular bridges connect the cells with one another and with the inner enamel epithelium. Their cytoplasm contains mitochondria, a central apparatus and a Golgi network near the nucleus. Prenant found mitotic figures in this layer after mitotic activity had ceased in the inner enamel epithelium.

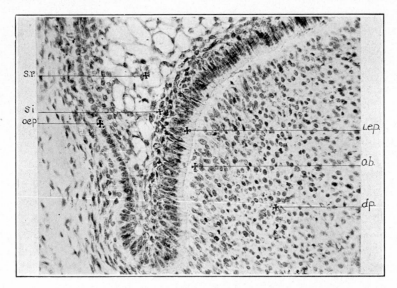

Fig. 40.—Portion of Fig. 39. *dp*, Dental papilla; *oep*, outer layer of enamel epithelium; *iep*, inner layer of enamel epithelium; *si*, stratum intermedium; *ob*, future odontoblastic layer; *sr*, stellate reticulum. (× 640.)

The stratum intermedium is probably concerned with amelogenesis since ameloblasts do not form enamel except when lying next to it. Leon Williams considered that the cells of this layer take up materials from the blood and elaborate them, to be used by the ameloblasts in the development of enamel. According to Lehner and Plenk, these cells may replace ameloblasts that have died or may serve for the enlargement of the stellate reticulum.

**Inner Odontogenic Epithelium.**—At the bell stage the cells of this layer no longer show mitotic figures, but differentiate into the high columnar ameloblasts or enamel-forming cells. Prior to apposition their polarity changes, so that their nucleus is situated at what was formerly the distal end of the cell. The ameloblsts show a concentration of alkaline phosphatase which may be active in the synthesis of proteins needed for the organic matrix of the enamel. A distinct basement membrane (Fig. 91) separates the ameloblasts from the odontoblastic layer of the pulp.

## FUNCTIONS OF THE ODONTOGENIC ORGAN

The odontogenic organ performs the following functions:

1. It determines the pattern and size of the future dentino-enamel junction and with it the shape and size of the future crown. An examination of the enamel organ at the bell stage will thus indicate the shape of the tooth that will develop. Fig. 39 shows the odontogenic organ of an incisor. Fig. 43 shows the development of the odontogenic organ of a molar.

2. Its inner odontogenic epithelium, which consists of tall columnar cells, the ameloblasts, is responsible for enamel formation.

3. It plays an active rôle in stimulating the underlying connective tissue cells to form the dentin.

4. It gives rise to Hertwig's epithelial sheath which guides the shape of the forming root just as the odontogenic organ proper determines the form of the crown. The inner odontogenic epithelium joins the outer odontogenic epithelium at the cervical growing rim, termed the cervical loop of the odontogenic organ (Fig. 48). This loop shows prominent mitotic activity and gives rise to Hertwig's epithelial root sheath after the outline of the dentino-enamel junction of the crown is completed.

5. It produces the primary calcified enamel cuticle as its final product of amelogenesis.

6. The cells of the various layers of the odontogenic organ join to form a stratified squamous epithelium, the reduced enamel epithelium. A desmolytic function during early eruption has been ascribed to this epithelium.

7. After eruption into the oral cavity, the reduced enamel epithelium becomes the epithelial attachment. The latter elaborates the secondary cuticle in response to stress.

## ACCESSORY STRUCTURES

**Enamel Knot.**—During the cap stage of the enamel organ, the cells at the center of the base of the enamel organ become high columnar, proliferate and arrange themselves to form a conical thickening which extends chiefly into the enamel organ, and which also projects somewhat toward the dental papilla (Fig. 37). Thus, the general concavity of the inner tunic is interrupted at its center by a convex area. This structure was described by Ahrens as the enamel knot. According to Sicher and Tandler, it serves as a germinal center for the rapidly growing enamel organ. Figure 37 shows the concentric arrangement of the cells of the enamel knot, and suggests a whirlpool of activity. However, no greater mitotic activity can be observed here than in other regions of the enamel organ.

**Labial and Lingual Enamel Grooves.**—The projection of the enamel knot toward the dental papilla is at times bounded labially and lingually by what Ahrens calls the labial and lingual enamel grooves (Fig. 37). These are believed to play an important part in the formation of the crown of the tooth.

**Enamel Cord.**—The enamel knot is connected with the summit of the enamel organ by a central epithelial extension, which Bolk calls the enamel septum. Since this structure is located only centrally, Ahrens calls it more appropriately the enamel cord (Fig. 38). According to Schaffer, this enamel cord has a steadying

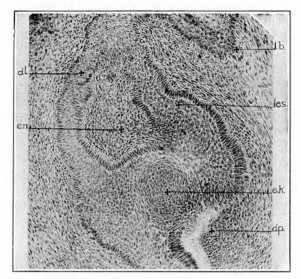

FIG. 41.—Transverse section of a 60.4-mm. human embryo. (Embryo H 44, Department of Anatomy, University of Chicago.) Tooth germ of lower deciduous cuspid, showing enamel niche and lateral enamel strand. *dl*, Dental lamina; *en*, enamel niche; *dp*, dental papilla; *lb*, lip furrow band; *ek*, enamel knot; *les*, lateral enamel strand. (× 215.)

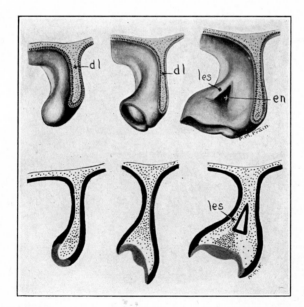

FIG. 42.—Schematic representation of different stages in the development of the anlage of the epithelial portion of the tooth. *dl*, Dental lamina; *les*, lateral enamel strand; *en*, enamel niche. (After Sicher and Tandler, Fig. 146.)

effect on the central portion of the enamel organ, thus enabling it to maintain the invaginated condition of the latter. Bolk regards this cord as a remnant of a partition that, in early phylogenetic development, divides the enamel organ into halves, and he employs it as evidence for his "dimer theory." According to this theory the teeth of the primates have a double origin, and have evolved through the fusion of two primordial teeth.

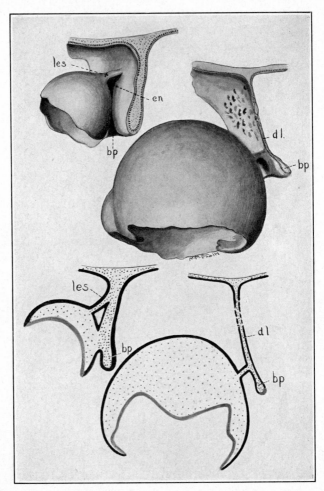

Fig. 43.—Schematic representation of different stages in the development of the anlage of the epithelial portion of the tooth. *bp*, Bud for permanent tooth; *dl*, dental lamina; *en*, enamel niche; *les*, lateral enamel strand. (After Sicher and Tandler, Fig. 146.)

**Enamel Navel.**—The enamel cord has been described as ending in a constriction at the summit of the enamel organ called the enamel navel. Both the enamel knot and the enamel navel disappear later.

**Lateral Enamel Strand.**—The enamel organ is connected with the dental lamina by means of a broad attachment which undergoes gradual constriction (Figs. 42 and 43). According to Sicher and Tandler the dental lamina is soon split into two

PLATE IV

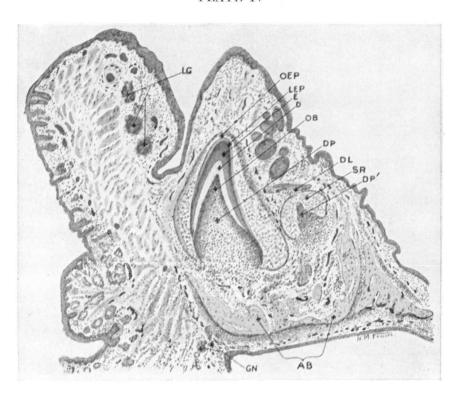

Primary and permanent tooth germ.   Upper jaw and lip of a human fetus.
(After Rauber-Kopsch.)

| | | | |
|---|---|---|---|
| AB. | alveolar bone | GN. | glands of nasal epithelium |
| D. | dentin | LEP. | inner layer of enamel epithelium |
| DL. | dental lamina | LG. | labial glands |
| DP. | dental pulp | OB. | odontoblastic layer |
| DP'. | dental papilla of permanent tooth germ | OEP. | outer layer of enamel epithelium |
| | | SR. | stellate reticulum |
| E. | enamel | | |

parts by the ingrowth of neighboring mesoderm. One part remains in immediate contact with the dental lamina. The other part is narrow and, because it connects the more lateral or labial portion of the enamel organ with the dental lamina, Bolk has described it as the lateral enamel strand (Figs. 41, 42 and 43). He considers it the remnant of a second dental lamina from which arose a separate tooth germ corresponding to the labial portion of the enamel organ. In his opinion the dental lamina and the lateral enamel strand have an equal share in the formation of the enamel organ which is, thus, a double structure.

**Enamel Niche.**—The space bounded by the dental lamina, the lateral enamel strand and the enamel organ is called the enamel niche (Figs. 41, 42 and 43). These relationships vary according to the stage of development and the type of tooth, and present different appearances according to the plane in which the sections are cut.

**Accessory Lamina.**—An accessory lamina sinking down into the mesoderm is sometimes found labial to the dental lamina. It is probably a rudimentary structure, and is associated by various observers with the prelacteal tooth anlagen, or the tooth glands found in reptiles. It disappears like the dental lamina. This structure presents an interesting field for further investigation.

## THE PERMANENT TOOTH BUDS

While the dental lamina breaks up for the most part prior to enamel formation, the deeper margins of its lingual aspect grow as a free end (Figs. 41, 42 and 43). This part of the dental lamina is called the secondary lamina, and extends further downward and lingual to the tooth germ of the deciduous tooth. It develops into the enamel organ for the corresponding permanent tooth and passes through the same phases of development as do the primary teeth (Plate IV).

### The Developmental Stages of the Tooth

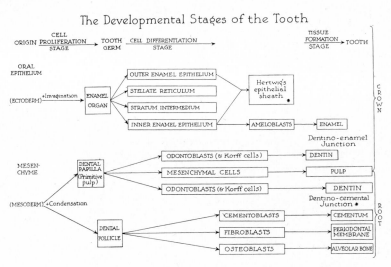

* Hertwig's epithelial sheath is formed by the union of the inner and outer enamel epithelium and determines the pattern of the dentino-cemental junction

Fig. 44.—The developmental stages of tooth. (Schour and Poncher, courtesy of Am. Jour. Dis. Child.)

**Permanent Molars.**—The origin and development of the permanent molars differ from that of the other permanent teeth. They are the only permanent teeth whose enamel organ springs directly from the dental lamina in the same way as those for the deciduous teeth. About the seventeenth week *in utero* at a point on the dental lamina distal to the enamel organs of the second deciduous molar, a bud develops into the enamel organ for the first permanent molar. At about the time of birth the tooth germ is complete and apposition has begun.

With the further growth of the jaws, the dental lamina extends distally back of the enamel organ of the first permanent molar, where it continues to give off buds for the second and third permanent molars. The permanent molars thus belong embryologically to the deciduous dentition.

**Fate of Dental Lamina.**—The dental lamina finally becomes fenestrated and resorbed. The process begins in the late bell stage of the enamel organ. The dental sac which surrounds the tooth severs the epithelial connection

---

LEGEND FOR FIG 45.

FIG. 45.—The embryology and growth-pattern of the deciduous central incisor.
(Schour and Poncher, courtesy of Jour. Dis. Child.)

*A*, Primary stage of proliferation of the oral epithelium (*O.ep.*) forming the bud-like dental anlage (*D.a*). This occurs at the sixth week of intra-uterine life for the deciduous central incisor. *B*, Secondary stage of epithelial proliferation and invagination forming cap-shaped enamel organ (*En.org.*). Note the condensation of the underlying mesenchymal tissue (*Mes.*) into the dental papilla (D.p.) (about the end of the second month *in utero*). *C*, Stage of cell differentiation. The cells of the bell-shaped enamel organ and dental papilla (*D.p.*) are differentiated for their various functions (about fourth month *in utero*). *D*, Primary stage of tissue formation. Dentin formation precedes enamel formation slightly. Note the first dentin cap (black) at the incisal tip. The permanent tooth bud (*P.b.*) is separated from its parent tooth germ and will undergo the same developmental stages (about fourth month *in utero*). *E*, Secondary stage in tissue formation. The enamel is apposed from within outward and the corresponding dentin from without inward. Note the development of Hertwig's epithelial sheath (*H.e.s.*) to guide the formation of the root. *F*, Neonatal stage of tissue formation. *G*, Midsagittal view of the deciduous central incisor, showing the pattern of formation as represented by the incremental bands of Retzius in the enamel (striated portion) and Owen's lines of contour in the dentin. *N* and *n* represent accentuated incremental lines associated with the neonatal period (about one year of age). *H*, Transverse view through the gingival portion of the crown as indicated by the arrow in *G*. The incremental bands of Retzius and Owen's lines of contour resemble the concentric seasonal rings of the tree.

*Am.*, ameloblasts
*Al.b.*, alveolar bone
*Cem.*, cementum
*D.a.*, dental anlage
*Den.*, dentin
*D.e.j.*, dentino-enamel junction
*D.f.*, dental follicle
*D.l.*, dental lamina
*D.p.*, dental papilla
*En.*, enamel
*En.org.*, enamel organ
*H.e.s.*, Hertwig's epithelial sheath

*I.e.e.*, inner enamel epithelium
*Mes.*, undifferentiated mesenchyme
*N.*, neonatal line in enamel
*n.*, neonatal line in dentin
*Od.*, odontoblasts
*O.e.e.*, outer enamel epithelium
*O.e.p.*, oral epithelium
*P.b.*, permanent tooth bud
*R.e.*, reduced enamel epithelium
*S.i.*, stratum intermedium
*S.r.*, stellate reticulum

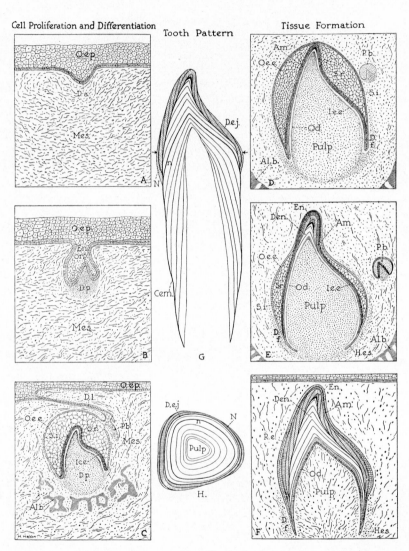

FIG. 45.

of the enamel organ to the oral epithelium.  Remnants of the lamina sometimes persist as epithelial isles, and may differentiate into cysts, enamel
masses or supernumerary teeth.  When a supernumerary tooth develops
between the deciduous and permanent teeth, the first tooth to erupt after
the loss of the deciduous tooth is usually the supernumerary.

## SUMMARY OF THE DEVELOPMENT OF THE TOOTH GERM

The tooth is a derivative of the skin.  It arises at the free margin of the
jaws primarily from an epithelial thickening called the *dental lamina* (Fig.
45*A*).  This epithelial base proliferates at its deeper end, invaginates
(Fig. 45*B*) and finally *differentiates* into the odontogenic organ (Fig. 45*C*).
The cells that line the invaginated portion constitute the *inner enamel
epithelium* (Fig. 45, *I.e.e.*).  The shorter peripheral cells constitute the
*outer enamel epithelium* (*O.e.e.*).  The more central portion consists largely
of the *stellate reticulum* (*S.r.*) and a thick layer of *stratum intermedium*
(*S.i.*) next to the inner enamel epithelium.  The connective tissue which
borders the invaginated portion condenses and forms the *dental papilla*
(*D.p.*), the primordium of the dentin and the pulp.  The boundary between
the enamel organ and the dental papilla constitutes the future permanent
dentino-enamel junction (*D.e.j.*).

Connective tissue cells arrange themselves about the outer surface of the
enamel organ and the base of the dental papilla, and form the *dental sac*,
which will contribute to the formation of the cementum, periodontal membrane and alveolar bone.  *The tooth germ* thus consists of the *enamel organ*,
the *dental papilla* and the *dental sac* (Fig. 45*C*).  This stage is reached in
the fourth fetal month in the case of lower central deciduous incisors and
is preparatory to the formation of the dental tissues.

## ROOT FORMATION

Hertwig's sheath is a double layered epithelium derived from the fusion
of the inner and outer enamel epithelium.  In contrast to the odontogenic
organ it contains no intervening stellate reticulum or stratum intermedium.
The sheath establishes the dentino-cemental junction of the root just as
the inner enamel epithelium of the bell stage previously outlines the blue-
print for the dentino-enamel junction of the crown.  Just prior to the
beginning of root formation and at the level of the future cemento-enamel
junction, Hertwig's sheath bends at a right angle to form the epithelial
diaphragm which narrows the cervical opening of the developing tooth
(Fig. 45, E).  This diaphragm, resting on a suspensory ligament, tends to
serve as a fixed base, the proliferation of the Hertwig's sheath occurring
largely at the edges of the epithelial diaphragm (Figs. 46 and 47).  In three
dimensions, Hertwig's sheath takes the pattern of one or more epithelial
tubes, depending on the number of roots.

In singled-rooted teeth, Hertwig's epithelial sheath is a single tubular structure. In multi-rooted teeth the central cervical opening becomes bridged by horizontal flaps of the epithelial diaphragm. These proliferate and fuse to form the bifurcation with two or more smaller cervical openings, one for each root. Thus a swimming trunk would represent a three di-

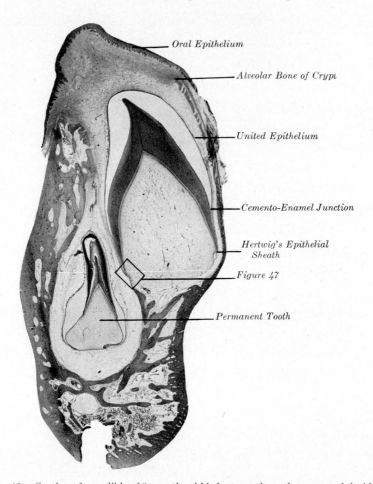

*Oral Epithelium*

*Alveolar Bone of Crypt*

*United Epithelium*

*Cemento-Enamel Junction*

*Hertwig's Epithelial Sheath*

*Figure 47*

*Permanent Tooth*

FIG. 46.—Section of mandible of 9-months old infant cut through unerupted deciduous canine and its permanent successor which lies lingually and apically to it. The enamel of the deciduous canine crown is completed and lost because of decalcification. Root formation has begun. Higher magnification of formative end of root is seen in Figure 47. (× 17.)

mensional model of a double rooted tooth in its post-coronal stage of development, and shorts or trousers would model the subsequent stages of root elongation. However, the "cloth" of Hertwig's sheath is resorbed and destroyed soon after it proliferates so that it is highly discontinuous and temporary. Remnants persist near the root surface as epithelial rests. (Fig. 166).

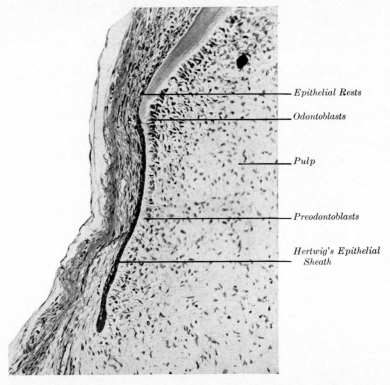

— *Epithelial Rests*

— *Odontoblasts*

— *Pulp*

— *Preodontoblasts*

— *Hertwig's Epithelial Sheath*

Fig. 47.—Higher magnification of area indicated in Figure 46. Hertwig's epithelial sheath organizes the formation of the preodontoblasts which soon differentiate into the dentin forming odontoblasts. Note the epithelial remains following the degeneration of the epithelial sheath. (× 200.)

## INTERDEPENDENCE IN TOOTH DEVELOPMENT

The classification of tooth development in terms of successive stages of growth, calcification, eruption and attrition and their further subdivisions is helpful in recognizing and understanding clinical anomalies in terms of the developmental stages at which they occurred (Fig. 33). However, it must be pointed out that these stages are not sharply delineated. They overlap and have reciprocal influences. Thus, the life history of the tooth involves not only a number of stages which proceed in orderly sequence, but also calls for the proper timing and a delicate balance and interdependence of a number of physiologic processes concerned with the formation of the dental tissues. For example, the developmental history of enamel and dentin proceeds in the following sequence. (Fig. 48).

A. Proliferation of the cells of the inner odontogenic (enamel) epithelium and their differentiation into preameloblasts.

B. Organizing influence of the preameloblasts upon the peripheral pulpal cells to differentiate into odontoblasts.

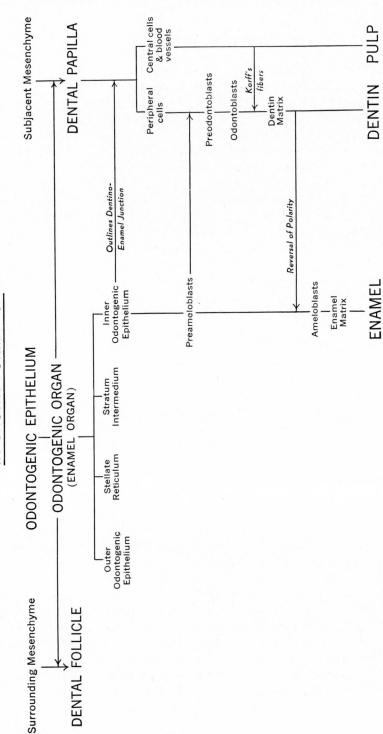

Fig. 48.—Schematic representation of the interrelationships and interdependencies in crown formation.

In tissue culture of tooth germs, odontoblasts differentiate only in the presence of the odontogenic epithelium. If, on the other hand, the latter is defective, the odontoblasts that do differentiate are abnormal in structure and function. This has been observed in the rat incisor in experimental Vitamin A deficiency.

C. Formation of dentin matrix.

D. Differentiation of the preameloblasts into ameloblasts.

This event illustrates the reciprocal influence of odontoblastic activity upon enamel formation. With the deposition of the first dentin, the preameloblasts are cut off from their original nutritive source of the dental papilla and instead depend on the follicular connective tissue surrounding the odontogenic organ for their nutrition. This leads to the reversal of the polarization of the preameloblast (nucleus shifts from the distal to the proximal end) and its concomitant differentiation into an ameloblast.

E. Formation of enamel matrix.

F. Calcification of outer dentin layer (Mantle Dentin).

G. Calcification of enamel.

These and other interdependent relationships outlined in Figure 48 for the crown forms are so essential that the arrest of any one step may lead to the omission or disturbance of the subsequent processes and thus upset the total balance in normal development.

**Root Formation.**—Hertwig's epithelial sheath continues the function of the odontogenic organ in respect to dentin formation in the root as shown in Figure 49. In addition, it probably plays a role in the organization of the periodontium, particularly in the formation of cementum.


## EXPERIMENTAL STUDIES IN TOOTH TRANSPLANTS

In recent years a number of tooth transplant experiments have been conducted in man and lower animals. These were based on our understanding of the principles of interdependence in tooth development and have added new knowledge to developmental oral histology. Crowns of third molars have been transplanted in the alveolar socket from which the first permanent molar was extracted. Some of the transplants were observed to continue to develop with the formation of part of the root and periodontal structures.

Recent transplantation research demonstrated experimentally that the developing root exerts its influence even on connective tissue of a non-oral site. Hoffman and Gillette removed molar tooth germs from the mesenchymal dental follicles in the hamster jaw before root formation began and transplanted them into connective tissue under the skin of the back. These transplanted tooth germs succeed in organizing new dental follicles, apparently from the connective tissue of the skin, and undergo root formation provided their epithelial root sheaths were not injured. Furthermore, they induce the surrounding connective tissue to form cementum, peri-

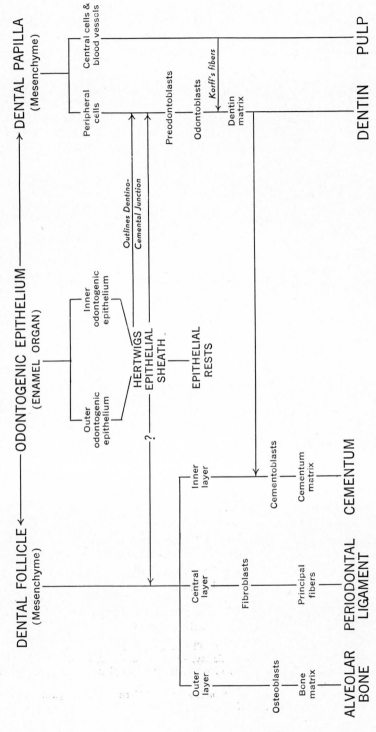

FIG. 49.—Schematic representation of the interrelationships and interdependencies in root formation.

odontal ligament, and alveolar bone. Thus the influence of the tooth germ seems to extend into the surrounding mesenchymal tissue for a considerable distance. (Fig. 50).

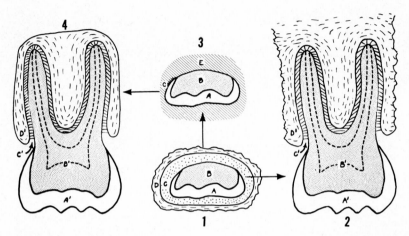

FIG. 50.—Diagram showing experimental results following transplantation of molar tooth germ of new-born hamster into connective tissue of skin. *1*, developing molar in situ; *2*, normal development of tooth and periodontium; *3*, transplantation of the enamel organ and dental papilla into connective tissue of skin, E; and 4, development of transplant.

*A*, enamel organ; *A*[1], enamel; *B*, dental papilla; *B*[1], dentin and pulp; *C*, mesoderm surrounding developing tooth; *C*[1], periodontal ligament; *D*, bone of the crypt; *D*[1], alveolar bone; *E*, subcutameous connective tissue not ordinarily forming periodontium. (Courtesy Hoffman and Gillette).

Such influences, passing from one tissue to another, are responsible for coordinating the development of the different tissues so that a harmoniously proportioned whole, the dental-periodontal unit results. While the sequence described in Figs. 48 and 49 suggests that such influences are occurring, the existence of such interdependencies can be proven only by experimental methods, that is, by experimentally separating, tissue-culturing, transplanting, or injecting tissues in various combinations. After proving that influences do pass from tissue to tissue, there still remains the problem of identifying the physical or chemical nature of these influences. These "odontogenic tissue hormones" are apparently short-range or local in their effects in contrast to the circulating hormones produced by the endocrine glands.

### BIBLIOGRAPHY

BEAMS, H. W., and KING, R. L.: The Golgi Apparatus in the Developing Tooth With Special Reference to Polarity, Anat. Rec., *57*, 29, 1933.

BEVELANDER, G., and JOHNSON, P. L.: Alkaline Phosphatase in Amelogenesis, Anat. Rec., *104*, No. 2, 125, 1949.

BOLK, L.: On the Development of the Enamel-Germ, Odontological Essays No. 2, Jour. Anat., *55*, 152, 1921.

HOFFMAN, RICHARD L.: Formation of Periodontal Tissues Around Developing Roots of Subcutaneously Implanted Hamster Molars, J. of Dent. Res., *39*, May–June, 1960.

MEYER: Histology and Histogenesis of Human Teeth, transl. by Churchill, Chapter 7 discusses Bolk's Dimer Theory.

ORBAN, B.: Editor. Oral Histology and Embryology. 4th Ed., St. Louis, C. V. Mosby Co., 1957.

SCHOUR, I.: Early Human Tooth Development With Special Reference to the Relationship Between the Dental Lamina and the Lip-furrow Band, Jour. Dent. Res., *9*, 699, 1929.

SCHOUR, I., and MASSLER, M.: Studies in Tooth Development, The Growth Pattern of the Human Teeth, Jour. Am. Dent. Assn., *27*, 1778–1793, 1918–1931, 1940.

CHAPTER 5

# The Development of Enamel

**Introduction.**—Considerable controversy has centered about the histogenesis of the enamel. The principal theories of enamel formation by the transformation of the ameloblasts into prisms (Waldeyer, 1871, and Tomes, C. S., 1876) and by secretion (Kölliker, 1880; Le Gros and Magitot, 1880) have been variously modified by v. Ebner, Williams, Studnicka, Mummery, Lams, and Orban. The evidence without doubt favors the view that the enamel is a cuticular secretion of the ameloblasts which later becomes impregnated with lime salts.

In its initial stages the development of enamel is so closely interdependent with that of dentin that it is difficult to treat each separately. Figures 48 and 49 outline some of the significant interdependent steps that lead to normal development. This is particularly true of the initial stages at the growth center (Fig. 48) which involve the transition from the advanced *bell stage* to what may for convenience be termed the *shell* stage. The latter is characterized by the forming and calcifying enamel and dentin at the growth center (Plate IV and Fig. 51).

## STAGES PREPARATORY TO ENAMEL FORMATION

The following changes occur in the odontogenic organ preparatory to the formation of enamel:

1. The stellate reticulum becomes reduced (Fig. 51).

2. The outer enamel epithelium approaches the stratum intermedium and the inner enamel epithelium. When the three layers have approximated, they are called the united enamel epithelium (Fig. 51).

3. The outer enamel epithelium becomes irregular and connective tissue papillæ containing capillary loops project into it. This modification probably provides for a greater nutritive supply to the avascular enamel organ. An especially high development of this process is reached in the rodent incisor, where the enamel is being formed continuously and more rapidly than in the human tooth (Fig. 53). These changes occur only immediately preceding amelogenesis and are therefore observed first at the growth-centers, which are located at the tips of the cusps or at the incisal edges (Fig. 51).

4. The inner enamel epithelium becomes differentiated into the ameloblasts. The preameloblasts, before dentin formation occurs, are apparently in direct contact with the odontoblasts with only a basement or limiting

( 76 )

membrane separating them. The boundary between the ameloblasts and the odontoblasts at this stage shows the beginning of the scalloped contour of the future dentino-enamel junction whose form is already determined by the interface between these two layers.

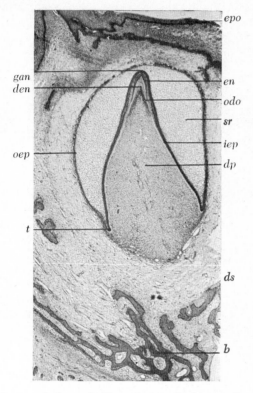

FIG. 51.—Tooth germ of a lower deciduous incisor of a five-months old human embryo immediately after the beginning of amelogenesis. The stellate reticulum is reduced immediately over the center of growth. Note the greater width of the dentin cone as compared with the enamel layer. *b*, Bone of mandible; *den.*, dentin; *dp.*; dental papilla; *ds*, dental sac; *en*, enamel; *epo*, oral epithelial; *gan*, ameloblasts; *iep*, inner enamel epithelium; *odo*, odontoblasts; *oep*, outer enamel epithelium, *sr*, stellate reticulum; *t*, Epithelial cervical loop. (From Schour, in Cowdry's *Special Cytology*, courtesy of Paul B. Hoeber, Inc.)

## CYTOLOGY OF THE AMELOBLASTS

At the beginning of their appositional activity the ameloblast show no mitotic figures. During formation they reach their greatest columnar height and are hexagonal in cross-sections (Fig. 54). They are on the average 40 $\mu$ in length and 5 to 6 $\mu$ in diameter. These cells are connected with one another and those of the stratum intermedium by fine intercellular bridges (Fig. 54). Their nuclei are oval and elongated in the direction of the long axis of the cell and are situated at the distal ends of the cell. They very often contain several distinct nucleoli. The cell body contains many mitochondria, some of which are especially long, a distinctly stained filament, and a diplosome situated between the nucleus and the surface of the cell facing the enamel. The cytoplasm is coarsely granular and acidophilic, and contains basophilic pre-enamel granules or drops.

The Golgi apparatus changes its position according to function. In the inactive ameloblasts it is situated between the stratum intermedium and the nucleus. In the actively secreting ameloblasts it is found between the nucleus and the enamel end of the cells. The ameloblasts become phosphatase positive just before enamel matrix formation occurs. The ribonucleic acid content is rich and equal to that of the active osteoblast.

The dentinal ends of the ameloblasts are united by a network of terminal bars, which are a condensation of the intercellular substance between the ameloblasts. The terminal bars give the appearance of a dot or line in cross or longitudinal section, but present a honeycomb network enclosing the ameloblasts when seen from the surface (Fig. 52).

## AMELOGENESIS

Amelogenesis, the development of the enamel, occurs in two well-defined phases. The first may be termed the formative phase. In it the enamel rods are formed by the ameloblasts and, as a primary step of calcification, about 30 per cent of the final mineral contents are deposited in the organic substance of the rod. The second phase is characterized by a gradual replacement of most of the remaining organic material of the rods and inter-rod substance by lime salts. This second phase has been termed enamel maturation.

### FORMATIVE PHASE

Although the presence and the differentiation of the inner enamel epithelium precedes and is essential to dentin formation, the ameloblasts do not show any secretory activity until a microscopic cuspal portion of dentin has been formed (Fig. 51). Amelogenesis thus lags slightly behind dentin formation in the crown.

Amelogenesis begins with the formation of Tomes' processes by the ameloblasts. This process is a protoplasmic outgrowth of the dentinal end of each ameloblast in the shape of a $4\,\mu$ long hexagonal prism. Its structure does not essentially differ from the dentinal end of the ameloblast itself. The Tomes' processes are separated from each other by extensions of the terminal bars. In a complex sequence of changes the material of Tomes' process changes to the organic substrate of an enamel rod (prism). While the Tomes' process is transformed into organic-rod substance, the process itself is regenerated by a renewed outgrowth from the ameloblasts. Formation of the Tomes' process and its transformation into organic-rod substance occur in a daily rhythm. Formation of the rod segment is concomitant with primary calcification (30%). The resulting material is the enamel matrix. The daily rhythm of formation of Tomes' process, its transformation and primary calcification, leave their impress upon the rods. These remain segmented by the alternation of 4 microns long calcified segments, enamel globules, and the intervening thin transverse striations of less calcified substance.

While the secretion, transformation, and calcification of Tomes' process take place, the extensions of the terminal bars are transformed into the

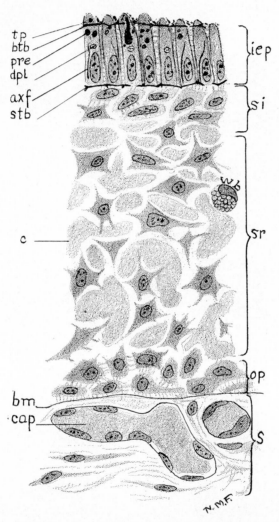

FIG. 52.—Longitudinal section of enamel organ of two-day kitten: *axf*, axial filament; *bm*, basement membrane; *btb*, distal terminal bars; *c*, colloidal intercellular substance; *cap*, capillary; *dpl*, diplosome; *iep*, inner layer of active ameloblasts; *op*, outer layer of enamel epithelium; *pre*, pre-enamel granules; *s*, dental sac; *si*, stratum intermedium; *sr*, stellate reticulum; *stb*, proximal terminal bars; *t*, Tomes' process; *wb*, white blood cell. (× 900.) (After Lams, in Cowdry's *Special Cytology*, courtesy of Paul B. Hoeber, Inc., 1921.)

interrod (interprismatic) substance.  The developing rod lies as a rule at an angle to the axis of the ameloblasts.

Each enamel prism is thus derived from a single ameloblast.  A cross-section of completely formed enamel presents a picture that is practically identical in form and arrangement with that of a cross-section of the ameloblasts and their intercellular spaces; the prisms corresponding to the ameloblasts and the interprismatic substance to the intercellular substance.

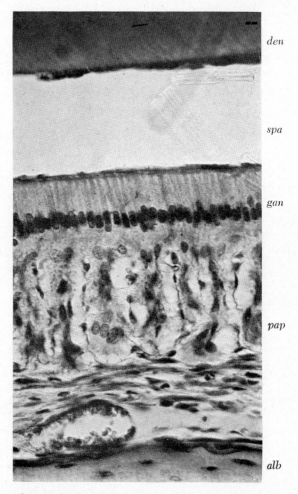

Fig. 53.—Enamel organ in the middle portion of the upper incisor of a ten-months rat:  *alb.*, alveolar bone; *den,* dentin; *gan,* ameloblasts; *pap,* epithelial papillæ; *spa,* space formerly occupied by enamel lost in decalcification.  (Schour in Cowdry's *Special Cytology,* courtesy of Paul P. Hoeber, Inc.)

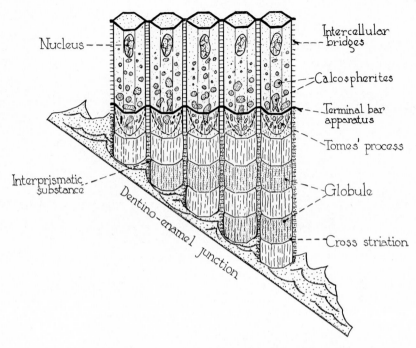

Fig. 54.—Diagrammatic representation of amelogenesis. Adapted from Lams. Truncated effect of Tomes' process is probably an artefact.

## PATTERN OF FORMATION AT GROWTH CENTERS

The formation of the enamel rod proceeds outward from the dentino-enamel junction to the surface of the enamel. This process begins on the future dentino-enamel junction at certain "high points" which correspond to the number of the individual cusps on posterior or incisal edges of anterior teeth, and which constitute the growth-centers of the tooth. Amelogenesis begins at these individual growth-centers and extends cervically in graded daily intervals. Successively adjacent ameloblasts begin their formation at successively later intervals. The enamel surface at any given time will thus be highest at the cuspal tip and will grade to a sharp edge cervically at the dentino-enamel junction (Fig. 55). The form of any given incremental layer is that of a cone in three dimensions, the apex pointing occlusally and the base resting upon the dentino-enamel junction.

Incremental cones of enamel are apposed successively one above another over each growth center in an outward direction until the enamel reaches the full height of the cusp (Fig. 57). The subsequent layers are apposed in the form of truncated cones at the sides, until the size of the tooth is established and the surface of the crown is complete (Figs. 57 and 87). When the incremental cones of adjacent growth-centers meet they fuse at their peripheral margins and, with subsequent formation, complete the

6

particular incremental pattern of a given tooth. The time of formation of any given incremental layer is in proportion to its distance from the growth-center on the dentino-enamel junction. The demarcations between successive incremental layers have been called the striæ of Retzius in the enamel. These striæ end at the enamel surface in shallow grooves, the perikymata (Figs. 57 and 58).

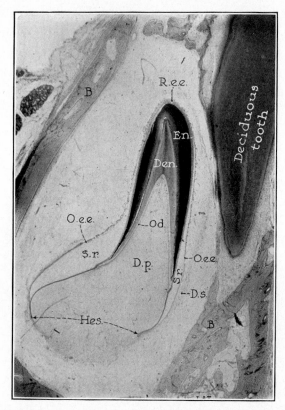

FIG. 55.—Tooth germ of a lower permanent incisor of a nine-months-old human infant. *B*, Bony crypt; *D.p.*, dental papilla; *D.s.*, dental sac; *Den*, dentin; *En*, enamel; *Hes*, cervical loop; *O.e.e.*, outer enamel epithelium; *Od.*, odontoblasts; *R.e.e.*, united enamel epithelium; *S.r.*, stellate reticulum. ( × 09.)

**Incremental Pattern.**—There is no doubt that the process of primary calcification follows that of formation in close succession and accentuates the demarcation between successive incremental layers in the form of the so-called striæ of Retzius. The enamel thus normally presents a stratification in the form of regularly recurring incremental lines (Fig. 60). Schour and Hoffman found that these incremental lines recurred rhythmically at intervals of approximately 16 $\mu$ in the enamel, as well as in the dentin, of a number of mammalian species ranging from opossum to man.

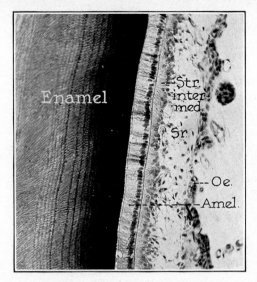

FIG. 56.—Decalcified section of enamel matrix during formation. *Oe*, outer enamel epithelium; *Sr.*, stellate reticulum; *Str. intermed.*, stratum intermedium; *Amel.*, ameloblasts. Note the incremental lines in the enamel matrix. These were produced experimentally by injections of sodium fluoride at different intervals. (× 240.)

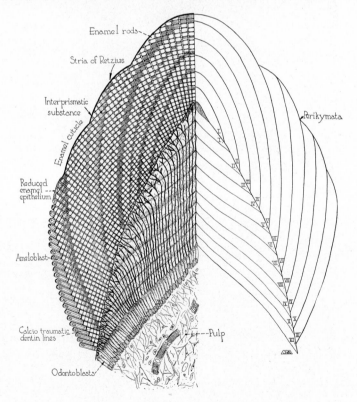

FIG. 57.—Diagrammatic representation of the pattern of formation in the enamel and dentin over a typical growth center. Stippled area represents the first dentinal caplet. Corresponding incremental layers of the enamel and dentin are labeled with corresponding numbers.

The striking constancy in the width of these increments suggests that they are the result of a physico-chemical phase in the calcification process, just as the cross-striations of the enamel prisms (recurring at intervals of approximately $4\mu$) are an expression of the daily appositional rhythm in the activity of the ameloblasts.

The striæ of Retzius as originally described by him are accentuations of individual 16 $\mu$ incremental calcifications rings and are produced by systemic disturbances. These accentuations may be produced by constitu-

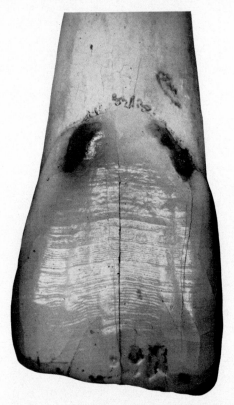

Fig. 58.—Perikymata on enamel surface of central incisor. ($\times$ 7.)

tional or environmental factors such as birth (neonatal ring), weaning, summer or winter seasons, or by diseases that disturb, among other tissues or organs of the body, the enamel that is forming and calcifying at that time.

**Final Product and Fate of the Enamel Organ.**—When the deposition of the enamel matrix is completed and the final thickness of the enamel established, the ameloblasts secrete a final cuticular product called the *primary enamel cuticle*. The ameloblasts now lose their columnar shape. They become indistinguishable from the outer cells of the odontogenic organ and together form stratified squamous epithelium which is termed the reduced enamel epithelium. It is 1 $\mu$ thick and may become calcified. In ordinary methods of histologic preparations, it becomes easily lost but can be isolated from the surface of the enamel by using dilute acids. A view of its inner surface shows the impression of the enamel prisms. In the erupted tooth, this cuticle is soon worn off the surfaces exposed to mastication. In the protected portion of the enamel surface, the reduced enamel epithelium remains attached to the enamel surface and constitutes the *epithelial attachment* or *attached epithelial cuff*.

**Epithelial Attachment.**—After the formation of the enamel cuticle the united enamel epithelium regresses to a stratified squamous epithelium which is called the reduced enamel epithelium and gives rise to the epithelial attachment. The ameloblasts become cuboidal or squamous. In the process of eruption the reduced enamel epithelium unites with the oral epithelium and then gradually peels off the erupting crown (Fig. 207).

The epithelial attachment is at first thin, consisting of only 3 to 4 layers of cells. However, with age it increases to 10 to 20 rows of cells and tends to migrate rootward along the cementum (Fig. 179). The mode of proliferation of the epithelial attachment in thickness and in down growth presents an interesting research challenge.

**The Secondary Enamel Cuticle.**—This is a layer 2 to 10 $\mu$ thick which is external to the primary enamel cuticle and is composed of the hornified cells of the epithelial attachment which adhered to the tooth surface. It was first described by Gottlieb in 1921 as a layer of hornified epithelial cells which is derived from the epithelial attachment. The secondary cuticle is called the *cuticula dentis*, because it may cover both enamel and cementum. He considered it of significance in the prevention of dental caries since it may form a protective barrier against the ingress of oral fluids and bacteria. It is resistant to acids and alkalies.

## MATURATION OF THE ENAMEL

The calcification of enamel differs from that observed in any other calcified structure. Mature enamel contains little organic matrix and water. (2-4%). The organic enamel matrix deposited by the ameloblasts is almost completely impreganted by inorganic salts. Just how this process occurs is not known.

The process of calcification apparently consists of the penetration of soluble mineral salts into an organic substance. It would seem in accordance with all known facts, that the structure of the enamel is first laid down in a material which is largely organic and that the calcification of this material proceeds by infiltration. There is nothing, however, in this protein material that relates it to living cytoplasm.

That the mineral compounds actually pass through the various layers of the enamel organ, and particularly through the ameloblasts, is indicated by microchemical findings. The calcification of the prisms appears to progress from the center toward the periphery. Later, the interprismatic substance also becomes calcified so that, after decalcification, practically no residue is left.

The secondary or final calcification of the enamel has been termed maturation of the enamel. At the beginning of this phase, the enamel matrix consists of organic substance (and water) and mineral salts in the ratio of two to one. During the maturation of the enamel, almost all of the organic substance becomes increasingly impregnated by mineral salts until the mature enamel consists of 2 to 4 per cent organic material and water and 96 to 98 per cent inorganic material.

The final impregnation of organic material by mineral salts starts only after, in the occlusal parts of the crown, the definitive thickness of enamel matrix has been attained. The maturation proceeds in an incremental pattern.

The maturation of the enamel is a gradual process when compared to the rhythmic process of development of enamel matrix. Maturation proceeds very slowly and the parts of the enamel close to the cemento-enamel junction may still be in the matrix stage when the tooth is in full function.

Chase and others have pointed out the role of the ameloblasts in the maturation of the enamel. The premature reduction of the ameloblasts to half their height is associated with incomplete calcification of the enamel. Further advances in our understanding of the maturation process will help to explain the fact that topical application of fluorides for the reduction of dental decay is more effective in recently erupted teeth and will also clarify the characteristic diffuse rather than incremental hypocalcification seen in endemic dental fluorosis and in amelogenesis imperfecta.

## BIBLIOGRAPHY

CHASE, S. W.: Histogenesis of the Enamel, Jour. Am. Dent. Assn., *19*, 1275, 1932.
————: The Nature of the Enamel Matrix at Different Ages, Jour. Am. Dent. Assn., *22*, 1343, 1935.
————: The Origin, Structure and Duration of Nasmyth's Membrane, Anat. Rec., *33*, 357, 1926.
————: The Interrelation of Maturation and the Histogenesis of Hypoplasia in Dental Enamel, in: Proceedings Dental Centenary Celebration, Baltimore, edited by Anderson, G. M., Waverly Press, 1940.
CRABB, H. S. M.: The Pattern of Mineralization of Human Dental Enamel. Proc. of the Roy. Soc. of Med., *52*, (2), 118–122, Feb.
ENGFELDT, BENGT, and HAMMARLUND-ESSLER, ERNA: Studies on Mineralized Dental Tissues, IX. A Microradiographic Study of the Mineralization of Developing Enamel, Acta Odontologica Scandinavica, vol. *14*, 273–289, No. 3, 1956.
HUGGINS, C. B., McCARROLL, H. R., and DAHLBERG, A. A.: Transplantation of Tooth Germ Elements and the Experimental Heterotopic Formation of Dentin and Enamel, Jour. Exp. Med., *60*, 199, 1934.
KITCHIN, P. C.: Some Observations in Enamel Development as Shown in the Mandibular Incisor of the White Rat, Jour. Dent. Res., *13*, 25, 1933.
LAMS, H.: Histogenese de la dentine et de L'émail chez les mammifères, Compt. rend. Soc. d. biol., *83*, 800, 1920.

Schour, I.:   Ch. on Teeth, in: Willier, B. H., P. A. Weiss and V. Hambruger's Analysis of Development, Ch. VII, 492–498, Philadelphia, W. B. Saunders Co., 1st Ed., 1955.

Schour, I., and Hoffman, M. M.:   Experimental Demonstration of the Daily Apposition of 16 micra of Enamel and Dentin in Growing Mammalian Teeth, Jour. Dent. Res., *15*, 161, 1935.

Schour, I., and Poncner, H. G.:   The Rate of Apposition of Human Enamel and Dentin as Measured by the Effects of Acute Fluorosis, Am. Jour. D. Child., *54*, 757–776, 1937.

Weinmann, J. P., Wessinger, G. D., and Reed, G.:   Correlation of Chemical and Histological Investigation on Developing Enamel, Jour. Dent. Res., *21*, 171, 1942.

# CHAPTER 6

# The Structure of Enamel

**Definition.**—Enamel may be defined as the hard translucent tissue covering the anatomical crowns of the teeth in man and many animals.

**Distribution of Enamel.**—The enamel forms a cap over the coronal dentin. Its distribution is best studied in ground sections cut longitudinally through the entire tooth (Figs. 30 and 31). It gives the detail of crown form to the tooth.

The enamel extends to the cemento-enamel junction but is often slightly overlapped by the cementum at its gingival termination (Fig. 85). It extends farther apically on the labial, buccal and lingual than upon the proximal surfaces, especially in the incisors, canines and premolars.

**Thickness of Enamel.**—The enamel is thickest over the cusps and incisal edges and grades down to a very thin edge at the cemento-enamel junction. Hopewell-Smith gave the following measurements: at the incisal edge of the incisors the enamel is 2 mm. thick; over the cusps of the bicuspids, 2.3 mm.; and over the cusps of the molars, 2.6 mm.

**Physical Properties and Functions of Enamel.**—Enamel is the hardest animal tissue and yields sparks when struck with steel, but is brittle and inelastic. It forms the hard protective surface of the crown and has a translucency which increases with the degree of its calcification. The functions of enamel are to resist the abrasion of mastication and to protect the underlying dentin. It depends upon the support of the underlying elastic dentin for strength.

**Chemical Analysis of Enamel.**—The enamel contains less organic matter than any other tissue of the body. It resembles the mineral apatite in its composition. Chemically, it is composed almost entirely (97 per cent) of inorganic salts, 90 per cent of which consists of calcium phosphate in the form of hydroxyl-apatite ($Ca_{10}(PO_4)_6$-$(OH)_2$) the rest being distributed in the order of greatest amount among calcium carbonate, magnesium phosphate, calcium fluoride and traces of other salts.

Dr. H. C. Hodge, of the University of Rochester, gives the following "best" analysis:

Water . . . . . . . . . . . . . 1.2– 4.0 per cent
Organic matter . . . . . . . . . 0.2– 0.8 per cent
Inorganic matter . . . . . . . . . 95.0–97.0 per cent

( 88 )

## Inorganic Matter.

| *Principal Components.* | | *Lesser Components.* | |
| --- | --- | --- | --- |
| Ca | 34.5–37.1 per cent | NA | 0.20 per cent |
| P | 17.1–18.0 per cent | K | 0.05 per cent |
| $CO_3$ | 2.0– 2.8 per cent | Fe | 0.02 per cent |
| Mg | 0.2– 0.6 per cent | Cl | 0.30 per cent |
| | | F | 0.02 per cent |

The balance up to 100% is made up of oxygen.

**Organic Substance.**—The view that enamel contains no organic matrix had been nurtured by the fact that in routine decalcification of teeth the enamel is completely lost. With improved methods, involving careful process of decalcification and embedding, the minute amount of organic framework is preserved and subject to histologic and chemical analysis. Studies of the human enamel under the electron microscope show the existence of a fine submicroscopic fibrillar network. These delicate organic fibrils surround the inorganic crystals and permeate both the enamel prisms and the interprismatic substance (Figs. 59 and 64).

Fig. 59.—Electron micrograph of thin section of demineralized mature human enamel. Note prism sheaths and submicroscopic fibrillar network within and between prisms. × 20,000. (Courtesy of D. B. Scott).

In the normal adult and fully calcified dry teeth the enamel contains less than 1 per cent organic matter. The bulk of the organic protein matter is a keratin-like substance. In addition, there is a small amount of widely spread glycoprotein ground substance. Sognnaes has suggested that this carbohydrate protein complex may act as a coating of the organic fibers and possibly serve as a bond between the crystals. The enamel contains no soluble protein and no enzymes and when fully formed is not the seat of any vital substance or process. It is permeable to various solutions and dyes.

**Differences Between Enamel and Other Calcified Structures.**—The enamel differs from all other calcified tissues in:

1. Origin.
2. The form of the structural elements of the tissue.
3. Degree of calcification.
4. Non-vitality.

It is well to emphasize these points of difference, for throughout dental and medical writings, reasoning by analogy from bone conditions to tooth conditions, and especially to changes in the enamel, is often found. For instance, the argument has been advanced that because there may be changes in the bones of the mother during pregnancy, "softening" of the teeth should be expected. Many similar, though less crude, arguments would not be made if it were remembered that histogenetically, histologically, chemically and physiologically the enamel stands alone.

**Origin.**—In mammals the enamel is the only calcified tissue derived from epithelium. All other calcified tissues are mesenchymal. Histogenetically, then, the enamel is ultimately derived from ectodermal epithelium, while the other calcified tissues arise from the mesoderm. Thus, even at the first step in the differentiation of the cells, enamel is different from bone, cementum or dentin.

**The Form of the Structural Elements.**—The enamel is made up of prismatic rods of inorganic matter held together by an inorganic cementing substance. All other calcified tissues are made up of fibrous intercellular substance containing inorganic salts, and are usually arranged in layers. The structure of the enamel differs so greatly from all other calcified tissues that it is difficult to compare them briefly. The subsequent paragraphs on the structural elements of enamel will clarify these differences further.

**Degree of Calcification.**—The enamel is the hardest known structure in the body and shows the highest percentage content of inorganic salts. If bone or dentin is subjected to the action of acid the inorganic salts are dissolved out of the organic matrix. However, enough organic matrix is left to retain the form of the original tissue. If enamel is similarly treated with acid, there is little trace of tissue or structure left. If bone or dentin is burned or ignited the organic matter will be driven off and the inorganic portion will be left in the form of the original tissue, still showing its structure. If enamel is ignited, water of combination and whatever foreign matter has clung to the pieces is given off, but the form of the tissue is unchanged. The enamel may be compared to a fossil in which, by molecular change, the organic matter has been removed and inorganic matter *substituted*, so that little organic matter remains, but the structure is preserved. If the inorganic salts were dissolved, (rapidly), no trace of structure would remain. On the other hand, by ignition, nothing but water can be driven off.

The enamel is produced by epithelial cells which are lost and destroyed after the tissue is completed. After the enamel is formed and calcified, it can be changed only by the chemical and physical action of its environment, but it has no power of repair or regeneration.

Fig. 60.—Photomicrograph of ground section of human enamel. Note the vertical course of the enamel rods and the oblique course of the incremental bands of Retzius. The enamel rods show distinct cross striations. ( × 133.)

All other calcified tissues are formed by connective tissue, and remain in vital relation with connective tissue of undifferentiated character. Bone and dentin matrix are therefore simply calcified intercellular substances containing living cells or living cell processes in the spaces of the matrix which maintain its vitality and nutrition. A change in the character or amount of the matrix might possibly be brought about by the vital activity of these cells. The formed and calcified matrix remains in vital relation with its formative cells, which may at any time undergo specialization, under appropriate stimulus, for the purpose of repair. There is therefore no basis for comparisons between pathologic conditions of bone and enamel. While bone is capable of being resorbed physiologically and thus mineral salts become released, all the experimental and clinical evidence available shows that enamel does not undergo changes comparable to those in bone.

## THE STRUCTURAL ELEMENTS OF THE ENAMEL

The enamel is composed of two structural elements:

1. The enamel rods or prisms.
2. The interprismatic substance which unites the rods into a continuous structure.

**Enamel Rods.**—**Shape and Size.**—The enamel rods may be described in general as long, slender prisms, irregularly five- or six-sided (Fig. 61). The

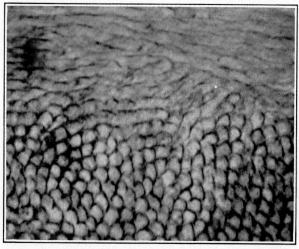

FIG. 61.—Human enamel rods. Decalcified section. In the upper part of the photomicrograph the enamel rods are cut longitudinally, in the lower part, transversely. The dark lines between the prisms are the interprismatic substance. Magnification × 850. (Kronfeld, Dental Histology).

polygonal form is the result of mutual pressure. The outlines are never regular, and unevenness in the distribution of the pressure, or lack of balance in direction, will modify the form of the prisms. The shape of the cross-section of the rods therefore often deviates from the original hexagonal type of the ameloblasts, so that many of them are arched convexly on one side and channeled by one or more longitudinal grooves on the concave side. This modification is believed to result from the uneven pressure exerted on the rods during development, and the calcification which proceeds from the center toward the periphery.

The rods vary about an average of 4 $\mu$ in diameter. They show a longitudinal fibrillation which is probably the remains of the fibrils seen in the Tomes' processes. Supplementary rods have been described.

**Cross-striations.**—The enamel rods contain transverse striations which appear at rather regular intervals approximately 4 $\mu$ apart. They are especially prominent in sections treated with dilute acid in areas which have been slowly decalcifying during the progress of decay and in areas traversed by striæ of Retzius (Fig. 62).

The enamel rods are formed by globules which are deposited one on top of the other, and are separated by intervening striations (Fig. 60). Each cross-striation therefore demarcates a globule deposited in the rod formation and may be said to be a record of the appositional growth of the individual rods.

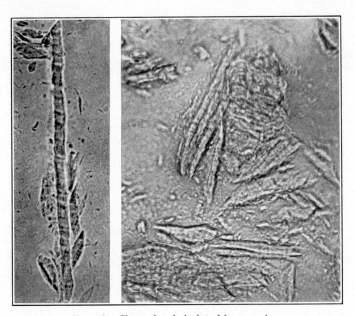

FIG. 62.—Enamel rods isolated by scraping.

In perfectly calcified enamel, the cross-striations are less prominent. The appearance of cross-striation is a sign of either incomplete calcification or decalcification by external factors. The decalcification is usually produced during the progress of decay and might occur in unetched sections through the use of slightly acid baslam. Carefully decalcified sections of enamel show the cross-striations through their difference in staining reactions. The cross-striations, together with the interprismatic substance, represent a system of lesser calcified areas which are richer in organic substance than the rest of the enamel.

**Prism Sheath.**—The surface border of the enamel rods represents the most readily stainable, and therefore the least calcified portion of the rod. This margin is called the prism sheath. That the prism sheath is richer in organic substance than the rest of the rod is indicated also by the fact that it

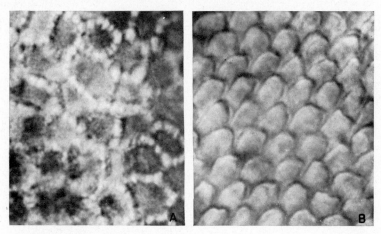

Fig. 63.—Photomicrographs of decalcified section of human unerupted tooth: *A*, cross-section of ameloblasts showing the intercellular bridges; *B*, cross and oblique section of enamel rods showing prism sheaths and interprismatic substance. × 2,000.

Fig. 64.—Electron micrograph of replica made from the surface of etched ground section of mature human enamel. Cross-section through enamel showing enamel rods and interprismatic substance. The fibrillar network extends within and between the prisms. × 20,000. (Courtesy of D. B. Scott and R. W. G. Wyckoff).

persists longer during acid treatment than the remainder of the prism (Fig. 59).

**Straight and Gnarled Enamel Rods.**—Upon the axial surfaces of the teeth the rods are usually straight and parallel, most of them extending from the dentin to the surface of the enamel. This is best illustrated by cutting sections labio-lingually through the incisors (Fig. 65).

Upon the occlusal surfaces of the molars and bicuspids the rods are usually straight and parallel for a longer or shorter distance from the surface, but as the dentino-enamel junction is approached they become twisted (Fig. 66).

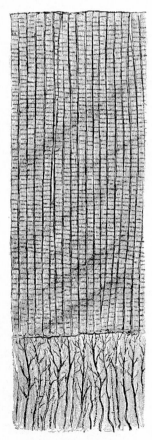

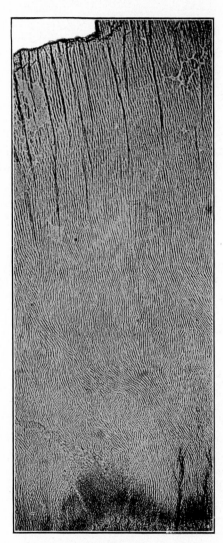

FIG. 65.—Straight enamel rods.

FIG. 66.—Gnarled enamel from etched section. (About 100 ✕.)

The gnarled condition extends farther toward the surface over the tips of the cusps, or the point at which the rods were first completed in the growth of the crown. These structural characteristics are important factors in the cutting of enamel during operative procedures.

**The Interprismatic Substance.**—The interprismatic substance differs from the prisms not only histogenetically as seen previously, but also morphologically, being glossy and homogeneous. Under high magnification, the interprismatic substance shows intercolumnar bridges which correspond to the intercellular bridges of the ameloblasts. The interprismatic substance represents a relatively softer and yielding portion of the enamel, and in that sense may serve a mechanical function. It is usually less than 1 micron in width.

FIG. 67.—Gnarled enamel.

## DIFFERENCES BETWEEN ENAMEL RODS AND INTERPRISMATIC SUBSTANCE

While both the interprismatic substance and the rods are composed almost entirely of inorganic salts, they differ in physical and chemical properties as follows:

A. The interprismatic substance is not as strong as the prismatic substance.

B. The interprismatic substance is more readily soluble in dilute acids.

C. The interprismatic substance is of slightly greater refractive index than the substance of the rod.

**Relative Strength of the Enamel Rods and the Interprismatic Substances.**—The most striking characteristics of the enamel, and the first to attract the attention of the student and the operator, are its hardness and its tendency to split or cleave in certain directions. On examination, it is found that this is determined by the direction of the rods, and is caused by the difference in strength between the prismatic and the interprismatic substances. The interprismatic substance is not as strong as the substance of the rods.

Sections ground at right angles to the rod direction are very difficult to prepare because of the tendency of the section to break into pieces. If a section that is beginning to crack is studied, the crack is found to follow the line of the interprismatic substance running around the rods. In some places a rod may be split through its center, but most of them remain perfect, and the interprismatic substance breaks. In the same way a section cut in the direction of the rods shows the crack following the lines of the interprismatic substance (Fig. 69), here and there breaking across a few rods, and then following the direction again; but the rods separate on the line of union, not at the centers of the rods. This fact becomes fundamental in the cutting of enamel and in the preparation of strong enamel walls in cavities.

**Relative Solubility of Enamel Rods and Interprismatic Substance.**—If a thin section of enamel cut parallel with the direction of the enamel rods is mounted in a 2 per cent hydrochloric acid solution, and the action ob-

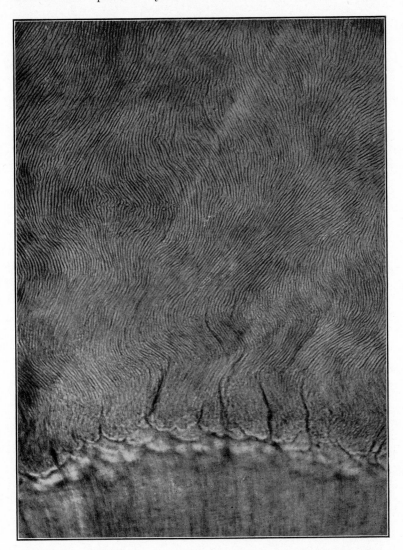

FIG. 68.—Gnarled enamel. Usually confined to inner third of enamel. (About 80 ×.)

served, it will be seen to attack the interprismatic substance more rapidly, dissolving it out from between the enamel rods and attacking their sides. If the action is stopped, the ends of the rods will be seen projecting like the pickets of a fence. The more dilute the acid the greater will be the distance to which the cementing substance is removed before the rods are destroyed. The action of acid produced in caries dissolves the interprismatic substance to a greater extent than has been possible by laboratory methods.

**Difference in the Refractive Index of the Rods and the Interprismatic Substance.**—The interprismatic substance is of slightly greater refractive index than the substance of the rods. If it were not for this fact it would be impossible to see the rods in unetched longitudinal or transverse sections.

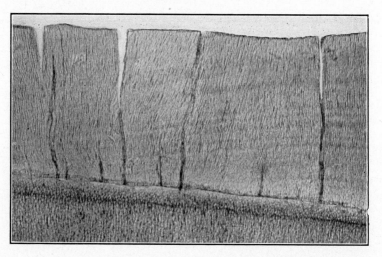

Fig. 69.—Enamel showing direction of cleavage. (About 70 ✕.)

## THE DIRECTION OF THE ENAMEL RODS IN THE TOOTH CROWN

From a study of sections it will be seen that the general arrangement of enamel rods in the architecture of the tooth crown is such as to give the greatest strength to the enamel and to furnish the greatest resistance to abrasion in the use of the teeth for mastication. The prisms are, therefore, arranged chiefly radially and often at right angles to the underlying dentino-enamel junction. An understanding of the shape and contour of the dentino-enamel junction thus facilitates the understanding of the direction of the enamel rods at any given point or level.

Over the tips of the cusps, occlusal ridges, or incisal edges the rods are in a plane parallel with the long axis of the tooth. As one progresses labially, buccally or lingually over the respective slopes, the rods gradually radiate and incline away from the axial plane toward a plane which is at right angles to the long axis of the tooth.

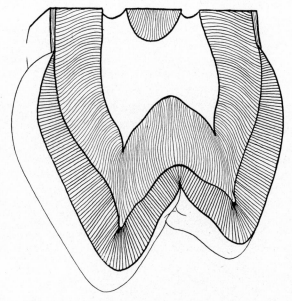

FIG. 70.—Diagram of the enamel rod direction in a bucco-lingual section of an upper premolar.

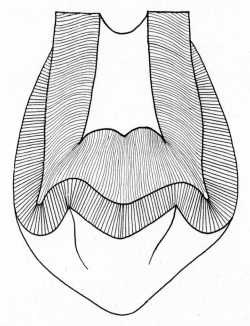

FIG. 71.—Diagram of the enamel rod direction in a mesio-distal section of an upper premolar.

There is considerable variation in the enamel rod direction in different teeth as the gingival line is approached. In permanent teeth the enamel rods in the gingival portion of the tooth incline toward the cemento-enamel junction. This inclination apically from the horizontal may be in some instances as much as 45 degress, as in Fig. 72. It may, however, on the proximal surfaces be very slight, or the rods may be almost in the horizontal

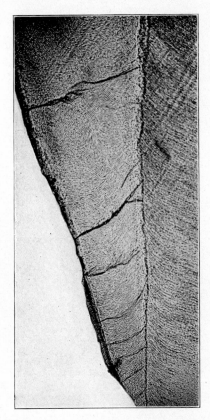

plane. The directions of the rods in these areas become very important in the preparation of the gingival wall of proximal cavities, and in buccal or labial cavities in the gingival third of the tooth.

At the developmental grooves or pits, the rods of the opposite slopes converge and tend to meet at the surface (Fig. 70). The enamel rods in those regions are therefore unusually short, and accentuate the depth of the grooves and pits at the surface of the enamel.

**Enamel Hypoplasia.**—Whenever a hypoplastic groove appears upon the surface of the enamel, the rod directions will be found to be more or less disturbed. The rods tend to be in whorls and the structure is more or less deficient (Fig. 73). The disturbance in structure is sometimes so great that it is difficult to determine the rod direction. Many such areas will be found in sections. Some condition which has affected the nutrition of the enamel-forming cells results in a local disturbance of formation and in deficient structural elements.

Fig. 72.—Direction of enamel rods in the gingival third of the buccal surface.

It has been possible to produce enamel hypoplasia experimentally in such conditions as chronic fluorosis, hypophysectomy, vitamin A deficiency and in mechanical injuries.

## STRUCTURAL CHARACTERISTICS

**The Striæ of Retzius.**—If longitudinal sections of moderate thickness are observed with low power, brownish bands are seen running through the enamel, which suggests the appearance of the stratification seen in rocks

Fig. 73.—Disturbance of enamel rod directions on labial surface of a canine. (About 80 ×.)

and trees. These were first described by Retzius and have been named the striæ of Retzius. Fig. 74 shows the tip of an incisor in which the bands are very well marked. They are seen to begin at the dentino-enamel junction and sweep in larger and larger zones or arcs around the incisal edge. Each band begins at the dentino-enamel junction. Some of them end at the den-tino-enamel junction of the other side of the tooth, but most of them end at the enamel surface. Where they meet the enamel surface, grooves are

formed which encircle the tooth, and are known as perikymata (Fig. 58).
Each band represents what was at one time the surface of the enamel
already formed, and the line along which formation was progressing. They
are, therefore, truly incremental lines. The zones reach the surface of the
enamel first at a point over the growth-center. The succeeding bands
extend along the sides from the surface of the enamel, near the occlusal, to
the dentino-enamel junction much farther apically. Corresponding lines
are seen on opposite sides of the section. In Fig. 75, the line which is at
the surface at $A$ and $A^1$ reaches the dentino-enamel junction at $B$ and $B^1$.

Fig. 74.—Tip of an incisor. (About 50 ×.)

This means that when the enamel rods which form the surface at *A* were completed, the rods at *B* were just beginning to be formed at the dentino-enamel junction. A layer of functioning ameloblasts occupied this position. The striæ of Retzius are always curved and usually pass obliquely across the enamel rods, but are parallel neither with the dentino-enamel junction, the surface of the enamel, nor the enamel rods (Fig. 74). As they pass toward the gingival level, the angle which they form with the axis of the

Fig. 75.—Incisor tip showing stratification or incremental lines. Rods at *A* were fully formed at the time the rods at *B* were beginning to form. (About 50 ×.)

tooth becomes greater. The particular depth of the curvatures followed by the striæ and the degree of their angles with the enamel surface and the dentino-enamel junction are characteristic for each tooth type.

Retzius described these striæ as being parallel. While two adjacent striæ give the appearance of being parallel, the various striæ of any given tooth are segments of a logarithmic spiral and are not parallel.

The striæ are especially distinct in the gingival portions of the tooth near the cemento-enamel junction. Their brownish coloration is related to the organic material of the striæ. It appears to be intensified with age and is related to a post-eruptive, gradual permeation of pigment from the oral fluids.

When the enamel surface is examined under low magnification one can readily see fine horizontal enamel ridges. Regularly spaced striæ of Retzius end at the enamel surface in shallow grooves, the perikymata, situated between two successive enamel ridges (Figs. 57 and 58).

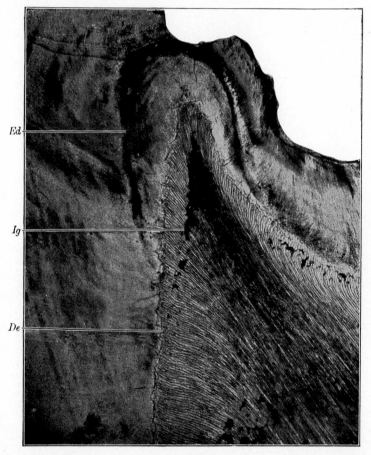

Fig. 76.—Stratification of enamel; the cusp of premolar: *De*, dentino-enamel junction; *Ed*, enamel defect showing in the heavy stratification band; *Ig*, interglobular spaces in the dentin. (About 40 ×.)

**Component Parts of the Striæ of Retzius.**—A stria of Retzius represents a poorly calcified portion of the enamel, because it is made up of the relatively less calcified components of an enamel rod. A microscopic study of a given stria under high power shows that it takes the structural pattern of a steep staircase which ascends uniformly and regularly, step by step, each step of successive enamel rods being higher than the preceding one by the height of one enamel globule. Each step thus consists of a transverse striation or enamel globule, which is joined to the striation or globule of the next highest level of the adjacent prism by means of the intervening inter-prismatic substance (Fig. 57).

**Cuspal Enamel.**—The portion of the enamel immediately overlying the tips of the dentino-enamel junction (the portion of the enamel first formed) contains, as a rule, very few striæ of Retzius. This portion presents a clear, bluish-white translucent appearance and may be termed the cuspal enamel (Figs. 75 and 76). Its outer limit appears to be the last stria of Retzius,

Fig. 77.—Photomicrograph of ground section of buccal cusp of lower premolar showing bands of Schreger as seen in reflected light. (× 14).

both of whose ends rest against the dentino-enamel junction. This might explain the origin of cuspal enamel, since the striæ in this region are not open to the surface of the tooth and therefore to the ingress of coloring matter from the oral fluids.

The incidence of the number of the striæ of Retzius appears to increase as one goes from the tip of the cusp toward the cemento-enamel junction. Here the enamel shows more prominent and frequent striæ, granular zones and a more wavy course of the prisms. These characteristics may be related to the retrogressive changes of the enamel organ at the time of the formation and calcification of this part.

**Bands of Schreger.**—These bands, first described by Hunter and by Schreger, extend from the dentino-enamel junction about halfway to the enamel surface (Fig. 77). They may be seen in sections of the enamel by reflected light and with very low magnification. The course of enamel rods is not the shortest path from the dentino-enamel junction to the enamel surface but is often complex. The rods are twisting about each other, and in one zone they are cut longitudinally (parazones) in the next obliquely (diazones). The alternations of these directions and the consequent zones cause the appearance of the bands (Fig. 77). In reflected light, the longitudinally cut zones are light (parazones) and the transversely or obliquely

Fig. 78.—Schreger's lines. Decalcified section through human enamel showing alternation of longitudinal and transverse cuts through groups of enamel rods. Magnification × 200. (Kronfeld, Dental Histology.)

cut zones appear dark (diazones) (Figs. 77 and 78). The structural significance of the bands of Schreger lies in the fact that the complicated course of the prisms increases the firmness and resistance of the enamel.

**Enamel Lamellæ and Enamel Tufts.**—The enamel lamellæ are imperfectly calcified areas of enamel which usually extend from the enamel surface through the entire thickness of the enamel. Gottlieb has described lamellæ which extend into the dentin for a variable distance (Figs. 79 and 80). They run approximately at a right angle to the surface of the enamel. The lamellæ are as result of poor calcification of part of the enamel or represent scars, tears or cracks in the enamel which occur in some way during formation and the early stages of calcification. The epithelial cells from the surface grow into these cracks and may become more or less hornified. In decalcified sections they appear as extensions from the enamel cuticle.

Fig. 79.—Ground section showing enamel lamella extending from enamel surface into dentin.

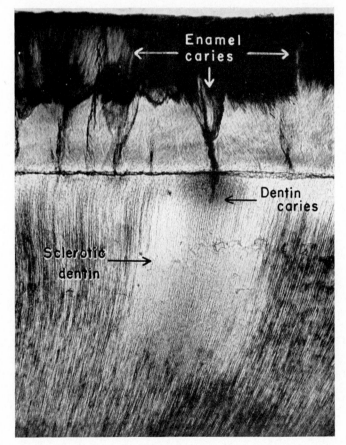

Fig. 80.—Ground section showing penetration of enamel caries from the surface into the dentin through an enamel lamella.

Another type of enamel lamellæ is the result of post-eruptive cracks which occur under masticatory stress. These, according to Sognnaes, are gradually filled with organic material from the saliva and from the food debris. Sognnaes has also pointed out that the organic matter within these post-eruptive lamellæ may serve as a nucleus for secondary deposits of inorganic matter.

The enamel tufts are also poorly calcified portions of enamel. They differ from enamel lamellæ in that they begin at the dentino-enamel junction and extend towards the surface only through a part of the thickness of the enamel (Fig. 81). Both the enamel lamellæ and tufts are significant because they contain more organic substance than normal and thus are structural defects which have been considered points of least resistance to the progress of decay.

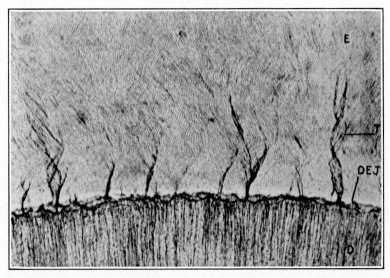

Fig. 81.—Enamel tufts. Ground section. D, dentin; DEJ, scalloped dentino-enamel junction; T, enamel tufts; E, enamel. Magnification × 150. (Kronfeld, Dental Histology.)

**Enamel Spindles.**—Peculiar spindle-like structures which may reach a length of approximately 100 $\mu$ are seen projecting from the dentino-enamel junction into the enamel, especially in the region of the cusps (Figs. 82 and 83). They appear to be continuations of the dentinal tubules and may contain Tomes' fibers. Their direction is rarely parallel to the enamel prisms and they often deviate sharply from the course of the dentinal tubule from which they arise. These structures are called enamel spindles. They may represent odontoblastic processes which originally extended between the ameloblasts to the stratum intermedium and stellate reticulum before enamel was formed. The enamel spindles probably constitute one of the factors that make for the greater sensitivity of the dentino-enamel junction.

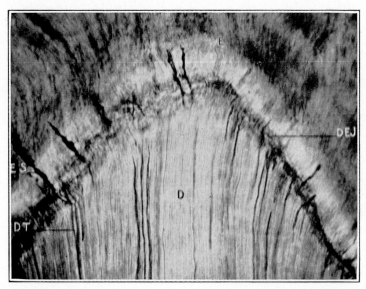

Fig. 82.—Enamel spindles. Ground section. Dentino-enamel junction at the tip of the cusp of an upper premolar. *D*, dentin; *DEJ*, dentino-enamel junction; *E*, enamel; *ES*, enamel spindle continuous with the dentinal tubules, *DT*. Magnification × 350. (Kronfeld, Dental Histology).

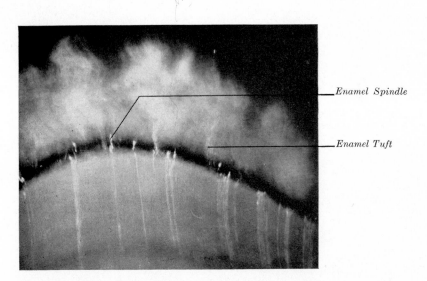

Fig. 83.—Fluorescent photomicrograph of ground section of enamel and dentin showing the enamel spindles and tufts at the dentinoenamel junction and the opaque appearance of the gnarled enamel. Courtesy of A. F. Forziati.

## THE DENTINO-ENAMEL JUNCTION

**Curvature.**—The dentino-enamel junction presents on the buccal and lingual surfaces in molars and premolars and on the lingual surfaces in the anterior teeth, a typical S-shaped curvature (Fig. 70). The concave portion of the curvature lies in the occlusal third of the tooth. This condition gives a greater thickness to the enamel in the region which will resist abrasion, and also gives it a firmer seat upon the dentin. Within the gingival half of the crown the curvature reverses to present a convex surface so that the thickness of the enamel becomes progressively less. This region is less subjected to a masticatory stress and therefore needs no great thickness of enamel. The dentino-enamel junction at the proximal surfaces of all teeth is similarly curved (Fig. 71).

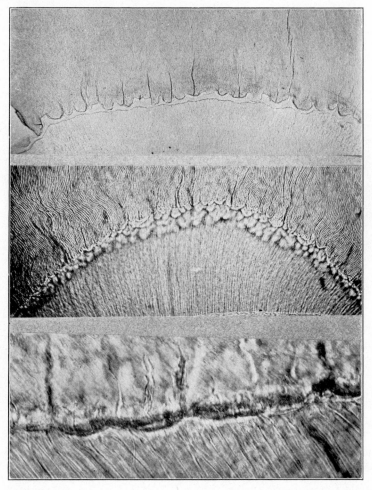

Fig. 84.—Dentino-enamel junction.

**Scalloped Surface.**—The dentino-enamel junction is seldom a smooth, even surface, but will appear scalloped in sections, projections of dentin extending between projections of enamel (Figs. 68 and 84).

The irregular surface of the dentino-enamel junction derives its origin from a corresponding waviness of the free border of the ameloblasts which faces the opposing odontoblasts in the bell stage of the enamel organ immediately preceding the formation of dentin.

In three dimensions, rounded projections of the enamel rest in rounded depressions of the dentin surface in an interlocking arrangement. This is similar but much less marked than the interlocking of the papillæ of connective tissue with the projections of the Malpighian layer of stratified

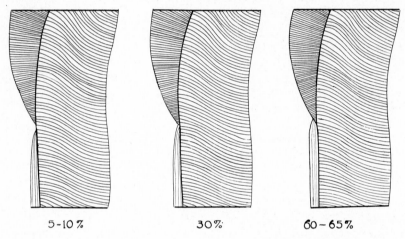

5-10 %          30%          60-65%

Fig. 85.—Diagram showing the relationship of the enamel and cementum at the cemento-enamel junction. (After Hopewell-Smith.) Figures indicate frequency of occurrence of each type.

squamous epithelium of the skin and mucous membrane. In some cases the scalloping may be quite prominent. This condition is more often found in the gingival third of the crown.

The scalloping of the dentino-enamel junction gives a stronger attachment of the enamel to the dentin, and accounts partially at least, for the difficulty with which the enamel is removed from the dentin in the preparation of teeth for crowns. Where the two tissues join with a smooth interface the enamel can be cleaved away with comparative ease; where the scalloping is marked it is removed with much greater difficulty.

**Organic Substance.**—The following conditions contribute to the relatively rich amount of organic substance at the dentino-enamel junction: (1) the proportion of interprismatic substance to enamel rods is greater in this region; (2) there is considerable crossing over of dentinal tubules; (3) the enamel spindles; (4) the dentinal parts of enamel lamellæ; (5) the greater branching of the dentinal tubules and (6) the persistence of some organic substance at the dentino-enamel junction (dentino-enamel cuticle). These factors favor the more rapid spreading of decay along the dentino-enamel junction and may account for the greater sensitivity of this region.

**The Cemento-enamel Junction.**—The cemento-enamel junction exhibits three types of relationships. The most common arrangement is an overlapping of the cementum over a small portion of the gingival enamel (65 per cent). The enamel and cementum meet end to end in about 30 per cent of the cases. In a smaller number of cases (5 per cent) the enamel and cementum do not touch, exposing the dentin surface in this region (Fig. 85).

## HISTOPHYSIOLOGICAL REMARKS

**Distinction Between Young and Adult Enamel.**—Enamel automatically records in its structure its own stages of formation and calcification as well as its response to systemic disturbances. These records remain permanent after the enamel has completed its formation and calcification, and has lost the kymographic properties of its growing period. The adult enamel, unlike the active young enamel, is non-vital and does not undergo alterations except through external and environmental interferences. The distinction between the actively growing and calcifying enamel and the passive adult or fully formed and calcified enamel cannot be pointed out too strongly.

## CLINICAL CONSIDERATIONS

Growing interest in the initiation of enamel caries and its prevention by topical application of fluorides have stimulated a re-examination of the membranes covering the enamel, the physical and chemical nature of the enamel surface and the outer layer of the enamel.

**Enamel Membranes.**—One of the unique features of enamel is the nature of the multiple layers which cover its surface. The primary and secondary enamel cuticles are of developmental origin and lie next to the enamel itself. In addition, there is the plaque or film which is derived from the organic parts of the saliva (especially mucin) and food and from micro-organisms. This acquired thin mucinous film serves to protect the enamel against the action of acids contained in foods. It has been termed the pigmented pellicle. The pellicle may invade the microscopic cracks of the enamel and thus contribute the organic content of the post-eruptive enamel lamellæ. Removal of this membrane during the prophylactic cleaning of teeth or grinding of the enamel surface is only transitory since it reforms rapidly, probably within several hours.

**Enamel Surface.**—Shadowed collodion replicas of the enamel surface have revealed finer details of the perikymata (or imbrication lines) than did direct optical microscopy. The perikymata show variations in their configuration and course which are of clinical and anthropologic interest. Both the perikymata and the surface endings of the rods are more pronounced in unerupted or recently erupted teeth. With advanced age and wear, however, this surface pattern gradually flattens and fades out as a result of external influences. Cracks and small depressions (micropits) are not uncommon.

**Outer Layer of Enamel.**—The outer layer of the enamel is more dense, harder, and less permeable than the deeper areas of the enamel. The thin surface layer (approximately 30 microns wide) is also more radiopaque and less soluble in acid.

Although decalcified histologic sections of the organic enamel of unerupted teeth show a different staining reaction in the outer layer, there are strong indications that the physical and chemical characteristics of the surface layer of the enamel are largely acquired through the adsorption of materials from the saliva after eruption of the enamel into the oral cavity. It is probably for this reason that the enamel of recently erupted teeth is more receptive to topically applied fluoride ions than the enamel of adult teeth. The inner layer of enamel within 20 to 30 $\mu$ from the dentinoenamel junction is hypercalcified.

**Permeability of Enamel.**—The permeability of the enamel has been restudied recently by means of radioactive isotopes. Wainwright and Lemoine found that substances of very small molecular size, such as urea labeled with radioactive carbon[14] as well as iodine and other radioactive substances, could pass from the surface of the enamel to the pulp within 2 to 48 hours. This diffusion occurs more rapidly along the paths of enamel lamellæ and tufts. Substances of larger molecular size, such as silver nitrate, penetrate the enamel much more slowly and only to a limited extent. The enamel may thus act as a semi-permeable membrane.

These new findings do not alter the fact that enamel possesses extremely high stability when compared with other structures neither should they be interpreted as proof for the vitality of enamel. Diffusion and exchange within the enamel are physical processes and do not necessarily signify biologic activity of the enamel.

The permeability of various filling materials has also been studied by means of radioactive tracers. These very fine tracer elements reveal the fact that a perfect seal between the filling material and the cavity wall is rarely, if ever, attained.

## BIBLIOGRAPHY

BERNICK, S., BAKER, R. G., RUTHERFORD, R. L., and WARREN, O.: Electron Microscopy of Enamel and Dentin, Jour. Am. Dent. Assn., *45*, 689, 1952.

BIBBY, B. G.: The Organic Structure of Dental Enamel as a Passive Defense Against Caries, Jour. Dent. Res., *12*, 99, 1932.

BRAIN, E. B.: A Method of Preparing Decalcified Serial Sections in Paraffin Wax of Human Enamel and Dentine in Situ, Brit. Dent. Jour., *87*, 8, 1949.

CHASE, S. W.: The Enamel Prisms and the Interprismatic Substance, Anat. Rec., *36*, 239, 1927.

————: A Critical Review of the Controversy Concerning Metabolism in the Enamel, Jour. Am. Dent. Assn., *18*, 697, 1931.

8

ERAUSQUIN, J.:   Histology and Development of Enamel, Int. Dent. Jour., *1*, 10, 1951.

GUSTAFSON, ANNA-GRETA:   A Morphologic Investigation of Certain Variations in the Structure and Mineralization of Human Dental Enamel, Lund, Berlingska Boktryckeriet, 1959; also published in Odontologisk Tidskrift, *67*, 361–472, 1959.

JANSEN, M. T., and VISSER, J. B.:   Permeable Structures in Normal Enamel, Jour. Dent. Res., *29*, 622, 1950.

KARLSTROEM, S.:   Physical, Physiologic and Pathologic Studies of Dental Enamel With Special Reference to the Question of Its Vitality, A. B. Fahlerantz, Stockholm, 1931.

LEFEVRE, M. L., and HODGE, H. C.:   Chemical Analysis of Tooth Samples Composed of Enamel, Dentine and Cementum, Jour. Dent. Res., *16*, 279, 1937.

ORBAN, B.:   Histology of the Enamel Lamellæ and Tufts, Jour. Am. Dent. Assn., *15*, 305, 1928.

PICKERILL, H. P.:   The Structure of Enamel, Dental Cosmos, *55*, 969, 1913.

ROSEBURY, T.:   A Biochemical Study of the Protein in Dental Enamel, Jour. Dent. Res., *10*, 187, 1930.

SARNAT, B. G., and SCHOUR, I.:   Enamel Hypoplasia (Chronologic Enamel Aplasia) in Relation to Systemic Disease, Jour. Am. Dent. Assn., *28*, 1989, 1941.

SAUSEN, R. E., ARMSTRONG, W. D., and SIMON, W. J.:   Penetration of Radio-calcium Through Acrylic Margins, Jour. Dent. Res., *31*, 485, 1952.

SCOTT, D. B., PICKARD, R. G., and WYCKOFF, R. W. G.:   Studies of the Action of Sodium Fluoride on Human Enamel by Electron Microscopy and Electron Diffraction, Pub. Health Rep., *65*, 43, 1950.

SCOTT, D. B., and WYCKOFF, R. W. G.:   Shadowed Replicas of Ground Sections Through Teeth, Pub. Health Rep., *62*, 422, 1947.

————:   Electron Microscopy of Tooth Structure by the Shadowed Collodion Replica Method, Pub. Health Rep., *62*, 1513, 1947.

SCOTT, D. B.:   Microscopic Studies of Dental Tissues.   II. Opitcal Microscopy of Tooth Surfaces, Oral Surg., Oral Med. and Oral Path., *5*, 638, 1952.

SOGNNAES, REIDAR F.:   Microstructure and Histochemical Characteristics of the Mineralized Tissues, Annals of the N.Y. Acad. of Sciences, *60*, (5), 545–572, April, 1955.

————:   The Organic Elements of the Enamel.   I. A Study of the Principal Factors Involved in the Histological Preservation of the Organic Elements of Enamel and Other Highly Calcified Structures, J.A.D.A., *38*, 280, 1949.

————:   The Organic Elements of the Enamel.   IV. The Gross Morphology and the Histological Relationship of the Lamellæ to the Organic Framework of the Enamel, Jour. Dent. Res., *29*, 260, 1950.

VALLOTON, C. F.:   An Acquired Pigmented Pellicle of the Enamel Surface.   I. Review of Literature.   II. Clinical and Histologic Studies.   III. Chemical Studies. Jour. Dent. Res., *24*, 161, 1945.

VILLA, V. G.:   Dentino-Enamel Cuticle Present in Adult Human Teeth, Jour. Dent. Res., *28*, 565, 1949.

WAINWRIGHT, W. W., and LEMOINE, F. A.:   Rapid Diffuse Penetration of Intact Enamel and Dentin by Carbon[14]-Labeled Urea, J.A.D.A., *41*, 135, 1950.

# CHAPTER 7

# The Development of Dentin

**Introduction.**—There has been an intense controversy regarding the question of dentin formation and more especially concerning the cells responsible for this process. Waldeyer and Tomes believed that dentin was a direct transformation product of the odontoblasts. Kölliker, on the other hand, believed that dentin was a secretion product of the odontoblasts and probably also of some other pulp cells. von Korff showed that

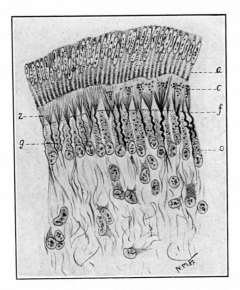

Fig. 86.—Fibers of Von Korff in tooth germ of cat. *o*, Odontoblasts; *f*, fan-like expansion of fiber bundles; *g*, corkscrew-like fibers; *z*, odontogenic zone; *c*, commencing calcification; *a*, ameloblasts. (From illustration to his paper.)

the dentin matrix is formed from particular fibers which he demonstrated by staining with silver. These have been called Korff's fibers (Figs. 86, 88 and 91).

There is now general agreement that the odontoblasts are responsible for the change of the Korff's fibers into the dentin matrix and later for the maintenance of circulation and nutrition in the dentin.

Without going further into the controversial literature on the subject, the evidence seems to point out that primary dentin is formed by the ac-

( 115 )

tivity of the odontoblasts from the Korff fibers, which contribute to the formation of the dentin matrix. The question still awaits further clarification.

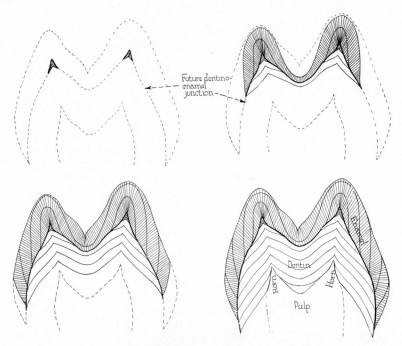

Fig. 87.—The coalescence of individual growth-centers in the formation of the crown of a posterior tooth.

## STAGES PREPARATORY TO DENTIN FORMATION

Prior to dentin apposition the formative organ, the dental papilla, consists of round, spindle- and star-shaped connective tissue cells which are joined with one another by long processes and are embedded in a loose, richly vascularized ground substance (Plate VI). Argyrophile fibrils ramify irregularly among the cells. At the periphery of the dental papilla, where a fibrous basement membrane between it and the ameloblastic layer has been described, a clear zone is present (Fig. 40). This zone has been thought to be a result of the tension that obtains between the inner enamel epithelium and the dental papilla. It disappears with the final functional differentiation of the odontoblasts.

During the bell stage of the enamel organ, apparently under the influence of the already differentiated ameloblasts, the peripheral cells of the dental papilla become tall columnar cells which arrange themselves in a palisade-like manner opposite the ameloblastic layer. Because of their role in dentin development, they have been named odontoblasts.

The ameloblastic layer in the crown and Hertwig's epithelial sheath in the root are essential to the formation of the dentin. Their outlines determine the outer surface of the dentin, the morphological pattern of the tooth thus being determined prior to dentin apposition. These epithelial cells in addition organize the dentin-forming cells and initiate dentinogenesis.

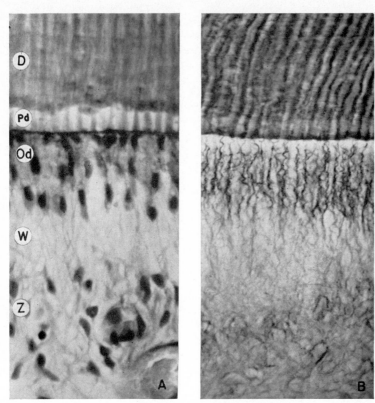

Fig. 88.—Photomicrographs of dentin and pulp of human incisor. Note the dentin *D*, the predentin *Pd*, the odontoblasts *Od*, the cell poor zone of Weil, *W*, and the cell rich zone, *Z*. The left section (*A*) was stained with hematoxylin and eosin. Compare with the right section (*B*) stained with silver. Note the Korff's fibers and the delicate network of reticular fibers in the cell poor zone of Weil in B. (× 525.)

## DENTINOGENESIS

Dentin formation just precedes enamel formation, although the ameloblasts differentiate earlier than the odontoblasts. Dentinogenesis begins at the individual growth-centers on the dentino-enamel junction, and proceeds from without inward, concomitant with the recession of the dentin-forming cells from the dentino-enamel junction (Fig. 87).

**Odontoblastic Process.**—As each odontoblast recedes, it leaves behind it a long cytoplasmic process which becomes embedded in the dentin tubule.

This can be demonstrated in teased preparations (Fig. 89). The deposition of the ground substance and the subsequent calcification of the dentin proceed around and between the odontoblastic processes, which thus become enclosed by the calcified matrix and establish the dentinal tubules. The odontoblastic processes completely fill the tubules *in vivo* and do not calcify. In dry extracted teeth they shrink and leave a hollow tubule in the calcified dentin matrix. The cytoplasmic processes extend through the entire width of the dentin which may be as much as 5 mm.

**Korff's Fibers.**—The Korff's fibers are present throughout the period of dentin deposition. They arise from the deeper cell layers of the pulp and unite at the base of the odontoblastic row. They then extend spirally in the intercellular spaces, pass between the odontoblasts, and unravel in the layer of ground substance which surmounts the odontoblasts (Figs. 86 and 91).

Orban finds that dentin develops through the transformation of precollagenous or argyrophile fibers (Korff's fibers) of the pulp into a collagenous matrix, which later calcifies. He suggests that the odontoblasts may, in the later stages, produce the interfibrillar substance in which the fibrils are embedded and also may produce some chemical substance which aids in the transformation of the precollagenous fibers into collagenous fibers.

The cytology of the odontoblasts and the structure of the Korff's fibers (Figs. 90 and 91) will be discussed in the chapter on the Dental Pulp.

**Pattern of Formation.**—**Crown.**—Dentin apposition begins at the individual growth-centers on the dentinoenamel junction and proceeds from without inward. Successively adjacent dentin-forming cells begin their formation at successively graded intervals. In three dimensions a given incremental layer of dentin has the form of a cone, with the apex pointed occlusally and the periphery of the base touching the dentino-enamel

Fig. 89.—Diagram of odontoblasts and their processes. (C. H. Stowell.)

junction. Successive incremental cones of dentin are deposited one within the other and cause a corresponding reduction of the dental papilla. Dentin formation always precedes formation of enamel although dentin and enamel deposition are synchronized so that for each layer of dentin that is apposed there is a corresponding layer of enamel in the crown (Figs. 45 and 57). This deposition occurs in a regular and rhythmic manner.

When the incremental cones of adjacent growth-centers meet, their peripheries fuse, and subsequent dentin apposition follows a pattern resulting from the fusion (Fig. 87).

**Root.**— When the cemento-enamel junction has been reached, the crown dentin is completed, and subsequent dentin formation procedes under the guidance and influence of Hertwig's epithelial sheath (Fig. 47). In the completed dentin structural as well as morphological differences exist between the crown and root portions. These may be explained on the basis of various influences exerted during their formative period.

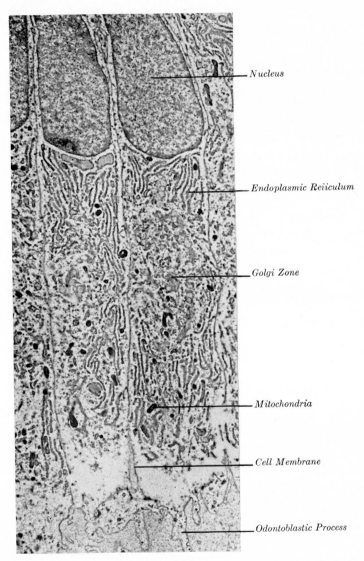

*Nucleus*

*Endoplasmic Reticulum*

*Golgi Zone*

*Mitochondria*

*Cell Membrane*

*Odontoblastic Process*

Fig. 90.—Electron micrograph of two odontoblasts showing their cytological organization. Courtesy of Nylen and Scott. ( × 5000.)

When the final width of the primary dentin is established, immediately under a given growth-center, the tip of the primary pulpal horn is reached. Subsequent incremental layers radiate apically in a fan-like manner, with the tip of the pulpal horn as a focal point, until the final width of the primary dentin of the sides of the tooth is reached (Fig. 87).

**Morphogenesis of Dentin and Pulp.**—The dental papilla, unlike the enamel organ, is a permanently functional structure. After dentin formation and calcification is completed, it persists within the central cavity of the dentin as the dental pulp. The formation of the dentin from without inward reduces the size of the dental papilla. While the rate of apposition

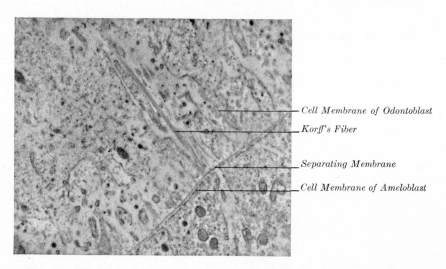

*Cell Membrane of Odontoblast*

*Korff's Fiber*

*Separating Membrane*

*Cell Membrane of Ameloblast*

Fig. 91.—Electron micrograph of junction between inner odontogenic epithelium and the odontoblasts. Note: The 640Å banding in the Korff's fiber. Courtesy of Nylen and Scott. (× 8,500.)

of the dentin decelerates gradually from a maximum at the growth center toward the apex of the root, the inherent primary life span of the individual dentin-forming cells approaches a relatively constant figure. The width of the primary dentin as determined by measuring the length of the dentinal tubules is therefore fairly constant in all regions of the tooth, ranging within very narrow limits from a maximum occlusally to a minimum apically. The primary outline of the pulp thus closely follows the form and contour of the dentino-enamel and dentino-cemental junctions, modified by the oblique course of the dentinal tubules in the gingival region of the tooth.

Under the stimulus of abrasion, caries or other factors, the dentin-forming cells in the pulp may be activated to form secondary dentin. This modifies the primary pulpal outline (Fig. 107). Secondary dentin will be considered in the chapter on Dentin.

## CALCIFICATION

As the dentin-forming cells recede pulpally, they continually form the new dentin matrix while the ground substance formed during the previous deposition is calcifying. This results in a pattern of calcification that closely follows the incremental appositional pattern in time and rhythmicity.

**Predentin.**—The most recently formed, and still soft and uncalcified, dentin matrix is called the predentin (Fig. 92). It can be seen in all actively

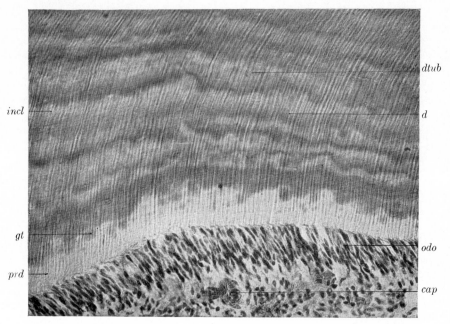

Fig. 92.—Calcification of dentin. Note the incremental layers of calcification. *cap,* Capillary in pulp; *d,* calcified dentin; *dtub,* dentinal tubule; *gl,* globule of calcified dentin; *incl,* incompletely calcified dentin; *odo,* odontoblasts; *prd,* predentin. (× 256.) (From Schour, in Cowdry's *Special Cytology,* courtesy of Paul B. Hoeber, Inc.)

forming teeth and corresponds to osteoid tissue. It apparently contains no inorganic calcium. The predentin layer is an argyrophilic, eosin staining zone next to the pulp which becomes calcified at the border farthest from the pulp as soon as it reaches a sufficient width, usually 10 to 20 $\mu$. This border tends to take a deeper purple stain with hematoxylin in decalcified sections and has been called the intermediate dentin. The intermediate dentin stains vitally with alizarine Red S. and represents without doubt an early stage of the calcification process.

Careful observation shows that the predentin itself often stains differently in its pulpal and dentinal halves. Next to the pulp it often does not stain at all (young predentin). The portion away from the pulp is eosinophilic (old predentin). The difference is due to the fact that the young predentin does not show fibrils. These, however, become visible in the layer of old predentin.

**The Mechanism of Calcification.**—The precipitation of inorganic calcium salts within an organic medium has been shown to occur, *in vitro*, in typical rhythmic *Liesegang* ring formations. Calcium is precipitated in the predentin as submicroscopical hexagonal crystals of tricalcium phosphate (apatite ($Ca_3(PO_4)_2$). The crystals are, however, at first not evenly distributed in the matrix but occur as rounded clusters, calcospherites, which consist of concentric lamellæ.

The concentric zones or lamellæ appeared alternately dark and light and were formed in a regular and rhythmic manner. The calcospherites in turn tended to aggregate and coalesce when they entered the sphere of influence of one another. This resulted in the formation of larger, regular layers.

Harting decalcified the calcospherites and found that the protein which remained was markedly altered. It was now remarkably resistant to the action of acids and alkalies and retained some calcium in a combined form. He termed this acid-resistant matrix calco-globulin.

In the dentin the calcification process appears to follow a similar Liesegang ring formation (Fig. 93). The soft organic matrix of the predentin layer is calcified at its "intermediate dentin" border by the precipitation of inorganic calcium salts in the form of individual globules of calcospherites. As these calcospherites enlarge and enter the sphere of influence of one another, a fusion occurs and results in the formation of a homogeneous incremental layer of calcified dentin (Fig. 93).

The formation of individual calcospherites is therefore the primary stage in the calcification process. They consist of an acid-resistant matrix of calcoglobulin in which are deposited the inorganic calcium salts in a Lisesgang ring formation. In the preparation of decalcified sections the inorganic salts are removed, leaving the calcoglobulin matrix, which stains deeply with carmine or hematoyxlin. If, during the calcification process, the globular fusion is incomplete, the dentin areas which are between the globules take an eosin stain and constitute interglobular dentin (Fig. 93).

**The Calcification Rhythm.**—Even under entirely normal conditions successive layers of the dentin are not equally well calcified. Well calcified layers which stain more readily with hematoxylin alternate regularly and rhythmically with less well calcified layers which stain more readily with eosin. Thus there arises in the dentin a stratification which consists of pairs of dark and light increments. These pairs are of uniform width (approximately 16 $\mu$), occur in dentin of all species studied, and give to the dentin its characteristically regular incremental calcification pattern. The rhythmicity of the calcification process is no doubt a manifestation of a broader physico-chemical phase in the calcification process.

**Secondary Calcification.**—The adult dentin appears to increase in its degree of calcification with age. This might be brought about either by the reduction in the size of the tubules or by the adding of inorganic constituents to the matrix.

While it is apparent that in young vital dentin the tubules are filled by cytoplasmic projections of the odontoblasts, it is by no means certain that all of the tubules of the dentin, in an old tooth, are still occupied by living cytoplasm.

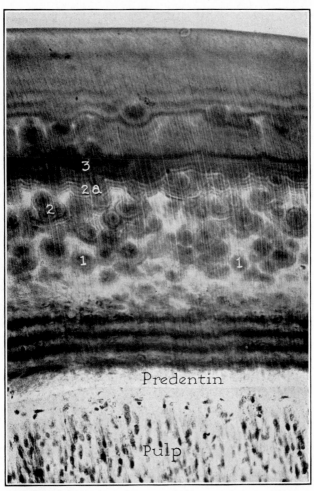

Fig. 93.—Calcospherite formation in the calcifying dentin of an incisor of a rachitic rat. Note the Liesegang ring formation in the individual globules. *1*, Individual globules; *2*, partial fusion of calcospherites; *2a*, incomplete fusion of calcospherites; *3*, complete fusion of calcospherities into a homogeneously calcified layer of dentin. (× 380.)

## HISTOPHYSIOLOGICAL REMARKS

**Periodic Accentuations (Contour Lines).**—The incremental formative pattern in the dentin of various teeth is constant and characteristic for the type of the tooth. Accentuations of the basic incremental pattern may occur periodically as a result of systemic or environmental disturbances. These accentuated incremantal lines were first described by Owen and have been called Owen's lines of contour (Fig. 94). They are analogous to the striæ of Retzius, which are found in the corresponding layers of the enamel and which are similarly related to periodic disturbances in calcification. When these disturbances affect the formative cells of the dentin so that the tubules remain sharply bent, in a direction different from their original course, they give the appearance of markings that represent *incremental*

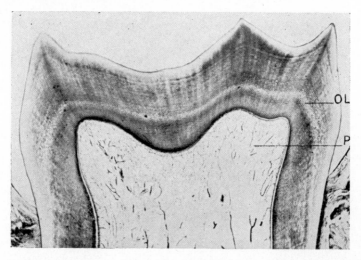

FIG. 94.—Contour lines of Owen. Mesiodistal section through the crown of an upper first deciduous molar of a child, aged one and one-half years. Owen's lines appear as light lines in the dentin encircling the pulp chamber; they indicate those periods of life during which the forming dentin was poorly calcified. *P*, pulp; *OL*, Owen's lines. Magnification × 12. (Kronfeld, Dental Histology).

*lines of deviated growth.* If the disturbances cause a slight arrest in growth with no change in direction of the dentinal tubules, the effect is seen as lines of arrested growth (neonatal line). Incremental lines of disturbed formation may be secondarily accentuated by concomitant disturbances in calcification (Table 4).

Disturbances in calcium metabolism are manifested in the form of either prominent or interglobular incremental layers of dentin. They have been associated with constitutional adjustments such as birth (the neonatal ring) or weaning; with dietary disturbances (rickets) or with diseases that affect calcium metabolism directly (parathyroprivic tetany). In rickets, for example, the apposition of the dentin matrix continues, but calcification has stopped or is delayed. This results in the formation of a very wide layer of predentin. Globular fusion is incomplete and individual calcospherites in typical Liesegang ring formation are found scattered in the dentin matrix. Interglobular dentin is characteristic of rickets (Fig. 93).

**Distinction Between Young and Adult Dentin.**—One can appreciate that no tooth can be perfectly formed and calcified if one realizes how many systemic factors may disturb calcium metabolism. Various disturbances in both formation and calcification are recorded permanently and clearly

TABLE 4.—THE CALCIFICATION PATTERN OF THE HUMAN TEETH

| The calcification zones and rings | Age period | Quality of calcification and histologic characteristics |
|---|---|---|
| Prenatal zone | 4 months in utero to birth | Very homogenous calcification. Striæ of Retzius and Owen's contour lines rare |
| Neonatal ring | Birth to 2 weeks | Dark, distinct arrest line or ring in enamel and dentin |
| Infancy zone | Neonatal period to about 10 months | Generally poorer calcification as reflected in interglobular dentin. 85% of all enamel hypoplasias occur during this period |
| Infancy ring | About 10 months | Acute susceptibility to hypoplastic defects. Chronic hypoplasias of infancy tend to terminate at this age |
| Early childhood zone | About 10 months to $2\frac{1}{2}$ years | Calcification better than during infancy period, but not as good as prenatal period. Hypoplasia relatively rare |
| Early childhood ring | About $2\frac{1}{2}$ years | Sharp arrest line which demarcates the early from later childhood periods. Acute hypoplasia may occur at this time |
| Later childhood zone | About $2\frac{1}{2}$ to 5 years | Calcification generally poor. Hypoplasias due to exanthems occur during this period |
| Later childhood ring | About 5 years | Sharp arrest line appears at the end of the later childhood period. Period of acute susceptibility to enamel hypoplasia |
| Grade school zone | 5 to 10 years | Calcification generally good; hypoplasia rare |

in the adult dentin. The extra-cellular dentin matrix, once deposited and calcified, may be destroyed through external sources such as caries or surgical removal. It does not serve as a storehouse for minerals, as does bone. However, unlike enamel, it reacts acutely to painful stimuli, since the odontoblasts remain in vital contact with the dentin matrix by means of their processes.

### BIBLIOGRAPHY

CAPE, A. T., and KITCHIN, P. C.: Histologic Phenomena of Tooth Tissues as Observed Under Polarized Light, Jour. Am. Dent. Assoc., *617*, 193, 1930.

HARTING, P.:   On the Artificial Production of Some of the Principal Organic Calcareous Formations, Quart. Jour. Micr. Sci., London, *12*, New Series, 118, 1872.

VON KORFF, K. V.:   Uber die Entwicklung der Elfenbeinzellen und ihre Beziehungen zur Dentingrundsubstanz, Anat., *64*, 383, 1928.

MASSLER, M., SCHOUR, I., and PONCHER, G. H.:   Developmental Pattern of the Child as Reflected in the Calcification Pattern of the Teeth, Am. Jour. Dis. Child., *62*, 33–67, 1941.

NYLEN, MARIE U., and SCOTT, DAVID B.:   An Electron Microscopic Study of the Early Stages of Dentinogenesis, Public Health Service Publication, No. 613, 1958.

ORBAN, B.:   The Development of the Dentin, Jour. Am. Dent. Assn., *16*, 1547, 1929.

OWEN, R.:   Odontography, London, Balliére, 1840–1845.

THOMPSON, D'ARCY W.:   On Growth and Form, Cambridge University Press, 1917.

# CHAPTER 8

# The Structure of Dentin

**Definition.**—Dentin is a calcified connective tissue which is penetrated by definitely arranged small canals containing protoplasmic processes belonging to cells which remain outside the tissue in the pulpal cavity. Dentin may be considered a modified bone and represents one of the most highly specialized connective tissues in the body. Normal human dentin is avascular and acellular.

**Distribution of Dentin.**—The dentin forms a layer of comparatively even thickness and surrounds a central cavity which is occupied by its formative organ, the pulp. The dentin constitutes the chief mass of the tooth and determines its morphological form. The cusps and ridges, as well as the number and shape of the roots, are represented in the dentin surface.

**Physical Properties of Dentin.**—Dentin gives to the tooth its general form and elastic strength. The enamel, being hard and very resistant to abrasion, is extremely brittle, and is dependent upon the elastic support of the dentin. Dentin is yellowish in color and semi-transparent.

The fact that dentin gives strength to the tooth should not be lost sight of in operating, and sound dentin should not be sacrificed unnecessarily in the preparation of cavities.

**Chemical Composition of Dentin.**—Dentin consists of about 21 per cent organic material, 62 per cent calcium phosphate, and 5 per cent of other inorganic salts similar to those found in enamel.

Dr. H. C. Hodge, of the University of Rochester, gives the following "best" analysis.:

| | |
|---|---|
| Water | 10.8–15.7 per cent |
| Organic matter | 20.3–22.4 per cent |
| Inorganic matter | 61.0–73.0 per cent |

### Inorganic Matter

| Principal Components | | Lesser Components | |
|---|---|---|---|
| Ca | 33.0–35.4 per cent | Na | 0.20 per cent |
| P | 16.0–18.0 per cent | K | 0.07 per cent |
| $CO_3$ | 3.8– 4.6 per cent | Fe | 0.02 per cent |
| Mg | 0.9– 1.1 per cent | F | 0.02 per cent |

The balance, up to 100% is made up of oxygen

## STRUCTURAL ELEMENTS OF THE DENTIN

The structural elements of the dentin consist of:

(a) The dentin matrix.

 (*b*) The dentinal tubules.

 (*c*) The contents of the dentinal tubules (the Tomes' fibers).

 **The Dentin Matrix.**—The dentin matrix is a solid, apparently homogeneous and very elastic substance, through which the dentinal tubules extend. In broken or split sections, to the unaided eye, it has a yellowish color and a characteristic luster due to the refraction of light by the tubules.

 **Relation of Organic to Inorganic Matter.**—The matrix, yielding gelatin on boiling, consists of collagenous fibrils, embedded in an organic cementing substance in which the inorganic salts are deposited. The relation of organic matter in the dentin matrix is similar to that found in the bone and the cementum.

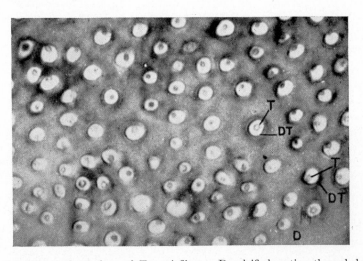

 Fɪɢ. 95.—Dentinal tubules and Tomes' fibers. Decalcified section through human dentin at right angles to the direction of the tubules. *D*, dentin; *DT*, walls of the tubules, formerly called Neumann's sheath; *T*, Tomes' fibers surrounded by lymph space. Magnification × 1250. (Konfeld, Dental Histology).

 Apparently the organic basis is first formed, and then the inorganic salts are combined with it in a weak chemical union. If the dentin is treated with dilute acid, the inorganic matter is dissolved and the organic basis is left retaining the form of the tissue. If the organic matter is burned out, it leaves the inorganic matter in its characteristic form.

 **Fibrillar Character.**—In the original condition no traces of the fibrillar character of the dentin can be seen. However, after maceration with acids and alkalies the intertubular material assumes a fibrillar appearance, as if bundles of white connective tissue fibrils had been fused. These bundles give the silk-like appearance to the dentin of ground sections. The fibrils are held together by an interfibrillar cementing substance which contains the calcium salts. The fibrils themselves, at least in young teeth, contain

no calcium salts. Studies with the electron microscope show the characteristic 640 Å banding of collagen in the dentinal fibrils (Fig. 90).

**Arrangement of Fibrils.**—Most of the fibrils are arranged longitudinally
and run parallel to the pulpal surfaces that obtained at the time of their
deposition, and at right angles to the dentinal tubules. Their course thus
gives an accurate record of the incremental pattern (Fig. 97). Not all
fibrils take this main course. A number of them cross one another and form
a network through which the dentinal tubules penetrate. There are also
radially directed fiber systems which are especially prominent in the mantle
dentin next to the enamel.

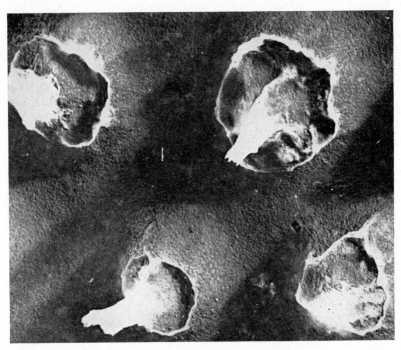

Fig. 96.—Electron micrograph of replicas made from the surfaces of an etched ground
section of dentin. Note the central process within the dental tubules, the distinct
structure at the periphery of the tubules, and the homogeneous nature of the matrix
between the dentinal tubules. × 9000. (Courtesy, D. B. Scott and R. W. G. Wyckoff).

**The Dentinal Tubules.**—**Size and Number.**—The dentin matrix is penetrated everywhere by minute branching tubules which radiate from the
central cavity or pulp chamber, and extend to the outer surface of the
dentin at the dentino-enamel or dentino-cemental junctions (Figs. 95 to 97).
Here they end blindly or in irregular arborizations that measure 1 $\mu$ in
diameter. The diameter of the dentinal tubules increases in the direction
of the pulpal surface where it is 3 to 4 $\mu$ (Fig. 95). The relative volume of
dentin matrix to dentinal tubules thus varies at different levels of the tooth.

9

The amount of ground substance between the tubules decreases from the periphery toward the pulp. Meyer found 75,000 dentinal tubules per square millimeter near the pulp, and 15,000 per square millimeter near the periphery of the dentin. Near the pulpal surface the tubuli are wider, and close together allowing relatively little space for the ground substance.

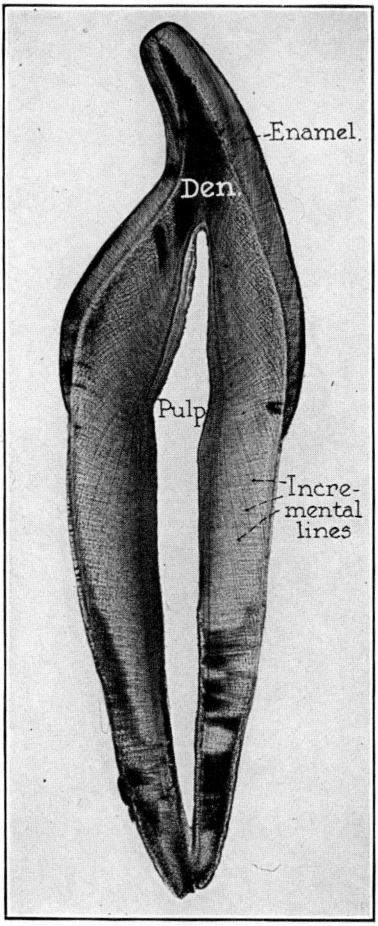

FIG. 97—Ground section shown in Fig. 30 photographed to show the incremental stratification in the dentin.

This is caused by the difference in the area of the outer and inner surfaces of the dentin.

**Direction of Tubules in Crown Portion.** — In the coronal and gingival portions of the dentin the tubules pass from the dentino-enamel and dentino-cemental junctions to the pulp in sweeping curves, which were called by Tomes the primary curvatures of the dentinal tubules (Fig. 98). These have been frequently described as S-shaped. The tubules tend to begin at right angles to the peripheral surface of the dentin and to enter the pulp also at right angles. The tubules thus make two primary bends in passing from the periphery of the dentin to the pulp chamber. In the first the convexity is directed occlusally, in the second it is directed apically. The outer extremities of the tubules of the crown are considerably closer to the occlusal than are the points at which they open into the pulp chamber.

The coincidence of the primary curvatures of neighboring dentinal tubules causes the appearance in the dentin of a macroscopic striping first described by Schreger in 1800. These lines have been confused with the microscopic bending of the tubules resulting from interruptions in dentin formation.

On closer study the directions of the tubules will be found to be more complicated. The course of the dentinal tubules is not a direct one but that of an open spiral. When longitudinal sections are examined under high power, this spiral course gives to the tubule the appearance of having little wavy curves throughout its length. These have often been called the secondary curvatures (Fig. 99). Each wave represents a turn in the spiral and as many as 200 have been counted in the length of a single tubule.

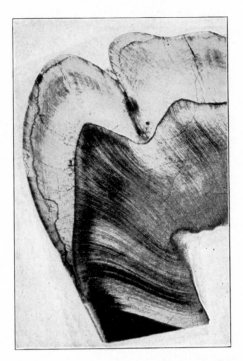

Fig. 98.—A section showing the primary curvature of the dentinal tubules in the gingival portion. (About 20 ×.)

Fig. 99.—A section showing compound curves near the dentino-enamel junction. (About 80 ×.)

The dentinal tubules give off minute lateral branches, which extend from one tubule to another (Figs. 100 and 101), and in the region of the dentino-enamel junction branch dichotomously, each fork having about the same diameter as the original tubule. The branches anastomose with each other freely. This anastomosis of the tubules at the dentino-enamel junction is very important in determining the spread of caries in this area. It probably also explains the sensitivity of this area in the preparation of cavities, and will be noted again in considering the sensitiveness of the dentin.

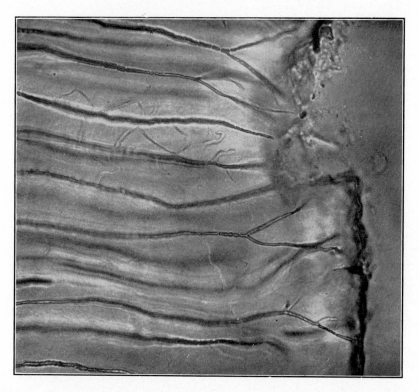

Fig. 100.—Dentin at the dentino-enamel junction, showing tubules cut longitudinally. (About 760 ×.)

**The Dentinal Tubules in the Root Portion.**—In the root portion of the dentin the tubules ordinarily show only the secondary curves, their general direction being at right angles to the long axis of the pulp canal (Fig. 97). Throughout their course they give off an enormous number of very fine branches extending from tubule to tubule. These are so numerous that in suitably prepared sections they appear like the interlacing twigs of a thicket or the rootlets of a plant in the soil. Figs. 100 and 101 give a very good idea of this condition. The tubules end at the dentino-cemental junction in the granular layer of Tomes (Fig. 102).

FIG. 101.—Dentin from the root, showing tubules cut longitudinally and the fine connecting branches.  (About 700 ×.)

From a consideration of the preceding it will be seen that it is usually not difficult to determine whether a field of dentin seen under the microscope was taken from the crown or the root of a tooth. The structural characteristics of the two regions may be summarized as follows: In the crown the tubules show both the primary and the secondary curves. In the root the tubules show only the secondary curves and are usually comparatively straight. In the crown the lateral branches are few and inconspicuous,

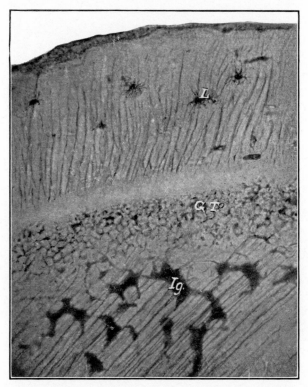

Fig. 102.—Granular layer of Tomes: *L*, lacuna of cementum; *GT*, granular layer of Tomes; *Ig*, interglobular dentin. (About 200 ×).

and the tubules branch dichotomously at the dentino-enamel junction. In the root the lateral branches are very numerous throughout the length of the tubule, and end in the granular layer of Tomes.

**The Sheaths of Neumann.**—There has been much discussion as to the character of these structures which were first described in 1863 by Neumann. Where the dentinal tubules come in contact with the dentin matrix, the latter takes on a deeper stain and is more resistant to acids and alkalies. This has led to the belief that there was a special structural sheath, that of Neumann, which clothed the tubules and could be isolated. Recent investigations indicate that Neumann's sheath does not exist as a separate structure, but that the matrix which forms the immediate wall of the tubules is more highly refractive and appears as a varying halo around the dentinal tubules (Fig. 95). These structures are therefore in no sense a sheath surrounding the dentinal fibril and lying in the tubule, but are that portion of the matrix which forms the immediate wall of the tubule. They correspond to the specialized layer of interstitial tissue which surrounds the lacunæ and canalicules of bone. That this material differs from that which occupies the rest of the space between the tubules is evident, and is shown by the examination of ground sections, the action of stains upon ground sections, and the action of the matrix when boiled with strong acids and alkalies. In Fig. 95 there is evidently a difference in the refractive index of the portion of the matrix immediately surrounding the tubules.

The Sheath of Neumann is afibrillar. It may be compared to the so-called capsule of the lacunæ in bone. Both the Sheath of Neumann and the capsule of the bone lacunæ stain intensively with hematoxylin but remain unstained in sections impregnated with silver stain. The sheath is very resistant to the action of acids and alkalies. After the remainder of the inter-tubular material has been destroyed by boiling with strong acid, the sheaths remain like hollow elastic fibers, having the appearance of pipe stems, which resist long continued action of the boiling acid.

**Sensitiveness of Dentin.**—Since nerve endings have not been found in the dentin or enamel, the sensitiveness of dentin may be explained on the basis of the irritability of the protoplasmic process of the odontoblasts which is transmitted through the body of the odontoblasts to the many adjacent nerve endings. The lateral twigs from the pulpal nerves extend to the walls of the pulp and the odontoblastic layer where they lose their myelin sheath and terminate as free nerve endings. (Fig. 115). Some of these nerve endings may enter the predentin and follow pathways which consist of simple and multiple loops which return to terminate in the odontoblastic layer (Fig. 116).

The rich distribution of the dentinal tubules assumes special significance in relation to the sensitivity of the dentin. In vital teeth these tubules are occupied by protoplasmic projections of the odontoblasts first described as the fibers of Tomes. As the dentin matrix is formed and calcified, a portion of their protoplasm is left in the tubules of the matrix as processes. These structures were first described by John Tomes, who recognized their true character. They may be demonstrated in decalcified sections, and will be seen projecting from the odontoblasts when the pulp is removed from a freshly extracted cracked tooth. In this way a portion of the process is pulled out of the tubules. Since the presence of a nerve supply in the fully formed dentin has not been proven, odontoblastic processes probably transmit external stimuli to the pulp and thus may subserve the function of nerve fibers. The dentinal fibers give off lateral branches which are especially numerous at the dentino-enamel junction. This region is more sensitive than the underlying dentin. A space has been observed between these processes and the walls of the dentinal tubules. This has been shown to be an artefact produced by the shrinkage of the protoplasmic processes during histological preparation.

## STRUCTURAL CHARACTERISTICS OF DENTIN

While the dentin matrix, the tubules and odontoblastic processes are the elements of which the dentin is composed, it also shows other structural characteristics.

**Interglobular Dentin.**—In 1850 Czermak described areas of imperfectly calcified dentin matrix, and called them interglobular spaces. These appear as spaces in dried dentin. In the discussion of the calcification of the dentin matrix it has been shown how the inorganic salts are combined with the organic matrix in spherical areas which enlarge and become united. When these calcospherites do not fuse, irregular areas of uncalcified matrix are left. These show concave facets where they join the spherical surfaces of the fully calcified matrix (Figs. 102 and 103).

Fig. 103.—Dried interglobular dentin. (About 80 ×.)

If the dentin is dried, the organic matrix in the above areas gives up water and shrinks; and true spaces appear, partially filled with the shrunken matrix. In this condition they may be filled with colored collodion or other material (Fig. 103). In sections of teeth which have never been allowed to dry, the uncalcified dentin matrix does not shrink, and the dentinal tubules continue in it without change of course or diameter. For this reason the term interglobular dentin, proposed by Meyer, is more appropriate than interglobular spaces.

Zones of interglobular dentin, as a rule, follow the incremental pattern (Fig. 104). They may occur at any portion of the dentin, either in the crown or root, but are more common in the crown and near the enamel.

A submantle layer of interglobular dentin occurs regularly in the crowns of permanent teeth in a manner that is characteristic of the type of tooth examined (Fig. 105). Like the mantle dentin, this layer does not follow the incremental pattern.

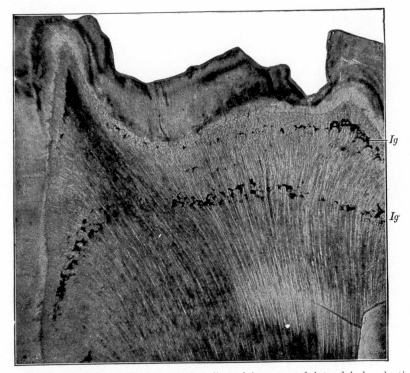

FIG. 104.—Interglobular dentin: *Ig*, first line of incremental interglobular dentin; *Ig′*, second line of incremental interglobular dentin. (About 30 ×.)

FIG. 105.—Submantle interglobular layer of dentin lying just beneath the homogeneous and well calcified mantle layer of dentin. (About 60 ×.)

Often more than one interglobular zone can be seen, as in Fig. 104, which shows two incremental disturbances in calcification. Disturbances in the structure of the enamel will be seen at corresponding positions. The zones of interglobular dentin appear in all gradations from a complete band of uncalcified matrix to widely scattered patches.

**Granular Layer of Tomes.**—In the dentin of the root next to the cementum there is regularly found a layer (of very small, crowded, and irregular areas) which resembles interglobular dentin and which in ground sections becomes filled with débris and appears granular (Fig. 102). It is called the granular layer of Tomes. Unlike the interglobular dentin it is not seen ordinarily in decalcified sections unless special staining is employed. It represents a physiologic disturbance in the calcification of the outermost layer of the dentin of the root and does not follow the incremental pattern.

**Owen's Lines of Contour.**—In 1840 Owen described contour lines in the dentin. They are incremental layers of interglobular dentin produced by a disturbance in the calcification of that layer at the time of its development (Fig. 104). They are analogous to the accentuated striæ of Retzius in the enamel and are seen in corresponding incremental levels of the crown.

Another type of contour line results when, "occasionally the tubes make a short bend along a line parallel with the outer contour of the crown" (Owen, 1840). An arrest in the formation of dentin sometimes occurs, and when appositional growth is resumed the dentinal tubules follow a slightly different direction. In longitudinal sections, this change in the direction of the tubules produces the appearance of a line at the pulpal surface that obtained at the time of the disturbance. Several such lines may be seen in a single section, though they are not common. These lines represent incremental deviations in dentin apposition, and offer an important contrast to the Owen's lines of contour, which represent interruptions in dentin calcification.

**Mantle Dentin.**—The dentin lying next to, and parallel with, the enamel and extending about 0.5 mm. from it, presents an appearance of better calcification and freedom from interglobular dentin (Fig. 105). It does not follow the incremental pattern and, because of its position, Weidenreich has named it the Mantle Dentin. He found that the mantle dentin was formed primarily by Korff's fibers and was analogous to fibrous bone.

**Predentin.**—The innermost layer of the circumpulpar dentin is called the predentin. Since, in dentin formation, the organic matrix is laid down first and then calcified, there is in young actively growing teeth a small border of uncalcified dentin next to the pulpal surface. This corresponds to the osteoid border of bone (Fig. 92).

**Transparent Dentin.**—There is a vital reaction of dentin to irritation, for instance, caries, in which the odontoblastic processes undergo fatty degeneration and may become calcified. Such dentin is called transparent dentin and may be a barrier to the progress of caries.

**Secondary Dentin.**—Dentinogenesis tends to continue throughout life, but proceeds at a steadily diminishing rate. The appositional rate of dentin is also different in different areas of a tooth. In the molars especially, more dentin is formed on the roof and floor of the pulp chamber than on the lateral walls. During the continuous apposition of dentin, the surface of the pulpal walls is gradually diminished and the odontoblasts become more and

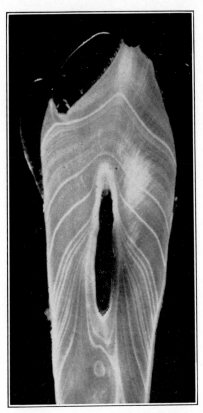

Fig. 106.—Fluorescent photomicrograph of ground section of premolar showing Owen's lines of contour in the dentin. Note the dentino-enamel junction. The enamel is outlined by the light surface borders. Courtesy of A. F. Forziati.

more crowded. When the crowding of the odontoblasts has reached a maximum, many of these cells degenerate and the remaining cells rearrange themselves on the wall of the pulp.

The dentin of the early period is called primary dentin; that formed in the later period is called secondary dentin. The secondary dentin is characterized by being formed on the entire pulpal surface of crown and root and by certain minor irregularities. At the boundary between primary and secondary dentin, the tubules sometimes change their direction and continue in a more wavy course through the secondary dentin. The latter contains, as a rule, fewer tubules per unit area. The characteristics of the secondary dentin may be explained on the basis of the overcrowding of the odontoblasts during the slowly progressing narrowing of the pulpal spaces.

**Irregular Dentin.**—Wherever dentinal tubules and odontoblastic processes become exposed by attrition, caries or cavity preparation, new dentin

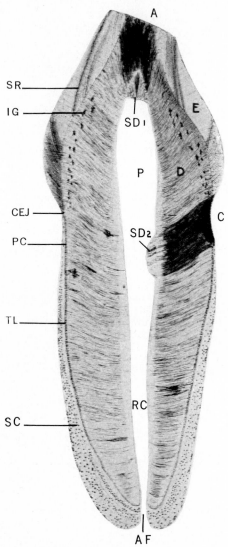

Fig. 107.—Longitudinal ground section through an upper central incisor of a middle-aged individual. The tooth is moderately abraded as well as affected by dental caries. *E*, enamel; *D*, dentin; *PC*, primary cementum; *SC*, secondary cementum; *CEJ.* cemento-enamel junction; *P*, pulp chamber; *RC*, root canal; *AF*, apical foramen; *SP*, stripes of Retzius; *IG*, interglobular spaces; *TI*, Tomes' granular layer; *A*, abraded incisal portion of crown; *SD*¹, secondary (irregular) dentin formed in response to abrasion; *C*, superficial dental caries at the cemento-enamel junction; *SD*², secondary (irregular) dentin formed in response to caries. Magnification × 7. (Kronfeld, *Dental Histology.*)

is rapidly formed in the exact area corresponding to the pulpal end of the exposed tubules. This dentin, characterized by its localized appearance, is termed irregular dentin. It may be regarded as a defense reaction of the pulp and may contain only a few irregularly scattered and irregularly twisted tubules (Figs. 107 and 108).

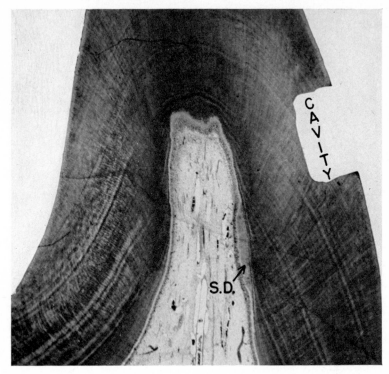

Fig. 108.—Photomicrograph of labiolingual section of canine of Macacus Rhesus monkey. Note cavity on labial surface and corresponding new secondary dentin formation, *S.D.*, at the pulpal ends of the cut odontoblastic processes. This cavity was filled with base plate gutta percha. The tooth was extracted 26 days later. × 12. (Courtesy of V. E. James).

## BIBLIOGRAPHY

Bernick, Sol.: Innervation of the Teeth and Periodontium, The Dental Clinics of North America, W. B. Saunders Company, July, 1959.

Bödecker, C. F.: A Consideration of Some of the Changes in the Teeth From Youth to Old Age, Dental Cosmos, *67*, 543, 1925.

Fish, E. W.: Experimental znvestigation of Enamel, Dentine, and the Dental Pulp, John Bale, London, 1933.

Murray, M. M.: The Chemical Composition of Teeth. IV. The Calcium, Magnesium and Phosphorus Contents of the Teeth of Different Animals, A Brief Consideration of the Mechanism of Calcification, Biochem. Jour., *30*, 1567, 1936.

Nylen, M. U. and Scott, D. B.: An Electron Microscopic Study of the Early Stages of Dentinogenesis. Health Service Publication No. 613, 1958.

Scott, D. B., and Wyckoff, R. W. G.: Electron Microscopy of Tooth Structure by the Shadowed Collodion Replica Method, Pub. Health Rep., *62*, 1513, 1947.

————: Electron Microscopy of Human Dentin, Jour. Dent. Res., *29*, 556, 1950.

# CHAPTER 9

# The Dental Pulp

**Definition.**—The dental pulp may be defined as the connective tissue occupying the cavity in the center of the dentin. It originates from the mesenchyme of the dental papilla.

## MORPHOLOGY OF DENTAL PULP

The pulp is located in the center of the dentin approximately equi-distant on all sides from the dentino-enamel and dentino-cemental surfaces when measured along the direction of the dentinal tubules. (See Morphogenesis of Dentin and Pulp, Chapter VII.) Because of the slanting of the dentinal tubules in the gingival third of the crown, the pulp lies closest to the outer surface of the dentin in this region. (See Direction of Dentinal Tubules, Chapter VIII.) This fact is of clinical importance in the preparation of proximal and gingival third cavities, particularly in the lower incisors.

**The Pulp Chamber.**—In the crown portion of the dentin, the primary outline of the pulp corresponds closely to the dentino-enamel junction and not to the surface of the enamel. This is more easily seen in three-dimensional models than in histological sections where the plane of section is often not exactly sagittal. The extensions of the pulp occlusally or incisally to conform with the projections of the growth centers on the dentino-enamel junction are called the pulpal horns. These horns must be constantly remembered during operative procedures lest the pulp be exposed.

**Pulp Canal.**—The pulp canal is the extension of the pulp chamber into the root. Its outline conforms to the dentino-cemental junction. Since the root is slender and tapers toward the apex, the pulp canal is narrow and tapers toward the apical foramen.

## FUNCTION OF DENTAL PULP

The pulp is a connective tissue originating from the mesenchyme of the dental papilla and performs multiple functions. It is the formative organ of the dentin. It is the source of nutrition and maintenance of the dentin. It also serves a sensory and defensive function.

**Formative Function.**—The formative function has been covered in Chapter VII, Dentinogenesis. In man the development of dentin slows down with age and the pulp cavity is gradually narrowed. In addition, irritation may stimulate the development of irregular dentin in localized areas (Fig. 108).

**Nutritional Function.**—The pulpal tissue in its similarity to loose connective tissue has a rich blood supply with a vascular network around the

( 142 )

odontoblasts. This affords a source of nutrition for the odontoblasts and their long terminal processes within the dentin. By maintaining the odontoblasts and their processes the dentin remains a vital tissue.

**Sensory Function.**—The nerves of the pulp react to stimulation, regardless of type of stimulus, by the sensation of pain. The pain is usually located correctly with reference to the median lines but apart from that is located only as it is referred to some known lesion. If several pulps were exposed on the same side of the mouth, including teeth of both the upper and lower arches, so that they could be irritated without impressions reaching the periodontal membrane, it would be impossible for a blindfolded patient to tell which of the pulps was touched. The pain originating from the pulp of a tooth may be referred to almost any point on the same side supplied by the fifth cranial nerve. This characteristic becomes extremely important in diagnosis.

The dental pulp is especially sensitive to sudden changes in temperature. This reaction has been utilized in testing the vitality of pulp. For instance, if a tooth is isolated and so protected by nonconductors that the soft tissues cannot be stimulated, and a jet of hot and then cold water be thrown upon its crown, it will respond to each with a sharp sensation of pain, but the patient cannot tell which is hot and which is cold. It is the sudden change that produces the reaction. This sensation of pain is a useful alarm system of the pulp to traumatic operative procedures.

**Defense Function.**—The similarity of the pulp to loose connective tissue is further evidenced by the defense mechanism of the pulp to injury by way of inflammation. The sequence of events of inflammation in other areas of loose connective tissue are also observed in the pulp following injury. Here, as elsewhere, the resolution of the inflammation is dependent on the extent and duration of the injury as well as the state of the pulpal tissue.

Another of the defense mechanisms of the pulp is the formation of calcified tissue in repair and resolution of inflammation. This is generally observed in localized areas where the deposition of the calcified tissue is more rapid than usually seen in non-stimulated secondary dentin formation. This calcified tissue of repair varies in the resemblance to dentin according to the amount of injury to the local odontoblasts. If not many odontoblasts are lost then the resulting repair tissue is very similar to regular dentin. If many of the odontoblasts are lost then the resulting reparative dentin may consist of a ground substance which contains only few or no dentinal tubules.

## STRUCTURAL ELEMENTS OF DENTAL PULP

The structural elements of the dental pulp are:

1. Odontoblasts.
2. Korff's fibers.
3. Connective tissue cells.
4. Intercellular substance.
5. Blood-vessels.
6. Lymphatic vessels.
7. Nerves.

**The Odontoblasts.**—The odontoblasts are highly specialized connective tissue cells of columnar shape which form the outer layer of the pulp adjacent to the dentin, and extend as cytoplasmic processes into the dentinal tubules. Their long axis lies at right angles to the surface of the pulp. The nucleus which is situated at the pulpal end of the cell is oval and contains several nucleoli. The diplosome and the Golgi apparatus are situated between the nucleus and the dentin side. The cytoplasm is rich in mitochondria which are especially abundant in the embryonic stages. Fat deposition has been found in the cytoplasm of the odontoblasts not only as an expression of degeneration but also as evidence of increased metabolism during active dentin formation (Figs. 90 and 91).

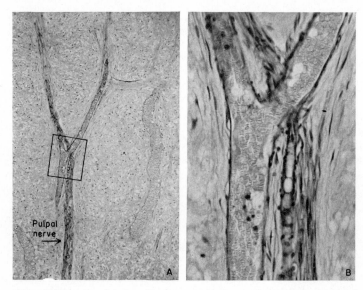

Fig. 109.—*A*, Pulp showing bundle of nerve fibers accompanied by a blood vessel. × 85. *B*, higher magnification of branching of nerve and vessel in field indicated in *A*.

Histochemical studies indicate the presence of calcium, phosphorus and potassium in active odontoblasts. Their cytoplasm as well as that of the odontoblastic processes contains alkaline phosphatase and glycoprotein, thus pointing to the role of the odontoblasts in the calcification of the dentin. The odontoblasts are furnished with a rich capillary network (Fig. 110).

The odontoblasts are connected with each other and with adjacent cells of the pulp by protoplasmic processes. Each odontoblast also sends out from the peripheral end multiple processes. The principal and central process increases in length in proportion to the increasing width of dentin and the recession of the odontoblasts (see Fig. 91). In the early stage of development, when the layer of dentin is still thin and enamel is not yet

PLATE V

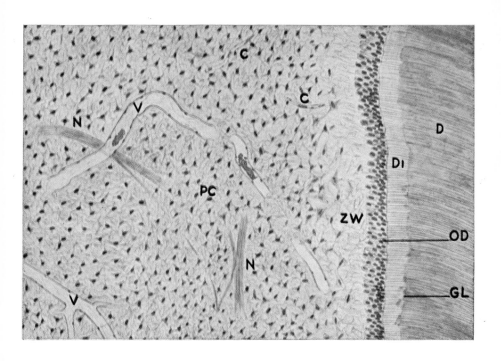

Pulp of a lower third molar of a young adult.

D, dentin; D₁, predentin (dentinoid); GL, globules of calcification; OD, odontoblasts; ZW, zone of Weil; PC, pulp cells; C, capillaries; V, veins; N, nerves. Magnification ×150. (Kronfeld, Dental Histology.)

formed, the main odontoblastic process which usually terminates at the dentino-enamel border may penetrate the latter and extend beyond the base of the ameloblasts or even lodge among the cells of the stratum intermedium remaining in the adult enamel as an enamel spindle (Figs. 82 and 83).

The shape and size of the odontoblasts vary with age and position. This is true not only of pulps from different animals and pulps at different periods of development, but also of different parts of the same pulp.

**Korff's Fibers.**—The Korff's fibers arise from the area lying more deeply in the pulp and extend between the odontoblasts into the dentin matrix (Figs. 86, 88 and 91). Their function in dentin formation has been discussed in Chapter 7.

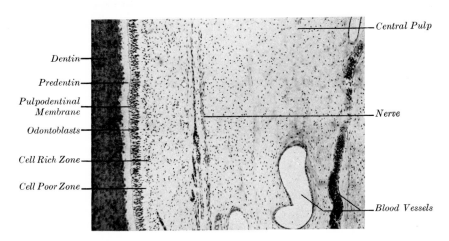

Central Pulp

Dentin—

Predentin—

Pulpodentinal Membrane—

Odontoblasts—

Nerve

Cell Rich Zone—

Cell Poor Zone—

Blood Vessels

Fig. 110.—Young human pulp. Courtesy Verda E. James.

**Connective Tissue Cells.**—Immediately beneath the layer of odontoblasts, for a space about one-half to two-thirds as wide as the odontoblastic layer, the cells and blood vessels are scarce. Weil described in ground sections of hard and soft tissue this layer next to the base of the odontoblasts, which is poor in cells. Weil's layer is indistinct or absent during early dentin formation or during active repair by secondary dentin.

This area contains many fine nerve fibers which are not stained by ordinary methods. Beyond the so-called layer of Weil, for a space perhaps twice as wide as the height of the odontoblasts, the cells are more closely placed. Through the remainder of the pulp they are much more widely but comparatively evenly scattered (Fig. 110).

The cells of the pulp are connected with one another by cytoplasmic processes and arranged in a syncytium. They are embedded in a gelatinous intercellular substance that resembles that of mucoid tissue (Plate V). While most of the cells are fibrocytes, there are also some histiocytes

10

undifferentiated mesenchymal cells, and wandering cells. The histiocytes have been studied after injections of vital dyes and during pulpal inflammations.

Histiocytes which show a granulated cytoplasm are often found near the blood-vessels. They are identical with resting macrophages of loose connective tissue. Undifferentiated mesenchymal cells are found along the capillaries.

**Intercellular Substance.**—The intercellular substance consists of fibers and a gelatinous cementing substance. The fibers are for the greater part fine collagenous fibers not arranged in bundles but in fairly regular network. In the outer layers of the pulp argyrophil fibers are found which, between the odontoblasts, fuse into the strong fibers of Korff. The gelatinous consistency of the cementing substance can be recognized by the fact that the pulp maintains its shape after it has been removed from the tooth and resists tear (Fig. 114).

**The Blood Vessels.**—The dental pulp is an extremely vascular tissue, and the arrangement of the vessels, the structure of their walls, and the nature of the intercellular substance through which they run render the tissue especially susceptible to the pathological conditions which are associated with alterations in the circulation.

The alveolar artery of the jaws sends pulpal branches to each root, and interdental or interradicular branches to the periodontal membrane. The pulpal artery sends its small branches into the periapical tissue before it enters the apical foramen. The interdental artery passes through the bony septum and terminates in branches which supply the gingiva (Fig. 168). The pulpal artery follows the central portion of the pulp, giving off many branches as it passes occlusally, and finally forms a very rich plexus of capillaries near the surface of the pulp about and between the odontoblasts (Plate VI). From these capillaries the blood is collected into the veins, which follow courses parallel to the arteries, leaving the pulp through the same foramina in the region of the apex. It is important to notice that an artery is entering and a vein leaving the tissue through very minute canals in the calcified dentin (Fig. 111). Since the pulp is enclosed by hard walls and constricted at the apical foramen or foramina, an engorgement with blood will produce a venous stasis and death much more readily than in connective tissues that are less confined spatially.

**Structure.**—The delicacy of the walls of the blood-vessels is one of the most striking histological characteristics of the dental pulp (Figs. 109, 110 and 112). The largest arteries show only a few muscle fibers in the tunica media and a very slight condensation of fibrous tissue for the tunica adventitia. There is no distinct boundary between the capillaries and the veins, and the vessels continue to have only a wall of endothelial cells after they have reached a size much greater than that of the capillaries. Because of this peculiarity many text-books of histology describe the pulpal vessels as large capillaries. Even in the largest veins the tunica media is very

PLATE VI

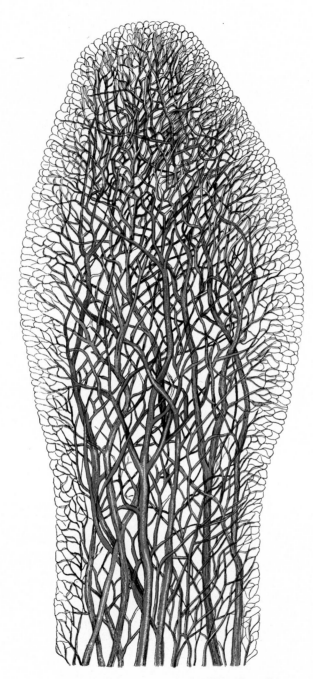

Blood vessels of the dental pulp. (After Stowell.)

A well-injected pulp studied under a binocular microscope makes a very beautiful object which no flat picture can represent. The larger bloodvessels lying at the center branch and divide, forming a network which becomes very fine at the surface.

imperfect, and there is only a slight condensation of fibrous tissue to represent the tunica adventitia. This peculiarity of the blood-vessel walls in the pulp renders the tissue unusually susceptible to hyperemia and inflammation. In a normal pulp there are many capillaries so small that a single corpuscle passes them with difficulty, but in pathological conditions they become distended to many times their normal diameter.

**Lymphatics of the Dental Pulp.**—For many years the dental pulp was said to be devoid of lymphatics and all attempts to inject vessels in the

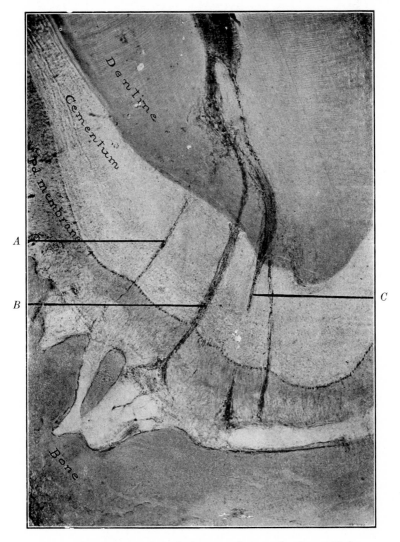

Fig. 111.—A section through the apex of a root showing multiple foramina, *A*, *B*, and *C*. (Talbot.)

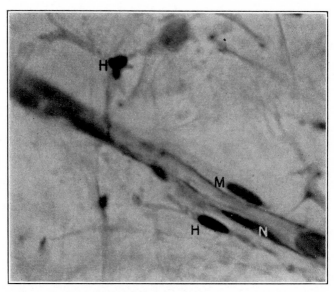

Fig. 112.—Photomicrograph of a capillary of a human pulp. Note the nucleus (N) of an endothelial cell; an undifferentiated mescenhymal cell (M) which is situated next to the vascular wall; a blood cell in the lumen to the right; and the histiocytes (H) with their branching granulated cytoplasm. (Courtesy, J. P. Weinmann), ×1300.

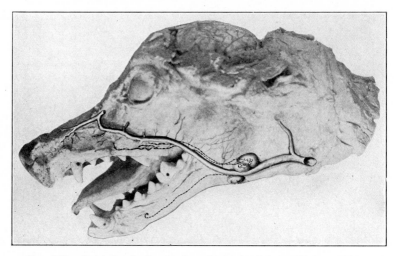

Fig. 113.—Dog's head, showing lymphatic glands injected from dental pulp.

dental pulp failed. In 1909 Schweitzer reported successful injections of the dental pulp, and in 1914 Noyes and Dewey repeated Schweitzer's results and succeeded in injecting lymph capillaries of the submaxillary lymph glands in the dog by injections into the dental pulp and followed the course of the vessels continuously from the pulp to the glands (Fig. 113). The blood-vessels were injected with gelatin carmin, the lymphatics with Berlin

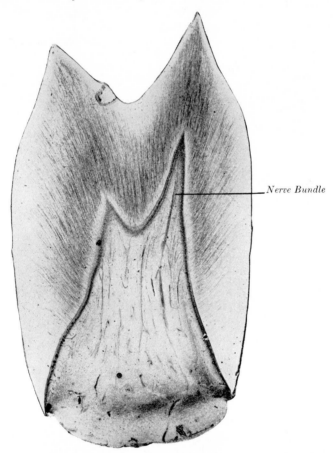

*Nerve Bundle*

Fig. 114.—Photomicrograph of decalcified longitudinal section of developing human premolar. The relatively firm consistency of the pulp is indicated by the absence of tearing within the pulp in spite of the forces in extraction. Courtesy Verda E. James and K. V. Katele. (×14).

blue. Very fine vessels were found close to the surface of the dentin (Fig. 110). From these, capillaries pass through the central portions of the tissue and the apical foramina where they anastomose with the vessels of the periodontal ligament. There is much work to be done in this field before our knowledge will be at all complete regarding both the perivascular lymph sheaths and the independent lymph vessels.

**The Nerves of the Dental Pulp.**—Few subjects in connection with dental histology have received more attention than the distribution of the nerves of the dental pulp, especially in relation to the sensitiveness of the dentin.

The nerve trunk entering the pulp through the apical foramen divides into branches containing from eight to forty medullated nerve fibers. They pass occlusally through the central portion of the pulp, but almost immediately begin to give off branches which pass toward the periphery, branching and anastomosing in their course. Most of the fibers lose their medullary sheath very soon after leaving the nerve trunk. Such nerve fibers are

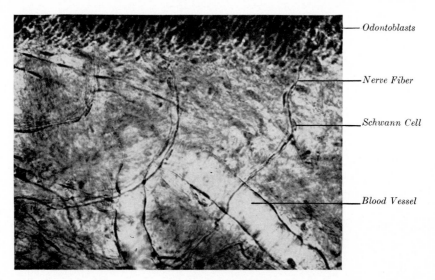

*Odontoblasts*

*Nerve Fiber*

*Schwann Cell*

*Blood Vessel*

Fig. 115.—Pulpal nerve fibrils coursing toward odontoblastic layer. Note nerve fiber which loses its myelin sheath as its approaches the odontoblastic layer. Courtesy Verda E. James and K. V. Katele.

covered only by the sheath of Schwann or the neurolemma. A bundle of such fibers, breaking up to be distributed to one horn of the pulp, is shown in Fig. 114. Other fibers retain their medullary sheath, following an independent course through the pulp tissue, until they reach the layer of Weil, where the sheath is lost and may join the plexus of non-myelinated fibers lying in this region. From the plexus in the layer of Weil, non-myelinated fibers are given off, passing between and around the odontoblasts, forming a network around each cell, and even passing over on to the end of the cell between it and the predentin or into the predentin (Fig. 116).

The sensitiveness of the dentin, in view of these observations, is due to the presence of living protoplasmic processes of the odontoblasts which are in physiological connection with nerve fibers. It is interesting to note that this is the only instance in which a connective tissue cell is intermediate between the outside world and the nerve fiber. In all other instances an epithelial cell is intermediate between the environment and the nervous system. The sensitiveness of the dentin is therefore due to the irritability of the cytoplasmic process, transmitted through the continuity of cytoplasm to the odontoblasts and their reaction upon the surrounding nerve fibers. The irritation may be physical, bacterial, chemical or thermal. For instance, if salt is sprinkled on exposed living dentin, a sharp sensation of pain is the result. It may be supposed that chemical changes are set up in the cytoplasm of the process which excite changes in the cytoplasm of

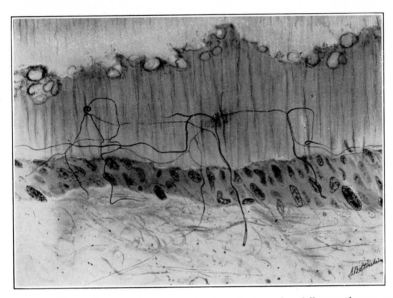

Fig. 116.—Nerve fiber entering the predentin. Its branches follow pathways consisting of simple and multiple loops in the predentin and odontoblastic layer. The nerve fiber divides in the predentin, its branches passing in a transverse direction and undulating between the dentinal tubules. (Courtesy, Sol Bernick and Dent. Clinics, N. A., and W. B. Saunders Company.)

the odontoblasts. These react upon the cytoplasm of the nerve fiber, and are transmitted to the nerve center, being recognized in consciousness as a sensation of pain. In the same way traumatic irritation caused by the cutting of dentin with a steel instrument sets up changes in the process.

Certain clinical facts are well explained by these structural facts. It is often noted in the preparation of cavities that the dentin is most sensitive at the dentino-enamel junction. This would be expected since especially at the dentino-enamel junction the sensitive odontoblastic processes branch and anastomose, so that an irritation to a few processes is not simply transmitted to their odontoblasts and the nerve endings in contact with them, but to all the fibers and so to the nerves in contact with all of the odontoblasts. The presence of dilute acids renders the cytoplasm of the fibers much more irritable. The dentin in a carious condition is therefore much more sensitive than that in a sound or normal area. The sensitiveness of extremely hypersensitive dentin can often be greatly reduced, if not entirely overcome, by cleansing the cavity thoroughly, washing with tepid water, followed by a dilute alkali, drying and sealing with zinc oxide and eugenol for a few days, when it will be usually found that the excavation can be performed without excessive pain. The sealing must be complete. If it is leaky, the cavity will be more sensitive than ever at the end of the delay.

Teeth in which the size of the pulp chamber has been reduced by the formation of secondary dentin are usually much less sensitive than those in which no secondary dentin formation has occurred. By this formation, as

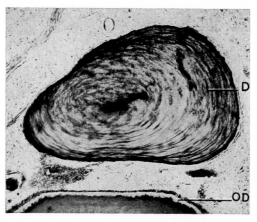

Fig. 117.—Pulp stone (denticle). A small calcific body of concentric lamellated structure is embedded in the pulp tissue. *D*, Denticle; *OD*, odontoblasts on the wall of the pulp chamber. Magnification × 60. (Kronfeld, Dental Histology and Comparative Dental Anatomy.)

has been seen in the chapter on dentin, many of the tubules are cut off and others reach the pulp only by anastomosing with tubules. The transmission to the nerves of the pulp is thus made more difficult and imperfect.

The nerves of the pulp not only respond to sensations of pain from the irritation of the fibers in the dentinal tubules, but also because of their confinement in a calcified chamber and the semifluid nature of the tissue, they are very sensitive to pressure, either increased or decreased. The normal response to changes of temperature, as well as most of the pain in pathological inflammatory conditions of the pulp, are probably caused by changes of pressure, through a disturbance of the blood circulation of the tissue.

Non-medullated nerve fibers of the autonomic nervous system control the blood supply of the pulp by giving off branches to the muscular elements of the walls of the blood vessels. Thus the blood supply of the pulp of experimental animals has been increased by the resection of the alveolar nerves.

## HISTOPHYSIOLOGICAL REMARKS

**Changes With Age.**—The pulp becomes constricted with age. This is a normal physiological process in the young tooth where primary dentin is still being formed. Later, in the adult tooth, the constriction continues with the deposition of secondary dentin. The apical foramen is wide open in the young tooth but becomes narrowed with age and may be further constricted by cementum formation. Multiple accessory foramina frequently arise and persist through the inclusion of blood-vessels and nerves during the narrowing of the foramina (Fig. 111).

The histologic character and structure is changed with age. The pulp becomes poorer in cells and shows an increase of collagenous fibrillar masses which are arranged in bundles. With fewer undifferentiated cells available for emergencies, the defense and repair processes are slower in getting started. This change may explain the lowered vitality of the pulp in older individuals.

**Pulp Stones.**—The propensity of the pulp to form calcified tissue is also seen in the frequent occurrence of calcified bodies in the central pulp, called pulpstones or denticles (Fig. 117). The initiation of this process is not necessarily pathologic since denticles are found even on young and unerupted teeth. They tend to increase in size and number with age.

The denticles have been classified according to their microscopic structure as being true or false. The true denticles consist of irregular dentin. The false denticles are evidence of degenerative calcifications of the pulp tissue, contain no dentinal tubules, and are formed by the deposition of concentric layers around a central nucleus in typical calcospherite formation.

According to their relation to the wall of the pulp chamber, all denticles are classified as being free, adherent and intersitital. The latter are denticles embedded within the dentin and have developed by the continued formation of dentin about an adherent denticle.

### Clinical Considerations

*Defensive and Reparative Power of Pulp.*—It is a mistake to *assume* that any injury or inflammation of the pulp will inevitably lead to degeneration and death of this tissue. The pulp is richly vascularized connective tissue and as such is endowed with the capacity to withstand injury and to repair itself. This capacity, however, is limited anatomically by the confined position of the pulp within non-yielding walls of dentin, and the subsequent lack of collateral circulation. Inflammation of the pulp can lead to recovery and healing and even repair (new dentin formation) under suitable conditions or to a degeneration when the conditions are unfavorable.

The response of the odontoblasts and adjacent pulpal cells varies with the degree of injury. A mild injury to the odontoblastic processes, such as in superficial caries or shallow cavity preparation, usually leads to an increased calcification. The resulting obstruction of the tubules by calcium salts serves as a barrier to the transmission of external stimuli (Fish, 1932). In addition, new dentin may be deposited along the pulpal surface of the

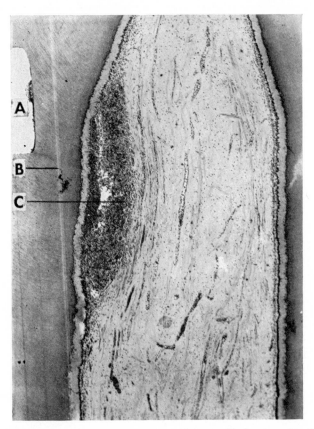

FIG. 118.—Photomicrograph of pulp of lower left cuspid showing the effects of insertion of silicate cement into cavity *A*. Note the dentin *B;* and the pulpal inflammation *C*. The tooth which was sound was extracted six weeks after the insertion of the filling. Compare with Fig. 119. (Courtesy of H. A. Zander).

tubules which have been injured. This favorable biologic response of the dentin and pulp does not occur when the injury is severe as in the case of rapid and deep cutting with a bur and toxic filling materials.

The particular effects in any given case depend not only on the type of cavity preparation and filling material but on a number of biologic variables; for example, the age and health of the patient and the posteruptive age of the tooth.

**Operative Procedures.**—It should be pointed out that for every square millimeter of dentin cut at the level of the dentino-enamel junction, there is a concomitant amputation of the living cytoplasmic processes of about 15,000 odontoblasts. This number increases fourfold as one approaches the pulp. Furthermore, the closer the injury to the cell bodies of the odontoblasts (perikaryons) the more severe the effect. No more dentin should, therefore, be cut than is necessary for the preparation of the cavity.

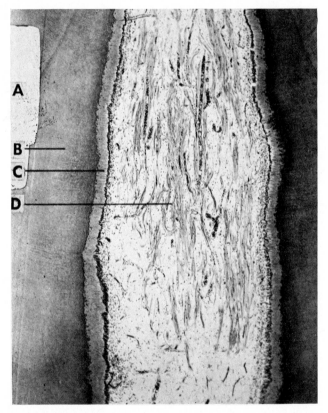

Fig. 119.—Photomicrograph of pulp of lower lateral incisor of same patient as in Fig. 118. The cavity *A* was filled with zinc oxide and eugenol. Note the dentin, *B;* the predentin, *C;* and the pulp *D.* The pulp is normal. The tooth was extracted six weeks after the insertion of the filling. Compare with Fig. 118. (Courtesy of H. A. Zander.)

In general, a slowly revolving sharp bur produces less heat and less injury to the pulp than does a rapidly revolving dull bur, and, furthermore, causes less pain.

**Filling Materials.**—Some filling materials (silicates) contain noxious substances (acids) which tend to injure the pulp (Fig. 118). Others transmit temperature differences too readily (amalgam) and thus tend to delay secondary dentin formation, especially in deep cavity preparations. An insulating base is, therefore, indicated to protect the pulp.

At the present time, we do not have an "ideal" permanent filling material; that is, one which is mechanically resistant to stresses, esthetic in appearance, and biologically favorable to pulpal regeneration. The selection of the filling materials is being increasingly based not merely on their physical and esthetic characteristics, but also on their biologic acceptability. The clinical principle of respect for living cells and tissues applies to cavity preparations and fillings since the dentin and the pulp are intimately related and interdependent. These integrated tissues are highly sensitive and responsive and react as a unit to disease, to operative procedures and to filling materials.

There is a general agreement that the temporary filling of zinc oxide and eugenol is biologically the best tolerated of the various filling materials (Fig. 119).

**Modifying Effect of Caries.**—The condition of the pulp at the time of placing the filling is also important. When the area involved in the cavity preparation has been previously affected by caries or attrition, there has, generally, already been some stimulus to the defensive and protective mechanism of the pulp. The odontoblastic processes may have already sealed the tubules by calcification, so that the impulse is not transmitted to the odontoblasts and the pulp. Injury of the odontoblastic processes during cavity preparation is, therefore, lessened. This protective response of the pulp may, however, be expected only when the carious process has been slow or arrested. In the case of rampant caries, the rapidity of the process may lead to pulp exposure and pulpal death.

## BIBLIOGRAPHY

BERNICK, SOL: Innervation of the Teeth and Periodontium, The Dental Clinics of North America, W. B Saunders Company, July, 1959.

COOLIDGE, E. D.: Anatomy of the Root Apex in Relation to Treatment Problems, Jour. Am. Dent. Assn., *16*, 1456, 1929.

FISH, E. W.: The Pathology of the Dentine and the Dental Pulp, Brit. Dent. Jour., *53*, 351, 1932.

HESS, W.: Formation of Root Canals in Human Teeth, Jour. Nat. Dent. Assn., *8*, 704, 1921.

HILL, T. J.: Pathology of the Dental Pulp, Jour. Am. Dent. Assn., *21*, 820, 1934.

HOPEWELL-SMITH, A.: Adventitious Dentin and Infection of the Dental Pulp, Dent. Items Int., *47*, 477, 551, 1925.

HUBER, G. C.: The Innervation of the Tooth-Pulp, Dental Cosmos, *40*, 797, 1898.

JAMES, V. E., ISAAC SCHOUR, and JOHN M. SPENCE: Response of Human Pulp to Gutta-percha and Cavity Preparation, Journal of the American Dental Association, *49*, 639-650, 1954.

KRONFELD, R.: Nerves in the Dentin; A Survey of Recent Literature on Dentin Innervation, Jour. Am. Dent. Assn., *23*, 1756, 1936.

MUMMERY, J. H.: The Innervation of Dentin, Dental Cosmos, *58*, 258, 1916.

NOYES, F. B.: A Review of the Work on the Lymphatics of Dental Origin, Jour. Am. Dent. Assn., *14*, 714, 1927.

ORBAN, B.: Contribution to the Histology of the Dental Pulp and Periodontal Membrane, With Special Reference to the Cells of "Defense" of These Tissues, Jour. Am. Dent. Assn., *16*, 965, 1929.

WASSERMANN, F.: The Innervation of Teeth. J. A. D. A., *26*, 1097, 1939.

# CHAPTER 10

# The Cementum

**Definition.**—The cementum is a bone-like tissue whose intercellular substance is calcified and arranged in layers around the circumference of a tooth root.

## DISTRIBUTION OF CEMENTUM

The normal distribution of cementum is confined to the root surface and to the inner apical end of the root canal. It begins at the enamel border as a thin layer about 20 $\mu$ thick and reaches its greatest thickness at the apex and bifurcations. But cementum is also commonly found slightly overlapping the enamel at the neck of the tooth (Fig. 85). This is made possible by the fact that cementum is laid down after the enamel is completely formed. In some cases the cementum just meets the enamel, or in others there is a space between the enamel and the cementum where the dentin is uncovered.

## FUNCTION OF CEMENTUM

The function of the cementum is to attach the tooth to the connnective tissue fibers of the periodontal membrane. These fibers extend from the cementum to the bone and the surrounding tissues, support the teeth against the forces of mastication, and hold the adjoining tissues and the teeth in proper relation. The primary purpose of cementum is thus to attach the periodontal membrane fibers to the surface of the root and to support the tooth as a whole and render it functional. In view of its function the cementum becomes one of the most important of the dental tissues, for no matter how perfect the teeth may be, without firm attachment they become useless and are soon lost.

## HISTOGENESIS OF CEMENTUM

Cementum is formed by the connective tissue cells lying at the inner border of the dental sac, adjacent to Hertwig's epithelial sheath and the dentin. There are two types of cementum: acellular cementum; and cellular cementum.

**Acellular Cementum.**—As soon as the dentin of the root begins to form, while the developing tooth is still within its bony crypt, connective tissue cells of the dental sac break through Hertwig's epithelial sheath, and arrange themselves along the dentinal surface (Fig. 120). The influence

( 157 )

of Hertwig's sheath on the formation of cementum presents an interesting problem for investigation.  It is possible that its cells stimulate cementum formation (Fig. 49).

The cementoblasts deposit the cementum, layer upon layer, and do not become embedded within the ground substance matrix as do osteoblasts, but remain outside the matrix as do the dentin-forming cells.  The acellular

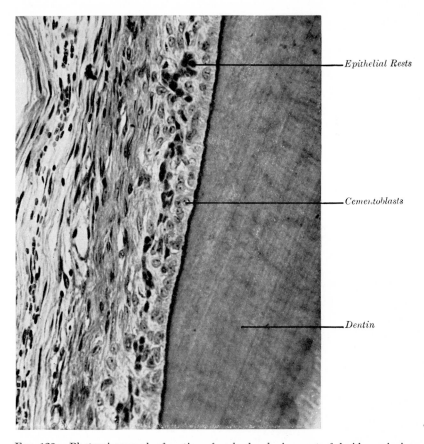

Fig. 120.—Photomicrograph of section of early developing root of deciduous incisor. The cementoblasts are differentiating from the follicular connective tissue adjacent to the surface of the root.  Note the longitudinal course of the fiber.  (× 450).

cementum is clear and structureless, and directly overlies the granular layer of Tomes in the dentin.  Although the connective tissue fibers are embedded in cementum, the developing tooth before its eruption is lying loosely within its bony crypt and can be picked out with very little effort.  Premolars are thus accidentally removed during the extraction of overlying deciduous molars.

As the tooth continues to form the root and begins its active eruption, new layers of primary cementum are formed. At the same time, perhaps under the stimulus of the active movement of the erupting tooth, a rich number of connective tissue fibers from the dental sac are observed to run, in bundles 3 to 6 $\mu$ in thickness, at right angles to the dentin surface. These fibers become embedded in the newly forming cementum matrix. The cementum matrix soon calcifies and embeds the fibers firmly within its

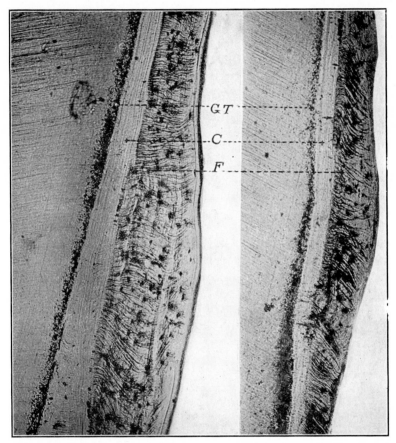

Fig. 121.—Two fields of cementum showing penetrating fibers: *GT*, granular layer of Tomes; *C*, acellular cementum, showing no embedded fibers (note the lamellæ and incremental lines of deposition); *F*, cellular cementum. Note the cementum lacunæ and the embedded periodontal fibers.

substance, attaching the tooth more firmly to the surrounding connective tissue and alveolar bone. Acellular cementum thus covers all of the root except the most apical portion. It is thinnest at the cemento-enamel junction and becomes thicker toward the apex.

**Cellular Cementum.**—As soon as the tooth is exposed to stress, before clincal eruption is completed, cellular cementum begins to form over the acellular cementum and the dentin at the apical end (since eruption occurs before the root is completed). The cementoblasts, under the stimulus of oral forces upon the partially exposed tooth, form new cementum matrix and, similar to the osteoblasts in bone, become incorporated within the forming and calcifying matrix (Fig. 121). The fibers of the periodontal ligament are firmly embedded wihtin the cementum during this process. The oral forces now are transmitted from the tooth *via* the embedded periodontal fibers to the alveolar bone.

It is important to remember in connection with the formation of cementum, that the teeth move microscopically throughout life. Every slight change in position must be accompanied by the formation of a new layer of secondary cementum, to reattach the fibers of the periodontal membrane in new positions or to adjust them to new directions of strain.

Structurally, cementum, particularly secondary cementum, may be regarded as a bone substance which is adapted to special functional conditions and is built continuously by the cells of the periodontal membrane. In actively growng cellular cementum, a clear cementoid or precementum border is seen next to the periodontal ligament (Fig. 121). This border stains with eosin in decalcified sections. It is very wide in rickets.

Cementum is formed both before and after the teeth have erupted into occlusion. It is apposed continuously throughout the functional life of the tooth. The retention of the tooth depends on the continual building of cementum. The continuous growth of cementum is also important because it checks the widening of the periodontal space and the weakening of the investing apparatus.

**Chemical Analysis of Cementum.**—The chemical composition of cementum resembles that of bone, being about 35 to 40 per cent organic and 65 to 70 per cent inorganic matter.


## STRUCTURAL ELEMENTS OF CEMENTUM

The structural elements of the cementum are:

1. The matrix (intercellular substance).
2. The incremental layers.
3. Cementocytes enclosed in lacunæ.
4. The embedded fibers of the periodontal ligament (Sharpey's fibers).

**The Matrix.**—The matrix is finely fibrous, the fibers being connected to each other by a calcified cementing substance. The fibrils are arranged according to functional stresses, similar to those in bone.

**The Incremental Layers of the Cementum.**—Cementum grows by the apposition of new layers. This process appears to be interrupted from time to time by periods of rest. These interruptions leave permanent marks, similar to the resting lines of bone, which are darkly stained in decalcified sections stained with hematoxylin-eosin. The layers of the cementum separated by the resting lines are of variable thickness.

The cementum becomes gradually thicker in the middle third of the root, and is thickest in the apcial third. It will be seen that this increase in thickness is caused chiefly by cellular cementum and is due to the greater width of the incremental layers. In longitudinal sections the cementum is often found to become suddenly thicker at a certain level, and each layer continues apically from that point, but with increased thickness. Fig. 124 illustrates this condition near the apex of the root. From a study of its structure, therefore, it is apparent that the entire root is clothed with successive layers, and that these layers are formed intermittently, and continue

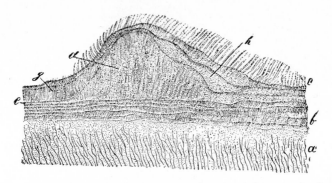

Fig. 122.—Hypertrophy of the cementum on the side of the root of a lower molar near the neck of the tooth. From a lengthwise section: (human) *a*, dentin; *b*, cementum; *c*, fibers of periodontal membrane. From *b* to *c* the cementum is normal and the incremental lines fairly regular, but at *d* one of the lamellæ is greatly thickened. At *e* this lamella is seen to be about equal in thickness with the others. The next two lamellæ are thin over the greatest prominence, but one is much thickened at *g*, and both at *h*. These latter seem to partially fill the valleys which were occasioned by the first irregular growth. (1 in. obj.) (G. V. Black.)

to be formed as long as the tooth is functioning. In a general way the number of layers is an index of the functional stresses to which the tooth has been subjected and is thus to some extent also an index to the age of the person at the time the tooth was extracted.

The rate of formation is not uniform; a number of layers may be formed within a short time, and again a considerable time may elapse between the formation of one layer and the next.

**Cementocytes and Lacunæ.**—The cementocytes can be studied in dried ground sections where the spaces formerly occupied by them and their processes are filled with air. The lacunæ differ from those of bone in that they are more irregular in shape, size, position, and in the number and direction of the canalicules radiating from them. In bone the lacunæ are fairly regular in shape, the long diameter exceeding the short diameter by about one-third. In cementum there is no regularity whatever, either in

11

size or in shape. Some are a little larger than the lacunæ in bone, some are very much smaller. The lacunæ of bone are fairly uniform in position. In the cementum, however, the lacunæ are unevenly distributed throughout the intercellular substance. The matrix immediately surrounding the lacunæ and canalicules stains dark in hematoxylin.

The number and direction of the canalicules which radiate from the lacunæ of cementum is extremely irregular, but in general there are more extending from the lacunæ toward the surface than toward the dentin.

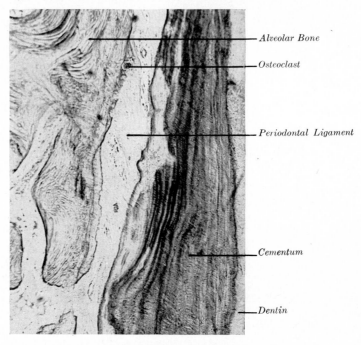

— Alveolar Bone

— Osteoclast

— Periodontal Ligament

— Cementum

— Dentin

Fig. 123.—Photomicrograph of decalcified section of root of human molar. The incremental lamellæ in the cementum show varying thickness. Note the embedded periodontal fibers and lacunæ and the record of cementum resorption and repair. (×65.)

**The Cementocytes**—These cementum cells are embedded cementoblasts found in the lacunæ. They are made up of granular cytoplasm and contain a faintly staining nucleus. Extensions of the protoplasm course into the canalicules and are directed chiefly toward the surface from which they obtain nutrition (Fig. 125). Their processes anastomose with one another. These cells bear the same relation to the matrix of the cementum that the osteocytes do to that of bone. There are many cementocytes in the lacunæ in the region of the apex of the root.

In the deeper layers various regressive changes of the cementum cells can be seen; pyknosis, disintegration and complete disappearance of the nucleus and fatty degeneration in the cell body.

When the osteocytes are killed or die, the matrix becomes a foreign body which is either resorbed or cut off from the portion in which the cells are living and cast out as a sequestrum. The same conditions are true of cementum.

If it is infected for a long time, the cementocytes are killed, and the tissue becomes saturated with toxic materials, so that tissue cells cannot lie in contact with it and live. In order to restore a healthy condition the ne-

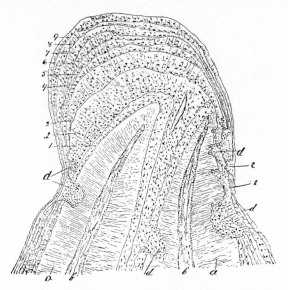

Fig. 124.—Apex of root of an upper bicuspid tooth with irregularly developed cementum: *a, a,* dentin; *b, b,* pulp canals. The lamellæ of cementum are marked 1, 2, 3, 4, 5, 6, 7, 8, 9; *d, d, d,* resorption areas that have been refilled with cementum. It will be seen that the apices of the roots were originally separate, but became fused with the deposit of the second lamella of cementum, and that in this the irregular growth began and was most pronounced. It has continued through the subsequent lamellæ, but in less degree. It will also be noticed that the resorption areas, *d, d, d,* have proceeded from certain lamellæ. That between the roots has broken through the first lamella and penetrated the dentin, and has been filled with the deposit of a second lamella. Other of the resorptions have proceeded from lamellæ which can be readily made out. The small points, *e,* seem to have been filled with the deposit of the last layer of the cementum, while others have one, two, or more layers covering them. (2 in. obj.) (G. V. Black.)

crosed cementum must be removed mechanically by root resection, until tissue is reached with which cells may lie in physiological contact without injury. Conditions which can only be understood through a knowledge of the structure of the tissue often arise in connection with the treatment of alveolar abscess. It should always be remembered that the treatment of an abscess is a biological problem.

**The Embedded Fibers of the Periodontal Ligament.**—The embedded fibers are in the strictest sense comparable with the fibers of Sharpey in bone. They are, however, in the oldest layers of the cementum calcified.

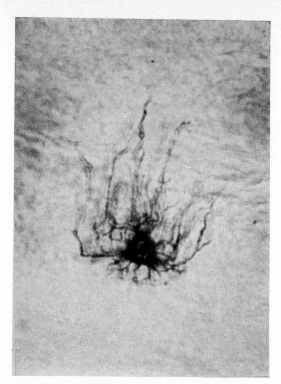

FIG. 125.—Cementocyte. Processes are directed toward the periodontal membrane. From a ground section of a human molar. (× 1000.) (From Schour, in Cowdry's *Special Cytology*, courtesy of Paul B. Hoeber, Inc.)

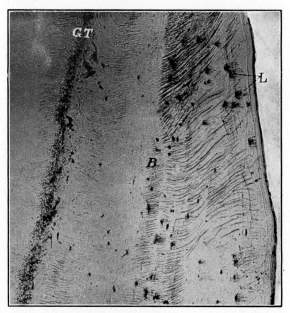

FIG. 126.—Cementum near the apex of the root: *GT*, granular layer of Tomes; *B*, point at which fibers were cut off and reattached by subsequent formation of secondary cementum; *L*, cementum corpuscle. Compare with Fig. 121. (About 54 ×).

( 164 )

To appreciate the relation of the embedded fibers to the matrix, the tissue must be studied both in ground and decalcified sections. In the cervical portion, from the study of ground sections, the presence of embedded fibers would never be suspected, but if decalcified sections are studied it will be found to contain calcified periodontal fibers since at this level the cementum grows slowly and represents the oldest protion. In the middle and apical thirds of the root, where the cementum is thicker, the fibers are not calcified in the superficial layers.

In the preparation of ground sections the imperfectly calcified fibers shrink and spaces which give the appearance of canals are seen in the cementum. These artificial spaces have often been mistaken for canals. They are usually not seen unless the section happens to be cut in their direction. In Figure 126 several layers of acellular cementum in which no fibers appear are seen next to the dentin, then in the cellular cementum the fibers are plainly seen, and finally the surface layer of precementum shows no fibers.

A change in the position of a tooth causes many fibers to be severed and detached. A new layer of cementum is then laid down in which the fibers become reattached in their new position and direction. The fibers are now adapted to the new direction of strain. It should be noted that whenever special stresses are exerted upon a given bundle of fibers, the cementum around them is thickened. This may be seen in ground sections Figures 121 and 126.

## HISTOPHYSIOLOGICAL REMARKS

**Resorption and Repair of Cementum.**—From what has already been said about the cementum, it will be understood that under normal conditions, cementum grows continuously by apposition of new layers. Resorption of cementum, sometimes even involving part of the dentin, is a pathologic sign. When the resoprtion process cuts into the dentin, the excavation in the dentin may be filled by the cementum subsequently formed (Fig. 127). In that event the dentino-cemental junction is not smooth but appears buckled. This process can be recognized by the absence of the granular layer of Tomes and by the sharply cut ends of the dentinal tubules. In many teeth, resorption of the roots is repaired by the formation cementum which often resembles bone so closely that from the histologic picture alone a differential diagnosis could not be made. Only the relation of this tissue to the root of the tooth permits its recognition. If small resorptions occur they are apparently reparied by a thickening of the lamellæ which are subsequently formed in the resorption area.

When the tooth outline is reestablished, the repair is termed anatomical. Functional repair is obtained with the reattachment of the periodontal fibers even though the surface outline is deficient (Fig. 127).

The lack of physiologic resorption of the cementum is characteristic for the biology of this tissue as compared with bone. In bone tissue periods of resorption and apposition alterntae under physiologic conditions. The cementum is found to react to irritation such as functional stress or inflammation, either favorably by means of hyperplasia of cellular cementum, or unfavorably by means of resorption and loosening of the tooth. The dentinal fracture surfaces of root fragments left from incomplete tooth extraction have also been found covered with cementum. The fact that teeth from which the pulp is removed remain normally functional and continue to oppose cementum is evidence that these cannot be called "dead" teeth. The type of reaction depends on the nature of the irritation and the condition of the tissue.

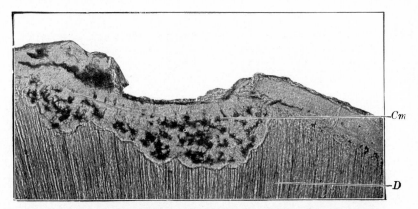

FIG. 127.—Record in the calcified tissue of a functional repair: *D*, dentin; *Cm*, cementum filling resorption cavity. (About 40 ×.)

**Dentino-cemental Junction.**—The dentino-cemental junction, unlike the dentino-enamel junction, normally presents a smooth outline. A crossing over of dentinal tubules into the cementum has been observed just as dentinal tubules are seen projecting into the enamel. Between the dentin surface and the cementum, an intermediate layer is occasionally present. This intermediate cementum has similar staining reactions as the dentin but does not contain tubules. It contains, however, embedded connective tissue cells which probably are derived from the original cells of the primitive periodontal membrane.

**Cementum Hyperplasia.**—This reaction may be regarded as a favorable response to irritation rather than as a pathological process. It results in an increase in tooth surface permitting more fibers to be attached to the tooth and consists of either acellular or cellular cementum. Gottlieb emphasizes the significance of the vitality of the cementum in the course of periodontal disease. The downward epithelial proliferation in diseased conditions is often checked by cementum hyperplasia. Such hyperplasias, however, are possible only in cementum of high vitality, that is, cementum which has a precementum layer and which contains corpuscles that are not yet degenerated.

## BIBLIOGRAPHY

Box, H. K.: The Pericementum as Influenced by Physical Functional Modifications, Int. Jour. Orth., *19*, 574, 1933.

BLACK, G. V.: Periosteum and Peridental Membrane, Chicago, W. T. Keener, 1887.

GOTTLIEB, B.: Tissue Changes in Pyorrhea, Jour. Am. Dent. Assn., *14*, 2178, 1927.

GUSTAFSON, ANNA-GRETA, and PERSSON, PER-ALLAN: The Relationship Between the Direction of Sharpey's Fibers and the Deposition of Cementum, Särtryck ur Odontologisk Tidskrift, Vol. *65*, No. 5, 1957.

HENRY, J. P., and WEINMANN, J. L.: The Pattern of Resorption and Repair of Human Cementum, Jour. Am. Dent. Assn., *42*, 270, 1951.

KRONFELD, R.: The Biology of Cementum, Jour. Am. Dent. Assn., *25*, 1451, 1938.

ORBAN, B.: Resorption and Repair on the Surface of the Root, Jour. Am. Dent. Assn., *15*, 1768, 1928.

SKILLEN, W. G.: A Report on the Formation of Dentin and Cementum Relative to the Structure of the Root End, Jour. Nat. Dent. Assn., *8*, 3, 1921.

STEWART-ROSS, W.: The Permeability of the Cementum and Its Reaction to Irritation, Brit. Dent. Jour., *55*, 177, 1933.

THOMAS, N. G.: Studies in Protective Cementum Development, Dental Cosmos, *64*, 385, 1922.

# CHAPTER 11

# Bone

**Definition.**—Bone may be defined as a connective tissue whose intercellular substance is calcified and arranged in layers around nutrient canals or spaces. The cells are placed in cavities (lacunæ) between the layers, and receive their nourishment through very minute channels, canaliculi, which radiate from them and penetrate the layers.

Bone tissue is the major component of the bones, which also contain the formative tissues of periosteum and bone-marrow. Most of the bones are covered at their articular surfaces by hyaline cartilage.

**Chemical Composition of Bone.**—Eastoe and Eastoe reported the following composition of air-dried bone (diaphysis of ox femur):

| | |
|---|---:|
| Inorganic matter (including citrate) | 70.91% |
| Collagen | 18.64% |
| Mucopolysaccharide-protein complexes | 0.24% |
| Resistant protein material | 1.02% |
| Water (lost below 105 C.) | 8.18% |

(All percentages by weight)

Estimates of the amount of water in fresh bone vary from 10% to 20% depending on the source of material and the method of measurement.

## FUNCTIONS OF BONES

The functions of bones are:

1. Support, protection and attachment.
2. Mineral reserve.
3. Hemopoiesis.

One of the interesting examples of the versatility of the mesenchyma is the formation of osseous tissue. The most obvious purpose of bone, because of its rigid and enduring gross characteristics, is that of support and protection. Early anatomists observed the protection of the brain by the skull, and also recognized the architectural significance of the skeleton as a framework for the support of the soft tissues and the mechanical advantage offered in locomotion.

While from an evolutionary point of view the principal function of bones may well be considered as supportive and protective, the adaptive character of the tissue from which it springs has incorporated two additional functions both of which, from the standpoint of the maintenance of life, are even

( 168 )

more important.   The first is the maintenance of the mineral balance in the tissue fluids and the second is the hemopoietic property of bone-marrow. In the light of our present civilization, we can support life in the presence of bone diseases which would seriously hamper or destroy its protective and supportive properties; but we can keep the individual alive for only a short time when he is no longer able to maintain a mineral reserve or to replace his blood elements.   Moreover, the very function of support is destroyed when the mineral reserve is too far depleted.

From the standpoint of oral structures and dental function, certainly the supportive and protective features predominate.   While the architectural character of the medullary portion of the bone of the jaws is unquestionably of significance in a study of oral pathology, it appears likely that in the maintenance of the mineral balance for the ordinary conditions of life, other areas are more important.   The hemopoietic property is perhaps even less evident in the bone of this region and would seem to exist more in the nature of a potentiality rallying to the assistance of other active areas when stimulated to action in conditions of both primary and secondary anemias.

## STRUCTURAL ELEMENTS OF BONE TISSUE

The structural elements of bone are:

1. The bone cells or osteocytes which are embedded in the matrix.
2. The bone matrix, or intercellular substance, which in mature bone is arranged in layers or lamellæ.
3. The lacunæ, or the spaces in which the cells are found.
4. The canaliculi, or the channels through the matrix by which the embedded cells receive nourishment.

**Bone Cells.**—The bone cells or osteocytes are the differentiated derivatives of the mesenchymal osteogenic cells.   Each osteocyte contains a single well defined nucleus, lying in the center of a granular cytoplasm.   The cell apparently completely occupies the lacuna, and from the central mass fine projections of cytoplasm extend through the canaliculi which bring the bone corpuscles in intimate relation with certain areas of bone matrix.   The processes of one cell anastomose with those of its neighbors through the canaliculi, so that there is a continuous network of living cytoplasm throughout the matrix.   These cells are vitally concerned with bone metabolism, as is demonstrated by the resorption of bone in which they have died.   The cells lie in flat oval spaces in the bone matrix, the lacunæ.   Radiating from the lacunæ are the anastomosing canaliculi which harbor the cytoplasmic processes of the osteocytes.   The cells originally formed the bone matrix and may possibly liberate an enzyme, phosphatase, which is believed to be an important factor in calcification (Fig. 128).

**Bone Matrix.**—The bone matrix is composed of a dense organic collagenous basis of ossein which yields gelatin upon boiling with water.   Its fibrillar character can be demonstrated by silver impregnation (Fig. 129). In adjacent lamellæ the fibrils lie at alternately different angles as can be seen by polarized light. In the cementing substance between the fibrils mineral salts are precipitated. Their chemical compound may be basic hydroxy-apatite, $Ca_{10}(PO_4)_6(OH)_2$.

These salts may be removed by treatment with acids, leaving the organic substance which retains the form of the tissue. In this condition the rigidity of the bone is destroyed, but the basis of much of osseous strength

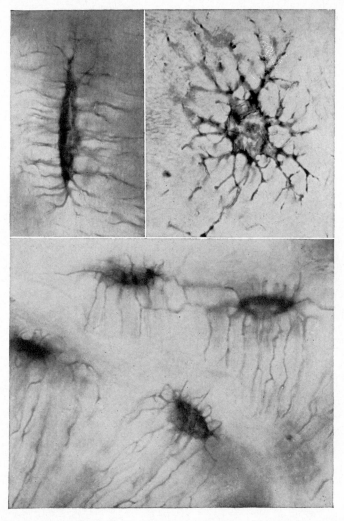

Fig. 128.—Lacunæ and canaliculi. Dried ground section of human bone. *A*, Longitudinal section. *B*, Surface view. Note the cross sections of canaliculi opening on the surface of the section. *C*, Cross section through lamellæ of two Haversian systems. Note the looping of the peripheral canaliculi. (Courtesy Weinmann and Sicher *Bone and Bones*, and C. V. Mosby Co., 1955.)

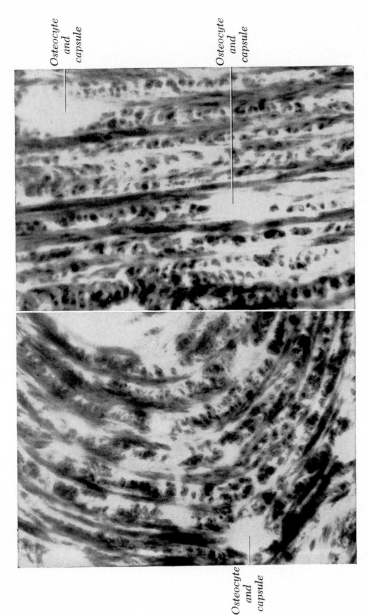

Fig. 129.—Alternating course of fibrils in adjacent lamellae of the intercellular substances. Decalcified section through a human mandible. Silver impregnation. A, Part of a Haversian system in cross section. Striped and stippled lamellae. B, Part of a Haversian system in longitudinal section. (Courtesy Weinmann and Sicher Bone and Bones, and C. V. Mosby Co., 1955.)

rests in its organic constituents.   By calcining at red heat or by micro-incineration the organic basis can be removed, leaving the inorganic substances.   In formation, the organic basis is apparently produced first, and then the inorganic salts are combined with it.

**Lacunæ.**—The lacunæ are flat, oval spaces about 20 $\mu$ long, 10 $\mu$ wide, and 5 or 6 $\mu$ in depth.   Their shape in sections depends upon the way in which they are cut, as illustrated in Fig. 128.   When cut lengthwise they would appear about 20 $\mu$ long and 6 wide in profile, or about 20 $\mu$ long and 10 wide when seen from above.

**Canaliculi.**—These radiate from the lacunæ in all directions, opening from them by larger channels which branch and divide, becoming smaller as they pass further into the matrix.   They anastomose freely with those from adjoining lacunæ (Fig. 128).

## CLASSIFICATION OF BONE TISSUE

Depending upon the particular arrangement, and distribution of these structural elements in response to the functional needs, the bone tissue is classified into three major types (Table 5).

TABLE 5.—CLASSIFICATION OF BONE TISSUE.

|  | Lamellated Bone (*Mature*) | Coarse Fibrillar Bone (*Immature*) | Bundle Bone |
|---|---|---|---|
| Distribution | 95% – 97% of adult skeleton. | In embryo | Insertion of ligaments. Alveolar bone proper. |
| Cells | Regular arrangement. Many processes. | Irregular arrangment, and shape. Few processes and many cells. | Few cells. Fairly regular. |
| Fibrils | Delicate, regular arrangement within each lamellæ. Direction alternating in adjacent lamellæ. | Coarse fibers. Irregular arrangement. | Few delicate fibrils, plus Sharpey's fibers. |
| Cementing Substance (Ground Substance) | 45% of total mass. | Less. | More. |
| Function | Resists pressure, tension and shearing forces. | Rapid growth in emergency. Fracture healing, etc. | Resist tension forces primarily. |
| X-Ray | Radiopaque. | More radiolucent. Difficult to differentiate from connective tissue proper. | More radiopaque. |

Courtesy, Dr. J. P. Weinmann.

*Immature Bone.*—This type is found in the embryo or in emergencies in the adult, when bone tissue is formed at a rapid rate and volume is temporarily more essential than organization (Fig. 202).

At these times bone growth proceeds rapidly within the mesenchymal substratum. The fibroblasts differentiate into osteoblasts. These are quickly transformed into osteocytes as they become surrounded by irregularly arranged coarse fibrillar ground substance, which becomes calcified. This bone is, therefore, called coarse fibrillar bone. The thickness of added increments varies with the functional demand.

*Bundle Bone.*—This type is formed in response to tension, as in ligaments and tendons. Its main characteristic is the regular insertion of embedded Sharpey's fibers, as seen in alveolar bone (Fig. 171). Due to the predominance of cementing substance, which is highly calcified, it is more radiopaque than the surrounding mature bone.

*Mature Bone.*—This type comprises the greatest portion of the adult skeleton and is formed by slow regular growth. The arrangement of the cells, fibrils and cementing substance is very regular as is the width of the added increments or lamellæ. This type has therefore been called lamellated bone. In the adult skeleton, bones consist of a heavy outer portion of compact bone (cortical bone) and a lighter strutlike inner portion of trabecular or cancellous bone (Figs. 142 and 145).

## THE ARRANGEMENT OF MATURE BONE

**Compact Bone.**—A knowledge of the structural elements of mature bone can best be obtained by observing transverse and longitudinal sections ground from the shaft of a long bone. From a study of these the arrangement of the lamellæ, and the shape and character of the lacunæ may be observed. Upon the outer surface of the transverse section will be found a varying number of layers of subperiosteal bone which encircle the shaft, and consequently are called the circumferential lamellæ.

This form of bone must be regarded as primarily a formative arrangement which is more or less transitory. It contains Volkmann canals which have blood-vessels (Fig. 130) and connective tissues, and which, unlike the Haversian canals, are not surrounded by concentrically arranged lamellæ.

The number of the layers will depend upon the position from which the section is taken, and the age of the bone. If the bone is increasing in circumference at the point from which the section is cut, there will be a considerable number of layers, and they will be easily seen. If the bone has not been growing in circumference at this point, there will be very little subperiosteal bone, and it may be comparatively hard to recognize. Normally, when a considerable thickness is formed it is resorbed from within (beginning in the canals) and bone is rebuilt with layers arranged concentrically around the channels formed. In this way subperiosteal bone is converted into the Haversian system type.

The inner boundary of the section next to the marrow cavity may show a few layers parallel with the surface. These are known as the inner circumferential lamellæ. It is a mistake, however, to think of them as surrounding the marrow cavity in the same sense as the outer circumferential lamellæ surround the outer surface of the bone. If the section has been cut

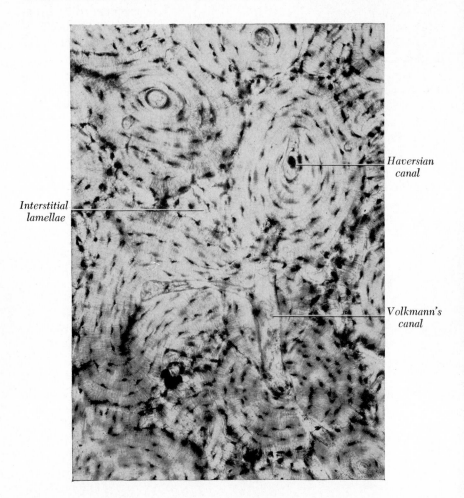

*Interstitial lamellae*

*Haversian canal*

*Volkmann's canal*

Fig. 130.—Haversian systems and interstitial lamellæ in cross section. Dried ground section through human bone. (Courtesy Weinmann and Sicher, *Bone and Bones*, and C. V. Mosby Co., 1955.)

a short distance from the center of the shaft, it will be noted that the marrow cavity is penetrated by very delicate spicules, and that in fact the marrow cavity is produced by the spaces in cancellous bone which become larger and larger until they are one continuous space. The inner circumferential lamellæ are therefore the layers which have been formed around enlarged nutrient or marrow spaces. From the outer and inner surface of the bone, Volkmann's canals penetrate the lamellæ to reach the Haversian canals.

The greatest part of the section will be composed of Haversian systems, in which from four to twenty lamellæ are arranged around a canal.

These canals contain blood- and lymph-vessels, nerves and embryonal connective tissue from which the cells in the lacunæ are nourished. They are, in general, parallel with the surface of the long axis of the bone and anastomose with each other. A canal with the layers arranged around it constitutes a Haversian system. Between the Haversian systems are remains of the subperiosteal layers which were left by resorption, and for that reason have been called interstitial lamellæ (Fig. 131). Haversian system bone is often called compact bone, and makes up the greater part of the shafts of the long bones and the plates of the flat ones. Many Haversian systems will be imperfect in form as some of those shown in Fig. 174. This means that after these systems were completed, resorptions occurred in a neighboring canal which attacked the layers of the system, and later a new system was formed in the space by the deposition of concentric lamellæ. While bone is thought of as a hard and fixed tissue, it is continually being built and rebuilt in this manner. It is only by the understanding of these possibilities that we obtain the conception that bone, while hard and rigid, is a plastic tissue and is continually being moulded by the mechanical conditions to which it is subjected. It is never allowed to become greater in thickness than is necessary for strength, and when sufficient thickness has been formed, the deeper part is cut out by resorption in the Haversian canals, converting them into large irregular spaces. The formation of these medullary areas transforms the compact into cancellous bone.

**Cancellous Bone.**—In this type the lamellæ are arranged in delicate plates of flattened spicules surrounding larger or smaller irregular spaces which connect with each other very freely. At first each spicule is composed of a few lamellæ arranged around a space. The structure of the spicules becomes complicated by resorptions and rebuildings. These processes change their direction. The tissue which fills the spaces, the bone marrow, is a connective tissue in which osteoblasts and osteoclasts appear in response to mechanical conditions. It is richly supplied with blood-vessels, nerves and lymphatics. The lacunæ and canalicules are in no respect different from those of the Haversian system and subperiosteal bone.

The plates of cancellous bone are not arranged haphazardly, as might be supposed from a casual observation of sections, but are disposed in definite arrangement determined by the directions of stress on the compact bone which they support (see Figs. 145 and 146). They are not permanent and unchanging, but are continually being rebuilt in new directions, in response to the mechanical conditions to which the bone as a supporting organ is subjected. This process, which illustrates Wolff's law, is admirably analyzed by Koch in his study of lines of stress in the femur.

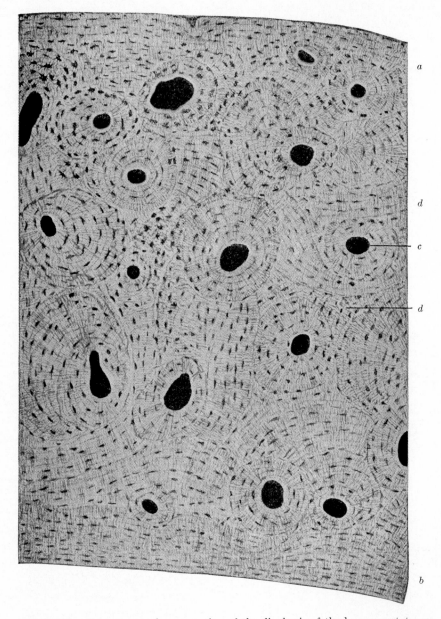

FIG. 131.—From a ground cross-section of the diaphysis of the human metatarsus. *a*, outer circumferential lamellæ; *b*, inner circumferential lamellæ; *c*, Haversian lamellæ; *d*, interstitial lamellæ. All canals and bone cavities are filled with coloring matter and appear black. (90 ×.)

## HISTOGENESIS OF BONE

Phylogenetically, in response to the demand for support, the mesenchymal tissue responded in two distinct adaptive reactions. The two types are cartilage and bone. Bone is the latest type and will withstand greater stresses than cartilage because of its calcified matrix which is laid down around connective tissue fibers. Cartilage however maintains the ability to grow under presure and in some areas serves as an expanding scaffold upon which bone is added.

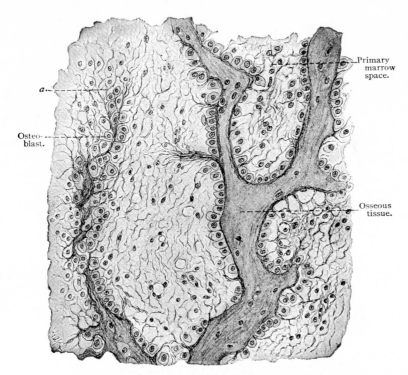

Fig. 132.—Section of immature bone through the lower jaw of an embryo sheep (decalcified with picric acid). At *a* and immediately below are seen the fibers of a primitive marrow cavity lying close together and engaged in the formation of the ground substance of the bone, while the cells of the marrow cavity, with their processes, arrange themselves on either side of the newly formed lamellæ and function as osteoblasts. (Bohm, Davidoff, Huber.) (300 ×.)

Bone formation in the flat bones of the skull is called endomembranous bone because it rises directly in the connective tissue.

Bone replacement of the cartilage scaffold is called endochondral bone formation and occurs in the skull base and long bones of the skeleton.

**Endomembranous Bone Formation.**—Endomembranous bone is formed directly from fibrous tissue. The primitive mesenchyme in the region of the future bone differentiates into an osteogenic tissue containing a fibrous connective tissue composed of specialized cells, osteoblasts. The cells elaborate a homogeneous matrix and deposit it within the mesh of the fibrous tissue framework. This matrix calcifies through the attraction of mineral salts from the tissue fluids. The resultant bone trabeculæ follow the direction and assume the form of the mesenchymal mesh, so that the product is a cancellous type of bone or spongiosa. Once begun, more bone is added to the surface of these trabeculæ. As this network of bone lamellæ, containing vascular connective tissue in its primary marrow spaces, begins to take on definite form, there is a specialization of the mesenchyme

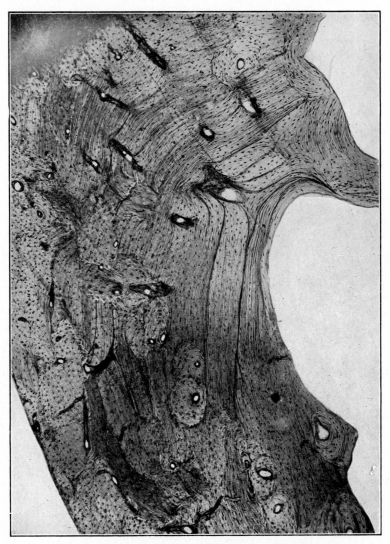

Fig. 133.—The record in the arrangement of the lamellæ of the growth of the mandible. A decalcified section from near the lower border of a human mandible.

surrounding it.  This develops into the periosteum.  The osteogenic layer
of the periosteum contributes to the peripheral extension of the bone (compact cortical plate) by addition of circumferential lamellæ (Fig. 131).

In flat bones increase in size as well as configuration is effected chiefly
through the periosteum.  Internally the osteogenic cells select the bone
trabeculæ as a base line for the addition of matrix (Fig. 132).

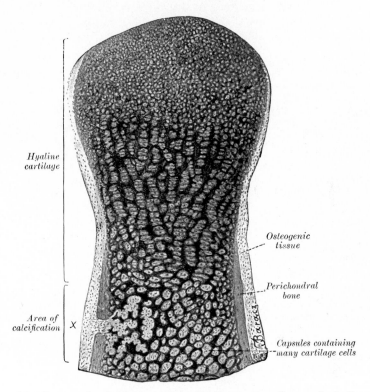

FIG. 134.—From a longitudinal section of a finger of a three-and-a-half-months
human embryo.  Two-thirds of the second phalange is represented.  At × a periosteal
bud is to be seen.  (85 ×.)

**Endochondral Bone Formation.**—Increase in size of the long bones is
effected by additions to both length and circumference.  Longitudinal
growth is accomplished by the following steps:

1. The formation of new cartilage at the ends of the shaft;
2. The degeneration and calcification of the older cartilage;
3. Resorption of parts of the calcified cartilage; and
4. Addition of bone along border of remaining calcified cartilage
   spicule.

Endochondral bone formation is a substitution and not a transformation,
for the original cartilage is destroyed in the process, and a new and more

highly specialized tissue, bone, is developed from connective tissue and is
apposed to the temporarily remaining cartilage.

1. **Cartilage Formation.**—The mesenchyme in the non-vascular region of
the future bone undergoes a transition through which cartilage cells are
developed. These cells form the cartilage matrix in which they become embedded. Before ossification begins the cartilage has taken on the general
form of the bone and is covered by a definite perichondrium. Ossification
starts at separate centers and replaces the growing cartilage, but the
centers do not unite until the bone is almost fully formed. In the long
bones there are usually three centers—one near the center of the shaft,
forming the diaphysis, and one near either end, forming the epiphyses.

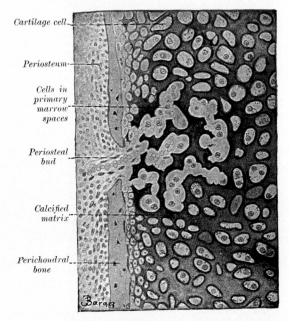

FIG. 135.—The place marked × in the preceding figure with
stronger magnification. (185 ×.)

These remain separated by a proliferating layer of cartilage until the length
of the bone has been fully attained.

2. **Degeneration and Calcification of the Older Cartilage.**—Prior to the removal of the cartilage the lacunæ become arranged in rows and as they increase in size in a direction generally parallel with the axis of the cartilage,
the amount of matrix separating them becomes reduced and calcifies.

3. **Removal of Cartilage.**—Opposite each center of ossification, osteoclasts appear, cut into the calcified cartilage, and remove the rows of
lacunæ. These areas are the primary marrow spaces and contain periosteal
buds of embryonal tissue (Figs. 134 and 135).

4. **Addition of Bone.**—Osteoblasts form and arrange themselves upon the spicules of calcified cartilage and develop a bone matrix which later becomes calcified.

At this stage the perichondrium around the central area of the cartilage model becomes more vascular and develops osteogenic cells. These cells lay down bone around the cartilage as a supporting collar and by apposition of circumferential lamellæ increase the width of the shaft.

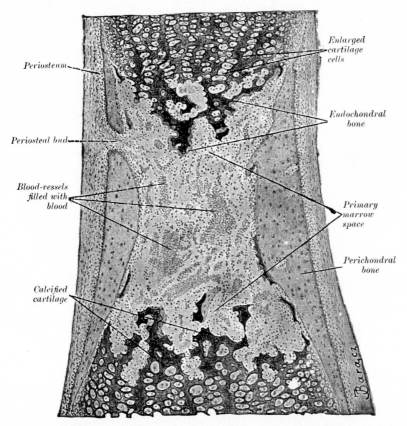

Fig. 136.—From longitudinal section of a finger of a four months embryo. Only the diaphysis of the second phalanx is represented. (85 ×.)

The replacement of cartilage by bone progresses from the diaphysis center in both directions, so that eventually the diaphysis is united to both epiphyses. All stages, from the typical hyaline cartilage to the formation of bone, may be seen in one section (Fig. 136).

Increase in length of the long bone is accomplished by the addition of new layers of cartilage over the old at the epiphyseal plates, while the latter are being replaced by bone.

In this manner the active formative area advances from the central portion of the shaft and the bone increases in length. Eventually no new cartilage is formed and the epiphyses become closed. In certain bones of some mammals the ossification and cartilage formation stop simultaneously, in which case the epiphyses are never united. The coordination in the formation of new cartilage, its degeneration, its removal by connective tissue, the development of osteogenic cells and reorganization through the ossification mechanism result in normal bone formation.

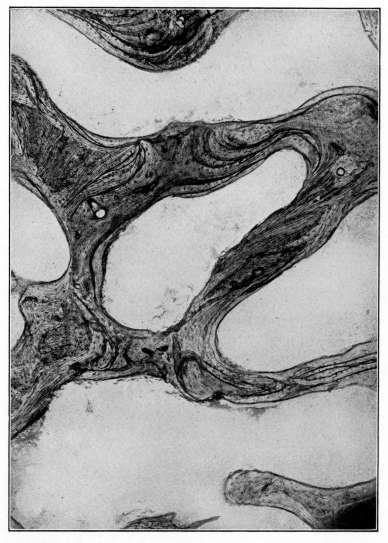

Fig. 137.—Decalcified section of cancellous bone from a human mandible, showing resorptions and rebuildings, changing the direction of the spicules.

**Increase in Diameter.**—Growth in diameter or width occurs through the deposition of lamellæ of bone on the periphery by the osteogenic layer of the periosteum and by concomitant resorptions on the internal surface lining the bone-marrow cavity. In this way the weight of the bone is kept mechanically efficient. This process can be beautifully demonstrated by madder feeding or by vital injections of alizarine. The reorganization of subperiosteal bone to Haversian system bone and the transformation of the innermost strata to cancellous bone with characteristic marrow spaces keeps pace with new bone formation (Fig. 180). In this way an appropriate width of cortical layer or compacta is maintained throughout life.

## HISTOPHYSIOLOGICAL REMARKS

Unequal activity of osteogenic cells together with fluctuations between bone formation and bone destruction moulds the bone to both its general and individual characteristics. The architecture of the bone is continually moulded and reshaped in response to the physiological demands of mechanical function and mineral reserve of the body.

**Bone Repair.**—The responsive activity of osteogenic tissue to varied stimuli is again demonstrated in its capacity for repairing injury. The mechanism of repair has been attributed to the osteogenic properties of the inner layer of the periosteum and to the tissue of mesodermal origin within the bone marrow. Of the two the former is the more active and it is for this reason that preservation of the periosteum in bone surgery, the setting of fractures, surgery incident to osteomyelitis or the uncovering of unerupted teeth is of utmost importance.

The rapidity of reaction of the various components of bone, in common with all body tissues, decreases with age. The potentiality for osteogenesis is never lost under normal circumstances. The earlier in the growth period that injuries are sustained the more complete will be the recovery. Thus a broken bone at birth in an otherwise normal infant will heal without immobilization and the reorganization of the bone in the natural growth which ensues removes all trace of the earlier damage.

An experimental method of observing the rate and direction of bone apposition and calcification is offered by vital injections of alizarine. Such injections demarcate by a red line the bone forming and calcifying at the time. This is a modern modification of the work of John Hunter with madder.

**Cementing Lines.**—The adjacent layers of bone are separated from one another by delicate lines of high refractibility which are called the *cementing lines*. If a bony surface is inactive for a period of time, the *aplastic line*, a peculiar layer of a basophilic substance is laid down which in sections stained with hematoxylin eosin appears as a dark-blue line. The latter is smooth if the inactive period followed a period of apposition; it is irregularly scalloped if the inactive period followed a period of resorption.

When after a period of inactivity the formation of new bone is resumed, the new tissue is apposed upon the aplastic line. In sections the newly formed bone is then separated from the old bone by a so-called *resting line* which demarcates the two layers of bone that were formed at different periods. If the new apposition followed a period of resorption, the demarcating line is called the *reversal line.*

A study of the cementing, resting and reversal lines thus permits the reconstruction of the history of any area of bone tissue, just as an analysis of the tree rings reveals the history of the tree and its environment, and an analysis of the rings of the enamel and dentin yields valuable clues on the nutritional status of the growing individual.

## BIBLIOGRAPHY

BOURNE, GEOFFREY H.: Biochemistry and Physiology of Bone, New York, Academic Press, Inc., 1956.

EASTOE, J. E. and EASTOE, L. B.: The Organic constituents of Mammalian Compact Bone. Biochem. J., *57*, 543–459, 1954.

HAM, A.: The Function of Bone as a Calcium Reservoir With a Consideration of the Cellular Pictures Seen in Resorption With Particular Reference to the Significance of Osteoclasts, The Angle Orthodontist, *2*, 142, 1932.

————: The Last Hundred Years in the Study of Bone, Jour. Am. Dent. Assn., *21*, 3, 1934.

HAM, A. W.: Cartilage and Bone, in Cowdry, E. V.: Special Cytology, New York, Paul B. Hoeber, Inc., *2*, 979, 1932.

HARRIS, H. A.: Bone Growth in Health and Disease, London, Oxford University Press, Humphrey Milford, 1933.

HUGGINS, C.: The Composition of Bone and the Function of the Bone Cell, Physiol. Rev., vol. *17*, No. 1, January, 1937.

KOCH, J. C.: Laws of Bone Architecture, Am. Jour. Anat., *21*, 177, 1917.

LERICHE, R., and POLICARD, A.: The Normal and Pathological Physiology of Bone; Its Problems, St. Louis, C. V. Mosby Company, 1928.

McLEAN, FRANKLIN C., and MARSHALL R. URIST: Bone, An Introduction to the Physiology of Skeletal Tissue, Chicago, Illinois, The University of Chicago Press, 1955, 177 pp.

MURRAY, F. D. F.: Bones ,Cambridge University Press, 1936.

WEINMANN, J. P., and SICHER, H.: Bones and Bones, Fundamentals of Bone Biology, 2nd Ed., St. Louis, C. V. Mosby Co., 1955.

# CHAPTER 12

# The Periosteum[1]

IRRESPECTIVE of the mode of formation there develops around ossifying centers a fibrous connective tissue sheath of mesenchymal origin known as the periosteum.

**Definition.**—The periosteum is the formative and protective membrane which covers the outer surface of the bone. All periosteum has certain structural characteristics in common, but because of structural differences two classes are recognized—attached and unattached—each of which may be simple or complex. Periosteum may thus be classified as follows:

1. Unattached simple.      3. Attached simple.
2. Unattched complex.      4. Attached complex.

## FUNCTION OF PERIOSTEUM

The importance to the dentist of a knowledge of the structure and function of the periosteum can scarcely be exaggerated. It has been the knowledge of this tissue and its function that has led to the advancement in bone surgery of modern time. Repair and regeneration of bone is largely accomplished through its agency.

The periosteum forms the immediate covering of all the bones and is continuous over their entire surface except the portion covered by cartilage. Each bone therefore has a periosteum of its own which does not continue around the articulation to the bones with which it joins. Bones that are united by suture are, however, covered by a common periosteum. If the flesh and overlying tissues are carefully removed from a long bone, the periosteum will be seen as a smooth white, lustrous membrane, having much the same appearance as a tendon on most of its surface. But at those places which correspond to the positions where muscles or fascia were attached it appears ragged and dull, for the tissues had to be cut to separate them from the outer layer of the periosteum, to which they were firmly adherent. In all other places the tissues separate easily in dissection; in fact, are not attached at all, except by the lightest of areolar tissue, which is very easily broken, and the tissues may be separated from the surface of the membrane with the finger or the handle of a scalpel. If the periosteum is slit along a smooth surface with the scalpel and the handle inserted between the bone

---

[1] In the presentation of this chapter it is impossible adequately to express our indebtedness to Dr. G. V. Black. Almost all of the illustrations are taken from Periosteum and Peridental Membrane, published by him in 1887.

and the membrane, it will be found to separate readily from the bone over most of its surface. If the process is watched closely, little strings will be seen apparently running from the periosteum to the bone, and being torn apart during separation. These are mostly small blood-vessels which are running into canals in the bone. In this process the periosteum seems like a closely adapted sac or elastic glove, clothing the surface of the bone, as if surrounding it in a fibrous bag. If the separation of the periosteum from the bone is continued, it will be found that it does not separate as easily in all places. As the articular ends are approached it suddenly becomes fastened to the underlying bone, and the blade of the knife must be used. Here the periosteum appears as a very thin, tough, and inelastic membrane, that is torn with difficulty, but it is so thin that it is difficult to separate it from the bone without cutting. When this point of attachment is reached it seems that the periosteum is sinking into the substance of the bone, and from the examination of its structure it is found that this is practically what has happened.

Comparing the periosteum to a sac surrounding the bone, it is found sewed firmly down at the margin of the cartilage around the articular ends. Besides the attachment around the cartilage, the periosteum will be found adherent in the following positions: Where muscles or fascia are attached to the outer layer of the periosteum; where it approaches the insertion of tendons or ligaments; and where the skin or mucous membrane seem attached to the underlying bone, as around the auditory meatus, the gums, mucous membrane of the nose, etc. In all such positions the periosteum is firmly attached to the bone—in fact, becomes a part of it—and through this medium is accomplished the connections between muscles, fascia, etc., and the framework of the skeleton.

This feature of the anatomy of the periosteum has never been studied in the detail it deserves, especially by the dentist. It is of the greatest importance in the management of the diseases of bone, especially those involving the formation of pus, for these lines of attachment determine the direction in which the pus will proceed along the surface of the bone. When pus generated within the bone reaches the surface, it will lift an unattached periosteum and run along the surface until it reaches a line of attachment. Here it can penetrate the periosteum more easily than it can separate it from the bone. When a line of attachment is reached, therefore, the direction of the burrowing is determined by the attached areas. The pus penetrates the periosteum more easily than it separates its attachments from the bone, but it lifts the unattached periosteum so easily that it will often run along a line of attachment for a long distance.

These factors often become of great importance in determining the position in which alveolar abscesses will point. For instance, if an abscess from a premolar root, or the mesial root of a molar, reaches the surface of the bone above the attachment of the buccinator, it cannot penetrate its attachment and pass downward to open on the gum, but may run out over the surface of the muscle and open on the cheek, producing the crow's foot scar so often seen. An abscess from an upper canine may reach the surface of the bone in the canine fossa between the attachments of the nasalis and caninus, and lift the periosteum extending upward, and open at the inner canthus of the eye between the orbicularis and the angular head of the quadratus labii superioris. If these abscesses had been reached with a lance, through the mucous membrane, at the proper time, a disfiguring scar would have been avoided. Accurate knowledge of the attached layers of the periosteum would have made it certain that they could never point in the mouth cavity without assistance.

## LAYERS OF THE PERIOSTEUM

Periosteum is always composed of two distinct layers:

1. An outer or fibrous layer, which is essentially protective and to which muscles and fasciæ are attached. This may be either simple or complex.

2. An inner or osteogenic layer which is essentially the vital functioning layer, and is, as its name indicates, concerned with the formation of bone. This may be either simple or complex.

## THE STRUCTURAL ELEMENTS OF PERIOSTEUM

The periosteum is composed of the following structural elements:

1. White fibers in coarse bundles (in the outer layer).

2. White fibers in very fine bundles (in the inner layer).

3. Elastic fibers.

4. The penetrating fibers, or white fibers of the periosteum, that in the growth of bone are included in its substance.

5. Embryonal connective tissue cells.

6. Osteoblasts or bone-forming cells.

7. Osteoclasts or bone-resorbing cells.

## UNATTACHED PERIOSTEUM

In the unattached periosteum the inner layer is always simple, and the outer layer may be either simple or complex, depending apparently upon the requirements of protection. In general, the more exposed the position the thicker is the layer, and the larger and stronger the bundles of fibers of which it is composed.

**Simple Unattached Periosteum.**—Where the periosteum is covered by a thick layer of muscles which are not attached to it, as in the thigh, the thinnest and simplest form of periosteum is found. An illustration, drawn by Dr. Black, of the periosteum from the femur of a kitten will illustrate its structure (Fig. 138). The outer layer is composed chiefly of bundles of white fibers, most of which run in a direction parallel with the long axis of the bone. The bundles are comparatively small and much flattened, so as to be quite ribbon-like. The inner layer contains a much greater number of cells lying among extremely delicate fibers. In its outer portion many of the cells are embryonal in character. In contact with the surface of the bone is a continuous layer of osteoblasts which are building subperiosteal bone in the young animal, processes of their cytoplasm extending into the

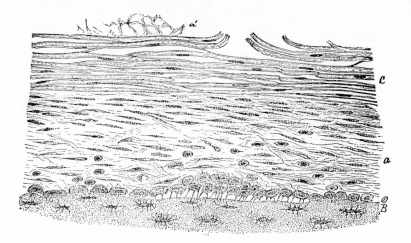

Fig. 138.—Non-attached periosteum from the shaft of the femur of the kitten $B$, bone; $O$, layer of osteoblasts. In the central portion of the figure they have been pulled slightly away from the bone, displaying the processes to advantage. It will be observed that the fibers of the periosteum do not enter the bone. $a$, Inner layer of fine white fibrous tissue (osteogenic layer) showing the nuclei of the fibroblasts and a number of developing connective tissue cells, which probably become osteoblasts; $c$, outer layer, or coarse fibrous layer, in which fusiform fibroblasts are also rendered apparent by double staining with hematoxylin and carmine; $d$, some remains of the reticular tissue connecting the superimposed tissue with the periosteum. ($\frac{1}{12}$ immersion.) (Black.)

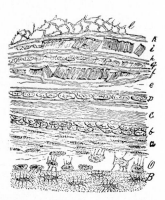

Fig. 139.—Periosteum from the shaft of the tibia of the pig, lengthwise section, showing the complex arrangement of fibers in the coarse or outer fibrous layer that sometimes occurs under muscles that perform sliding movements upon it: $B$, bone; $O$, layer of osteoblasts. The tissue has been pulled slightly away from the bone in mounting the section, and part of the osteoblasts have clung to the bone, some have clung to the tissues, while others are suspended midway, their processes clinging to each. $a$, Layer of fine fibers; inner or osteogenic layer of the periosteum; $b$, first lamina of the coarse or outer fibrous layer, the fibers of which are, in this case, circumferential, exposing the cut ends. It will be observed that there are ten lamina in the makeup of the outer layer, the lengthwise and circumferential fibers alternating. The ones marked $f$ and $i$ are very delicate ribbon-like forms, which have shifted from their normal position in the mounting of the section, so as to present their sides to view instead of their ends, thus displaying their structure to advantage. The illustration shows how readily separable these lamina are. $l$, Reticular tissue. ($\frac{1}{12}$ immersion.) (Black.)

canalicules of the matrix which they have formed. At one point in the illustration the osteoblasts are pulled off from the surface of the bone and show these processes stretched out of the canalicules.

**Complex Unattached Periosteum.**—In some places, especially where muscles or tendons perform sliding movements over an unattached periosteum, the outer layer, instead of being simple, may be very complex. This is illustrated in Dr. Black's drawing (Fig. 139), from the periosteum of the tibia of a young pig. In this instance the outer layer is composed of very much flattened bundles of white fibers, arranged alternately longitudinally and circularly. Ten layers may be counted in the section. The inner layer is of the same character as in a simple specimen.

## ATTACHED PERIOSTEUM

The attached periosteum differs from the unattached by having the fibers of the inner layer arranged in bundles which become attached and embedded in the deposited bone matrix. These fibers constitute the penetrating fibers. They were first described by Sharpey, and have been called Sharpey's fibers. The fibers of the inner layer are built into the substance of the bone in this way wherever tissues are attached to the outer layer of the periosteum.

**Simple Attached Periosteum.**—Where the pull of tissues attached to the outer layer of the periosteum is in one direction, the fibers of the inner layer are inclined in the same direction (Fig. 140).

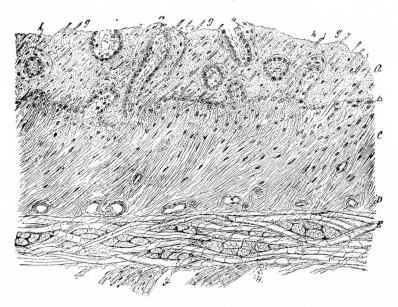

Fig. 140.—Simple attached periosteum: *a*, bone; *b*, osteoblasts; *c*, fibers of the inner layer; *D*, blood-vessels of the inner layer; *E*, outerlayer; *F*, muscle fibers attached to outer layer. (Black.)

As the surface of the bone is approached the fibers are gathered into strong bundles to be inserted in the bone, the osteoblasts covering the surface of the bone everywhere between the fibers. The outer and inner layers are united by the interlacing of their fibers. At the junction of the outer and the inner layers many blood-vessels are seen.

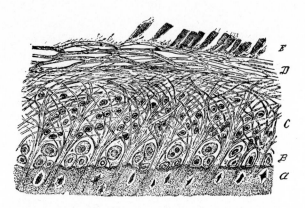

FIG. 141.—Attached periosteum from beneath the attachment of the muscles of the lower lip of the sheep: *A*, bone; *B*, osteoblasts, with the fibers emerging from the bone between them; *C*, inner layer with fibers decussating and joining the inner side of the coarse fibrous layer in opposite directions (this is rather an unusual form of this layer of the periosteum); *D*, coarse, fibrous layer; *E*, attachment of muscular fibers. (Black.)

**Complex Attached Periosteum.**—Where the pull upon the outer layer is in many directions, the fibers of the inner layer, after emerging from the bone, break up into smaller bundles and anastomose in all directions, arching around to interlace with the fibers of the outer layer, and in this way they sustain force in all directions (Fig. 141). This is illustrated in Dr. Black's drawing of a section of attached periosteum from beneath the attachment of the muscles of the lower lip of a sheep.

### BIBLIOGRAPHY.

BLACK, G. V.: Periosteum and Peridental Membrane, Chicago, W. T. Keener, 1887.

# CHAPTER 13

# The Alveolar Process

THE bone of the alveolar process, while structurally indistinguishable from other parts of the skeleton, is of especial interest to the dentist because of its functional aspects. The alveolar process plays a significant role in the investment of the functioning tooth and an understanding of the structure and distribution of this bone is essential to successful dentistry.

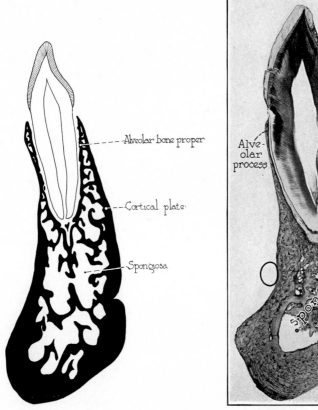

FIG. 142                          FIG. 143

FIG. 142.—Diagrammatic representation of the relationship of the alveolar process to both the lower incisor and the mandible.

FIG. 143.—A ground section through a human lower permanent canine showing the relationship of the alveolar process to the tooth and to the mandible.

**Definition.**—The alveolar process may be defined as that portion of the maxillæ and mandible which supports the teeth. It is the projection of the jaw bone which surrounds and forms the sockets in which the roots of the teeth are held by their periodontal membranes (gomphosis). The process develops with the teeth. Its structure is moulded in response to the functional demands of the teeth and disappears when they are lost. The alveolar process consists of (*a*) an outer cortical plate, (*b*) an inner plate (which is the alveolar bone proper and has also been called the cribriform plate) and (*c*) an intervening layer of supporting spongiosa (Figs. 142, 143 and 144).

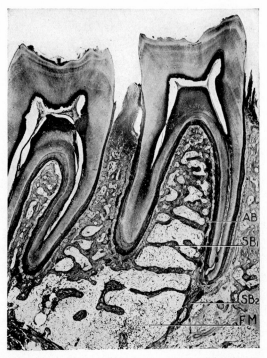

Fig. 144.—Alveolar bone proper and supporting bone. Lower first and second molars; age, forty-one years. *AB*, Plate of alveolar bone proper (cribriform plate) surrounding the roots; *SB₁*, trabeculæ of supporting bone running horizontally from one alveolus to the other; *SB₂*, trabeculæ of supporting bone running from the fundus of the alveolus downward; *FM*, fat marrow of the mandible. Magnification × 4. (Kronfeld, Dental Histology and Comparative Dental Anatomy.)

## FUNCTION OF THE ALVEOLAR PROCESS

The function of the alveolar process is to support and to attach the teeth. Although it has potentialities for both hemopoiesis and maintenance of mineral reserve, these properties are subservient to that of support of the dental units.

## DEVELOPMENT OF THE ALVEOLAR PROCESS

The tooth germ, during the early stages of its formation and calcification, lies loosely within a bed of connective tissue, the dental sac. It is, for the most part, enclosed within a bony crypt. The crypt of the developing deciduous teeth does not envelop the incisal or occlusal plane, thus leaving a rather wide opening. The permanent teeth, however, are almost completely circumscribed by the bony crypt. Epithelial strands pass through an opening of the crypt to connect the dental lamina with the tooth germ. During the eruptive process the roof of this crypt is resorbed to permit passage of the tooth.

With development of the dental sac, the mesenchymal tissue about it differentiates into the fibrous tissue anlage of membranous bone. The dental sac itself gives rise to cementum, periodontal membrane, and on its outer aspect to the bony crypt. The latter structure is thus formed by the outer layer of connective tissue of the primitive periodontal membrane. During and after eruption, the alveolar bone encloses and forms the socket within which the root of the tooth is suspended. The alveolar bone is later braced by the adjacent supporting bone of the alveolar process.

The position of the tooth determines the location of the alveolar socket; the functional demands determine the structural character. Should the tooth be lost, the alveolar process becomes unnecessary and is resorbed. The alveolar process thus develops along with tooth formation and eruption, and persists only as long as the tooth is present and functional.

## HISTOLOGICAL STRUCTURE OF THE ALVEOLAR PROCESS

The structural elements are not different from those of the bone elsewhere in the jaws. There is no clear-cut boundary line between the bone of the alveolar process and the bone of the maxillæ and mandible upon which it rests. The periosteum which forms the cortical plate of the alveolar process is continuous with that covering the cortical plates of the jaws.

The growth of the alveolar process is accomplished by (a) a direct extension occlusally (or vertically) of the membranous bone formation in the body of the maxillæ and the mandible (vertical growth); (b) by the deposition of subperiosteal bone on the labial and buccal and simultaneous resorption on the lingual surfaces, which results in the lateral and anterior extension of the cortical plates; (c) by the formation of alveolar bone about the growing roots of the teeth; and (d) by the reorganization of the spongiosa. Thus by a process primarily of surface apposition and resorption, growth of the alveolar process occurs vertically, laterally and anteriorly.

## THE STRUCTURE OF THE ALVEOLAR PROCESS

It has already been indicated that the alveolar process consists of the following structures:

1. The superficial cortical plate of bone.
2. The alveolar bone proper (cribriform plate), and
3. The supporting bone which intervenes.

**The Cortical Plate.**—The cortical plate is the outer portion of the alveolar process and is composed partly of circumferential lamellæ and partly of Haversian systems. It varies greatly in thickness, depending upon its position. It is generally thinner on the labial or buccal than on the lingual

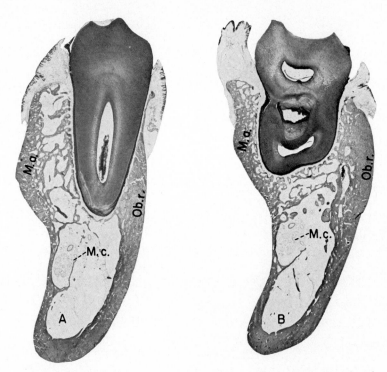

Fig. 145.—Bucco-lingual sections of a mandible through the lower second molar (A) and third molar (B). Note in B the reinforcement of the outer alveolar plate by the external oblique ridge (Ob. r.) and the high level of the mylohyoid attachment (M.a.) as compared with A. Note also the lingual placement of the mandibular canal (M.c.) and the wide marrow spaces in the mandibular body. These sections were prepared from jaws of a 42-year-old person.

surface. The thickness of the compact bone also varies horizontally. In dentures where vigorous function, as abrasion, is recorded upon the tooth surfaces, there is a corresponding thickening of the dense bone in the coronal third of the root (Fig. 143). The areas of thickening bear a direct relationship to the surfaces showing attrition.

**The Alveolar Bone Proper.**—This portion of the alveolar process bounds the alveoli (or sockets) into which the roots of the teeth fit. It represents a thin definite wall which is pierced by many small openings (lamina cribrosa) through which blood-vessels, lymphatics and nerve fibers pass. Because of its sieve-like character, this bone has also been termed the cribriform plate. It fuses with the cortical plates at the border of the alveolar process on the labial and lingual sides. The walls of the alveoli are thus composed of a thin layer of alveolar bone, which has been built on to the

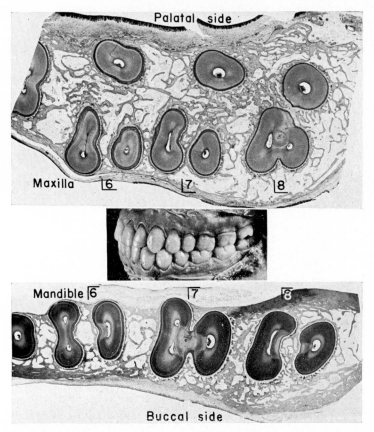

Fig. 146.—Photomicrograph of transverse sections at mid-root levels of maxilla and mandible. Note the spongy character of the trabeculæ in the maxilla and the more compact arrangement in the mandible. Note also the wide periodontal membrane on the distal sides and the narrower width on the mesial of all the teeth indicating physiologic mesial drift. Center insert shows original specimen from male 42 years old. See figure 148 for higher magnification of mesial root of lower first molar.

plates of the spongy bone, to attach the fibers of the periodontal ligament (Figs. 153, 154 and 144). This thin plate is recognized in the roentgenogram as the lamina dura.

**Bundle and Lamellated Bone.**—The alveolar bone proper contains an abundance of Sharpey's fibers, the continuation of the principal fibers of the periodontal membrane. Because of the predominance of enclosed bundles of fibers this bone has been termed bundle bone. The distribution of the bundle bone around a root is determined by the physiologic mesial drift of the teeth in a normal and complete human dentition. As a rule there is a fairly thick layer of bundle bone on the distal wall of the socket and at its fundus.

On the mesial surface of the socket, resorption of bone and reparative apposition alternate, the latter, however, leading to the formation of only thin layers of bundle bone.

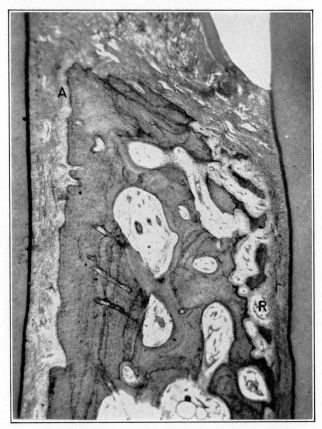

Fig. 147.—A mesiodistal section showing the inter-dental alveolar septum with bone apposition (A) and bone resorption (R). Taken from 11 years old individual. $\times$ 35.

**The Spongiosa.**—The cancellous portion of the alveolar process lies between the cortical plates and the alveolar bone proper. It contains marrow spaces and is continuous with the spongiosa of the body of the jaws (Figs. 142 and 145). There is less cancellous bone in the mandible, due partly to the variation in thickness between the upper and lower jaws and also to the increased width of the cortical plates in the latter. In both bones, however, the spongiosa is greater on the lingual than on the labial or buccal.

In the anterior region the alveolar bone is often fused with the cortical plate so that there is no intervening supporting bone. As the width of the alveolar process increases posteriorly, the proportion of cancellous bone becomes greater. The medullary spaces are larger at and below the level of the apices of the teeth (Fig. 134).

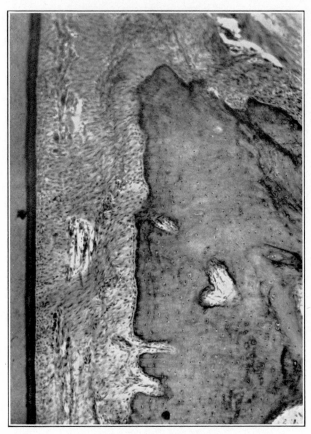

FIG. 148.—Higher magnification of portion of the crest of the alveolar bone shown in Fig. 147 at *A*. Note the row of osteoblasts along the periodontal surface.  ×95.

The arrangement and diameter of the trabeculæ of the cancellous bone are related to the demands for support, but they may be influenced by nutritional and other systemic conditions which interfere with their response to this function. The trabeculæ tend to be arranged about the alveolar bone in a horizontal plane connecting the latter to the adjacent cortical plate. Masticatory stresses are transmitted from the tooth through the periodontal ligament, to the alveolar bone. The trabeculæ of the spongiosa then transmit these forces to the cortical plate. In this way the *entire* alveolus is supported and braced as a unit to receive the load of masticatory

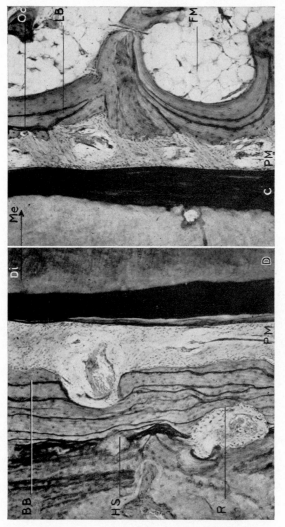

FIG. 149.—Distribution of bundle bone and lamellated bone in the alveolus of a tooth drifting mesially; The direction of movement is indicated by an arrow. *Di*, Distal side of root; *BB*, bundle bone which is laid down in layers parallel to the root surface; *R*, resorption of bundle bone; *HS*, area of lamellated bone; *PM*, periodontal ligament, 0.18 mm. thick, on distal side of root; *D*, dentin. *Me*, mesial side of root: *LB*, lamellated bone; *FM*, fat marrow; *Oc*, osteoclasts resorbing the bone surface; *PM*, periodontal ligament 0.12 mm. thick, on mesial side of root; *C*, cementum. Magnification × 60. (Kronfeld, Dental Histology and Comparative Dental Anatomy.)

stress. In the spaces between the roots of the teeth, the trabeculæ have a more nearly perpendicular direction and may extend to the base of the maxillæ or mandible. Support and resistance to vertical pressure is furnished in this way. The spongiosa of teeth having no antagonists is almost devoid of trabeculæ and shows very wide marrow spaces.

The marrow of the spongiosa is principally of the yellow or fatty type with infrequent patches of red or blood forming marrow. The amount of red marrow decreases with age and varies considerably among individuals. It usually persists to some degree in the cancellous bone at the distal of the last upper molar tooth in the region of the tuberosity. In systemic disturbances causing a prolonged destruction of blood cellular elements, where the hemopoietic capacity of the patient is taxed, there may be a conversion of yellow to red marrow.

## HISTOPHYSIOLOGICAL REMARKS

The normal growth and development of the alveolar process presupposes a normal growth-potential, dental development, function and systemic reaction. The very sensitive response of this tissue to regional influences may account for its delicate susceptibility, shared in a measure with all of the bones of the face, to systemic disturbances. This feature, together with the necessity for a high degree of coördination in the growth and eruption of the teeth, explains the frequent occurrence of deformities.

**Experimental Studies.**—By means of madder feeding, Brash has shown that the growth of the alveolar process in pigs is responsible for over 70 per cent of the vertical growth of the mandible and maxilla, and much of the vertical growth of the face. As a result of his experiments on pigs, Brash concludes that the growth of the alveolar process is the driving force in tooth eruption.

Schour and Massler used an alizarine injection technique in order to arrive at a quantitative estimate of the rate of apposition of alveolar bone. Application of this method in white rats indicates a mean growth-rate of $4\ \mu$ in twenty-four hours.

**Physiological Mesial Drift.**—One of the most interesting of the functional responses of the alveolar bone, physiological mesial drift, occurs during a period of relative stability and inactivity. The teeth normally tend to drift toward the median line. In this way they maintain their proximal contact. In the case of missing teeth, the distal teeth tend to drift mesially and fill in the space formerly occupied by the missing tooth.

While such a drift can be noted macroscopically, histological examination gives proof of its existence in almost all normal dentures. When physiological movement occurs the mesial periodontal membrane fibers are slackened and resorption of the alveolar bone along the mesial periodontal surface takes place. On the distal aspect, however, tension of the periodontal membrane occurs and is translated into a stimulating effect on the

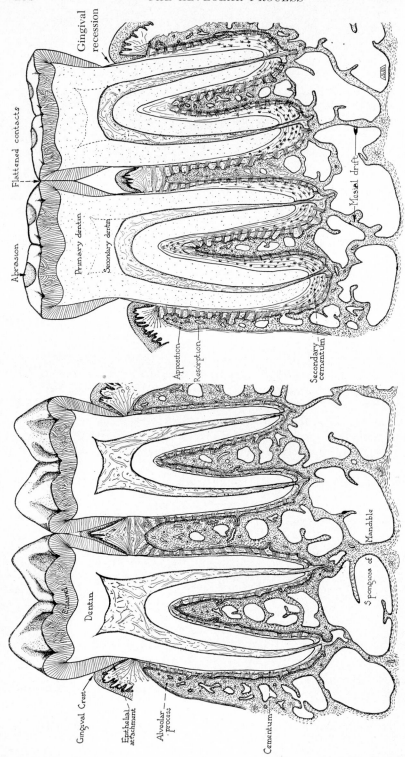

FIG. 150.—Diagrammatic representation illustrating the effects or abrasion and physiological mesial drift upon the dental tissues (changes in the dental tissues with age.)

alveolar bone with a consequent appositional response, and bundle bone is formed. Thus normally, the alveolar bone on the mesial surface of teeth shows resorption, the distal apposition of bundle bone (Fig. 149).

TABLE 6.—DEVELOPMENTAL CHARACTERISTICS AND ENVIRONMENT OF THE CALCIFIED DENTAL TISSUES*

|  | Characteristics | Enamel | Dentin | Cementum | Bone (Alveolar) |
|---|---|---|---|---|---|
| **Developmental** | Embryonic Origin | Epithelial | Mesenchymal | Mesenchymal | Mesenchymal |
| | Developmental Mechanism | Secretory | Endo membranous | Endomembranous | Endomembranous |
| | Uncalcified Precursor | Enamel matrix (Pre-enamel) | Pre-dentin | Cementoid tissue (Pre-cementum) | Osteoid tissue (Pre-osteum) |
| | Appositional Pattern | Incremental layers (bands of Retzius) | Incremental layers (lines of Ebner) | Incremental layers | Lamillæ |
| | Structural Type | Prismatic | Tubular | Cellular and acellular | Cellular |
| **Environment / Cellular Nutritive** | Nutritional Supply | None | Pulp | Periodontal ligament | Periosteum and Endosteum |
| | Internal cellular spaces | None | Dentinal tubules | Lacunæ and canaliculi | Lacunæ and canaliculi |
| | Cellular Elements | None | Odontoblasts (Dentinoblasts) and Odontoblastic processes | Cementocytes and processes | Osteocytes and processes |
| | Adjacent Cellular Elements | None | Odontoblasts Fibroblasts Odontoclasts (during shedding) | Cementoblasts Fibroblasts Cementoclasts (during shedding) | Osteoblasts Osteoclasts Fibroblasts |
| **Fluid** | Adjacent Tissue Fluid Environment | Saliva of oral cavity | Connective tissue fluid of pulp | Connective tissue fluid of periodontal ligament | Connective tissue fluid (of periosteum and endosteum) |

* Adapted from Sognnaes, R. F. Microstructure and histochemical characterists of mineralized tissues. Annals of the N.Y. Acad. of Sciences, *60*, Articles 5, 545–572, 1955.

This constant adjustment reveals the dynamic quality of bone. The alveolar process is not a static support of the teeth and its structure, and position is determined by the functional demand of the constantly moving dentition.

**Effect of Environmental Stimuli.**—The delicate balance, between the formation and destruction of the alveolar process, is swayed in one direction

TABLE 7.—COMPARISON OF STRUCTURAL CHARACTERISTICS AND
REACTIONS OF THE CALCIFEID TISSUES.

| | Enamel | Dentin | Cementum | Bone |
|---|---|---|---|---|
| Formative Cells | Ameloblasts | Odontoblasts | Cementoblasts | Osteoblasts |
| Location of Formative Cells | On enamel surface only in formative stage. | Perikaryon On pulpal surface | On cemental surface | On periosteal and endosteal surface |
| Cellular Contents | Acellular | Odontoblasts and processes | Cementocytes | Osteocytes |
| Spaces | Submicroscopic only | Dentinal tubules | Lacunæ and Canaliculi | Lacunæ and Canaliculi |
| Contents of Spaces | No protoplasmic content | Protoplasmic processes of odontoblasts | Cementocytes and processes | Osteocytes and and processes |
| Response to Stimuli in Adult Stage | Chemical changes only | Formation of reparative dentin | Resorption and repair | Resorption and repair |
| Response to Injury in Growing and Calcifying Stages | Sensitive to metabolic changes, leaving permanent record | Sensitive to metabolic changes, leaving permanent record | Sensitive to metabolic changes | Sensitive to metabolic changes, leaving temporary record |
| Degree of Calcification: Inorganic Contents | 97%+ | 68%+ | 60%+ | 66%+ |
| Response to Fracture | Cracks filled with protein aceous matter (possibly related to lamellæ). | Through pulpal response formation of reparative dentin and/or cementum | Through periodontal response formation of cementum | Through periostal and periodontal response formation of bone |

Adapted from B. G. Sarnat and I. Schour—Effect of Experimental fractures on bone, dentin, and enamel. Arch Surg., *49*, 23, 1944.

or the other by environmental pressure stimuli. These originate from the lips, tongue, facial and masticatory muscles, from external pressure, from habits of masticatory function and from loss of tooth structure or tooth units (Fig. 169). Only when the stresses are beyond the tolerance of the supporting tissues, which of course vary with age and fluctuating degrees of health and disease, do we find destruction when support is demanded (traumatogenic occlusion).

At this stage of study of Oral Histology, the student will find it of advantage to review the calcified tissues and compare then as outlined in Tables 6 and 7.

## BIBLIOGRAPHY.

Box, H. K.:   Twelve Periodontal Studies, University of Toronto Press, Toronto, 1940.

MacMillan, H. W.:   Structural Characteristics of the Alveolar Process, Int. Jour. Ortho., *12*, 166, 722, 1926.

Oppenheim, A.:   Tissue Changes, Particularly of the Bone, Incident to Tooth Movement, Oesterr-ung. Vrtljschr. f. Zahnheilk., vol. *4*, 1911.

    (For English version, see Kronfeld, R.:   Histopathology of the Teeth and Their Surrounding Structures, Philadelphia, Lea & Febiger, 1933.)

Schour, I.:   Measurements of Bone Growth by Alizarine Injections, Proc. Soc. Exper. Biol. and Med., *34*, 140, 1936.

# CHAPTER 14

# The Periodontal Ligament

**Definition and Distribution.**—The periodontal ligament is the connective tissue which (1) fills the space between the surface of the root and the bony wall of its alveolus; (2) surrounds the root occlusally from the border of the alveolus; and (3) supports the gingivæ. It is necessary to emphasize the three parts of the definition. The periodontal membrane does not stop at the alveolar crest, but continues to surround the root and crown as far as the tissues are attached. It also extends into the free margin of the gum and is the means of its support, holding the gingivæ close to the surface of the tooth and supporting them in the interproximal spaces. The importance of this segment of the periodontal structures and the functions which they perform have been strongly emphasized in the last few years, in their relation to the extensions of caries and the beginnings of periodontitis. Most of the diseases of the periodontal membrane which result in the final loss of teeth have their beginnings in this portion.

## FUNCTIONS OF THE PERIODONTAL LIGAMENT

The three major functions are: (1) a physical and adaptive function—it maintains the tooth in relation to the adjacent hard and soft tissues and renders it functional; (2) a vital function—the formation of bone on the alveolar wall and of cementum on the surface of the root; (3) a sensory function—the sensation of touch for the tooth lies exclusively in this membrane.

The periodontal ligament connects the tooth with the alveolar bone so that there is no ankylosed junction between the hard tissues, but a ligament-like connection which permits a certain amount of microscopic movement and adjustment. It is necessary to emphasize two parts in its physical function; the ligament not only supports the tooth in its alveolus and sustains it against the forces of occlusion and mastication, but also maintains the soft, investing tissues in their proper relation to the teeth. The second part of the physical function is fully as important as the first, and the adaptation and form of the gingivæ in their relation to the anatomical form of the teeth and alveolar process are important considerations, which should never be lost sight of in the preparation of operative restorations and crowns.

## HISTOGENESIS

The periodontal ligament is derived from the dental sac. During its early development, the tooth germ lies within a capsule of loose connective tissue, the dental sac, which occupies the space between the tooth germ and the walls of its bony crypt (Figs. 152 and 164). During the formation of the crown (prior to root formation, before any cementum is apposed), the fibers of the loose connective tissue encircle the tooth germ in a parallel arrangement (Fig. 201). However, as soon as the root begins to form, a marked change occurs in the arrangement of the fibers. These fibers become reorientated so as to run from tooth germ to bone. Two layers can be distinguished; an outer coarse fibrous layer next to the bone, and an

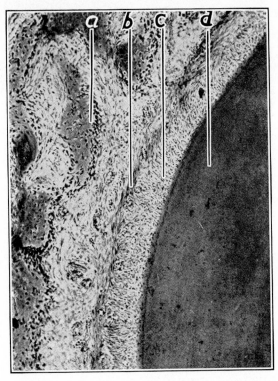

Fig. 151.—Cross-section showing the three layers of the periodontal membrane seen in the growing tooth germs of humans: *a*, bone; *b*, plexus intermedius; *c*, cemental fibers; *d*, dentin (Orban, courtesy of Jour. Am. Dent. Assn.)

inner loose layer next to the forming tooth. With the beginning of active eruption of the tooth, and the formation of cementum and alveolar bone, three layers of fibers may be distinguished: (1) the alveolar fibers; (2) the cemental fibers; and (3) the plexus intermedius between them (Fig. 151). Sicher considers this condition to be characteristic of the rapidly erupting tooth. It is seen normally in the continuously erupting rodent incisors. When the tooth has finished its more active eruption and comes into full occlusion, the plexus intermedius loses its identity, and with subsequent depositions of cementum and alveolar bone their respective fibers are replaced by the principal periodontal fibers, and the normal character of the adult periodontal ligament is reached (Fig. 152).

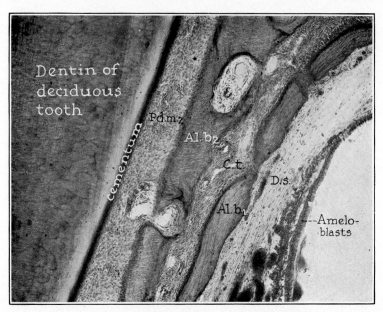

Fig. 152.—The periodontal membrane in two stages of development (Macacus rhesus monkey).    *D.s.*, Primitive undifferentiated dental sac of the permanent tooth germ; *Pdm.₂*, periodontal membrane of the deciduous tooth in functional occlusion; *Al.b₁*, bony crypt of permanent tooth germ; *al.b₂*, alveolar bone of deciduous tooth; *C.t.*, connective tissue between the two layers of bone.

## THE STRUCTURAL ELEMENTS OF THE PERIODONTAL LIGAMENT

(1) White connective tissue fibers.
(2) Cellular elements:
    (*a*) Fibroblasts;
    (*b*) Cementoblasts;
    (*c*) Osteoblasts;
    (*d*) Osteoclasts;
    (*e*) Histiocytes;

(2) Cellular elements:—*continued*
    (*f*) Primitive mesenchymal cells.
    (*g*) Epithelial rests.
(3) Bloodvessels.
(4) Lymphatic vessels.
(5) Nerves.

**The Fibrous Elements of the Periodontal Ligament and Their Arrangement—Classes of Fibrous Tissue.**—The fibrous tissue of the periodontal ligament is of the cellagenous variety, and is composed of the *principal* fibers and the *indifferent* or *interstitial* tissue. The former perform the physical function of the membrane; the latter simply fills in spaces between the bundles of fibers and surrounds and accompanies the bloodvessels and the nerves.

**The Principal Fibers of the Periodontal Ligament.**—These may be defined as the fibers which arise from the cementum and attach at their termination to the supporting and investing tissues of the tooth (the connective tissue supporting the epithelium, the fibrous matte of the gingivæ, the cementum of the approximating tooth, the outer layer of the periosteum at the border of the alveolar process, or the bone of the alveolar wall). These fibers are collagenous. They have a slightly wavy structure so that by alternate tension and relaxation a microscopic movement of the tooth is permitted.

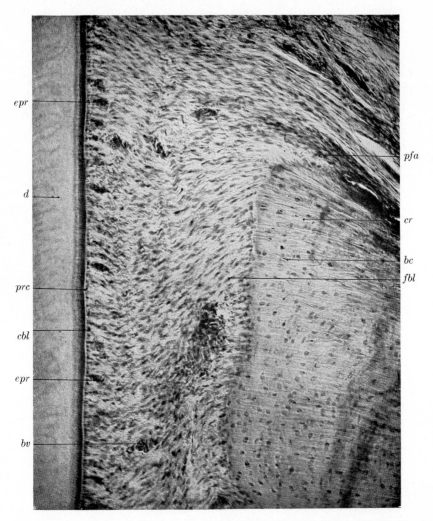

Fig. 153.—Periodontal ligament at alveolar crest: *bc*, bone corpuscle; *bv*, blood-vessel; *cbl*, cementoblast; *cr*, fibers embedded in crest of alveolar bone; *d*, dentin; *epr*, epithelial rests; *fbl*, fibroblasts; *pfa*, periodontal fibers attached to alveolar crest; *prc*, precementum. (× 152.) (From Schour, in Cowdry's *Special Cytology*, courtesy of Paul B. Hoeber, Inc.)

They perform the physical function of the membrane and may be considered, functionally and to some extent morphologically, as a ligament (Figs. 153 and 154). Their ends become embedded in the cementum or alveolar bone as Sharpey's fibers.

Sicher has pointed out the intertwining of the fibers particularly in the middle portion of the periodontal ligament. He compares this to a splicing effect which permits the fibers to function in the absence of an uninterrupted course from cementum to bone. This is the mechanism which is more highly specialized in the form of the plexus intermedius (Fig. 151) in rapidly erupting teeth.

Fig. 154.—Periodontal ligament about the middle of the root: *alb.*, alveolar bone; *c*, primary cementum; *cbl*, cementoblasts; *d*, dentin; *ep*, epithelial rests; *fbl*, fibroblast; *lam*, lamellæ of cementum; *opf*, oblique perodontal membrane fibers; *pfc*, periodontal ligament fibers embedded in cementum; *prc*, pre-cementum. (× 255.) (Schour, in Cowdry's *Special Cytology*, courtesy of Paul B. Hoeber, Inc.)

**Arrangement.**—The principal fibers are embedded in the cementum, the cementoblasts building up the matrix around them, the fibers thus becoming attached to the surface of the root. In most places the fibers, as they spring from the cementum, appear as bundles. A short distance from the surface of the root they may break up into smaller bundles which anastomose and interlace, passing around bloodvessels and fibers in their course and again uniting into large bundles for attachment at their other extremity (Fig. 155).

To arrive at an understanding of the arrangement of the fibers of the periodontal membrane, sections must be cut longitudinally, both in the bucco-lingual and the mesio-distal directions, and transversely through all portions of the membrane. There is a beautiful adaption of their arrangement to sustain the tooth against all the forces to which it is subjected, such as mastication, occlusal stress, lateral pressure and rotation; and to support the free margin of the gingiva so that it will lie close against the cervical of the enamel.

The fibers assume a direction which corresponds to the different stresses and needs of the various levels of the tooth (Fig. 156). Black (1887) has thus classified them into: (1) The *free gingival group* (Fig. 157), the fibers of which pass from the cementum occlusally into the gingiva to support it; (2) the *trans-septal group*, passing from the cementum of one tooth to the cementum of the adjacent one and supporting the interproximal gingivæ (Fig. 158); (3) the *alveolar crest group* passes from the cementum to the crest of the alveolar process (Figs. 153 and 157 and Plate VII); (4) the *horizontal group* in the occlusal third of the alveolar portion passes at right angles to the axis of the tooth from the cementum to the alveolar bone; (5) the *oblique group* in the apical two-thirds of the alveolar portion inclines occlusally as

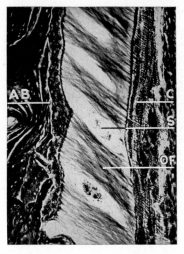

Fig. 155.—Oblique periodontal membrane fibers. Longitidunal section through the root. Silver staining. *C*, Cementum; *OF*, oblique fibers; *S*, spaces between the fiber bundles containing the bloodvessels and nerves of the periodontal membrane; *AB*, alveolar bone. (Kronfeld, Histopathology of the Teeth.)

the fibers pass from cementum to bone (Fig. 155); and (6) the *apical group* radiates from the apex of the root to the bone around the apical space. This classification is very helpful in the understanding of the structural pattern and function of the periodontal membrane. It must be pointed out, however, that this classification is more accentuated than can be seen in any one given section.

*The Free Gingival Group.*—Beginning at the gingival line, the fibers springing from the cementum pass out at a short distance at right angles to its surface and then bend sharply towards the occlusal, passing up into the gingivæ and uniting with the fibrous matte which supports the epithelium (Figs. 156 and 157). These are much more strongly marked on the lingual than on the labial gingivæ, since in mastication the lingual gingivæ receive greater pressure to crush them down. A little deeper, the fibers springing from the cementum on the labial and lingual, pass out at right angles to the cementum and are lost in the coarser fibrous matte of the gum tissue. The distance through which they extend before being lost in the coarser fibers is always greater on the lingual than on the labial.

14

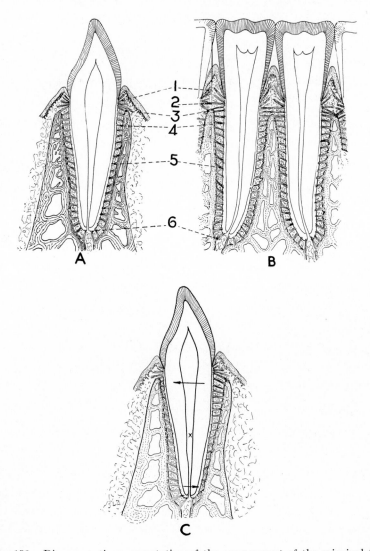

Fig. 156.—Diagrammatic representation of the arrangement of the principal fibers of the periodontal ligament. *A*, Labio-lingual, and *B*, mesio-distal sections through a lower central incisor. *1*, Free gingival group; *2*, trans-septal group; *3*, alveolar crest group; *4*, horizontal group; *5*, oblique group; *6*, apical group. *C*, shows the tipping of the tooth lingually and the changes in the periodontal membrane under incisal stress. *X* indicates approximate fulcrum point. The periodontal ligament is shown disporportionately wide for clarity.

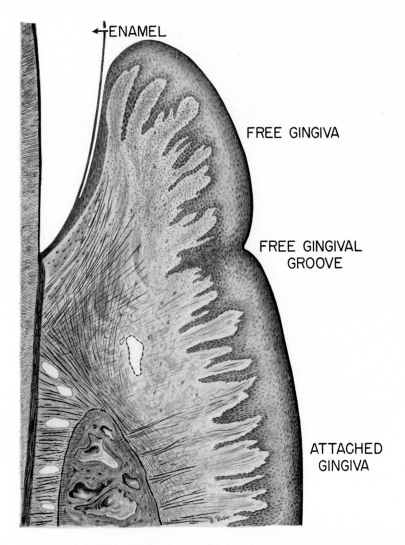

Fig. 157.—Drawing of longitudinal section of the free and attached gingiva separated by the free gingival groove. Note the free gingival, the alveolar crest, and the horizontal fibers.

The free ends of the gingival fibers interlace with circular fiber bands around the neck of the tooth which help keep the gingiva close to the tooth surface (Fig. 159).

*Trans-septal Group.*—On the proximal sides the fibers springing from the cementum at the same level branch and interlace, passing across the interproximal space to be attached to the cementum of the approximating tooth (Fig. 158). These fibers are of the greatest importance as they form a distinct layer which has been called the *dental ligament,* because they bind the teeth together across the septum. This group is naturally seen only in mesio-distal section or in transverse sections cut acclusal to the alveolar crest.

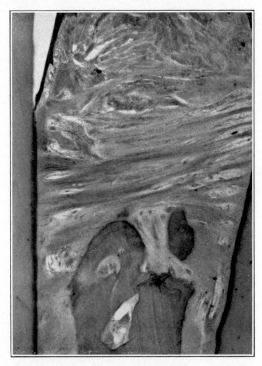

Fig. 158.—Transpetal fibers connecting the cementum of two adjacent teeth
×41. (Courtesy of J. P. Weinmann.)

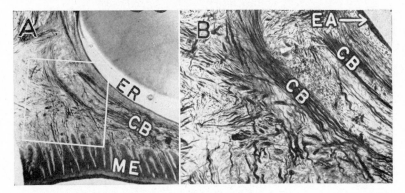

Fig. 159.—*A*, Photomicrograph of horizontal section of upper second premolar of
monkey at level oī alveolar crest. *ER*, enamel space; *CB*, circular band; *ME*, oral epithelium.  *B*, Higher magnification of circular band indicated in rectangle in *A*.  *EA*,
epithelial attachment.  (Courtesy Sumter S. Arnim.)

PLATE VII

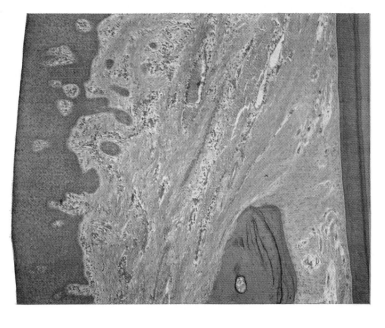

Gingiva    Alveolar   P.D.M. Cem.
           Crest

Longitudinal section at level of alveolar crest of human lower incisor. Note
direction of fibers in the periodontal membrane (P.D.M.).

*Alveolar Crest Group.*—A little farther apically the fibers as they come from the cementum are inclined apically (Fig. 130 and Plate VII). A short distance from the cementum they unite into very large and strong bundles which join with the fibers of the outer layer of the periosteum extending over the labial and lingual border of the alveolar process. On the proximal sides the fibers at this level are attached to the cementum of the adjoining tooth, or are inclined apically, to be inserted in the bone of the septum. These fibers hold the tooth down in its socket.

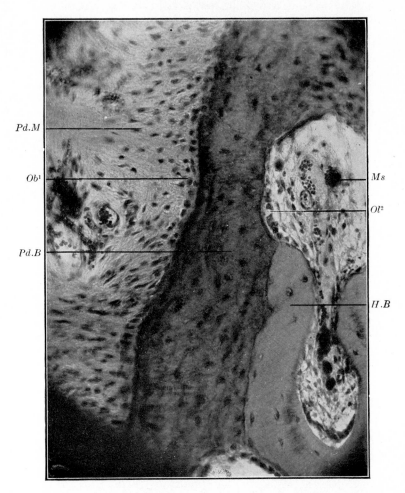

Fig. 160.—Penetrating fibers in bone. *Pd.M*, periodontal membrane; *Ob¹*, osteoblasts of periodontal membrane; *Ol²*, osteoblasts of medullary space; *Pd.B*, solid alveolar bone with embedded fibers; *Ms*, medullary space formed by resorption of the solid alveolar bone with embedded fibers; *H.B*, Haversian system bone without embedded fibers built around the medullary space. (About 200 ×.)

*Horizontal Group.*—At the border of the alveolar process and in the occlusal third of the alveolar portion, the fibers pass directly from the cementum to the bone at right angles to the axis of the tooth. In this position the fibers are larger and stronger, and show less tendency to break up into smaller bundles in their course than in any other portion of the ligament.

*Oblique Group.*—In the middle and apical thirds of the alveolar portion the fibers are inclined occlusally as they pass from the cementum to the bone (Figs. 154 and 155). They spring from the cementum in compact bundles, and show a strong tendency to break up into fan-shaped fasciculi, spreading out as they approach the bone to be attached over a larger area of the alveolar wall. These fibers literally swing the tooth in its socket, support it against the forces of mastication and occlusal stress and help it absorb shock. About the molar teeth they are sufficiently strong to maintain the tooth against one hundred or more pounds of pressure.

*Apical Group.*—In the apical region the fibers springing from the cementum pass out in all directions, radiating outward to be inserted into the bone forming the wall of the apical space.

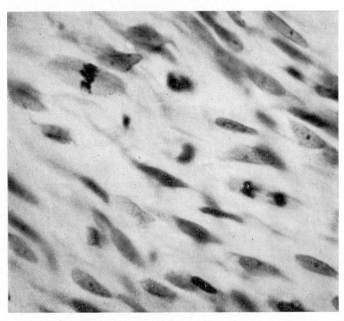

Fig. 161.—Fibroblasts of periodontal membrane of molar of normal white rat showing mitotic figures. (Courtesy of L. C. Macapanpan.)

If force is exerted against the lingual surface of an incisor, the fibers on the lingual side of the root in the *gingival third* will sustain part of the strain, preventing the crown from moving labially, and at the same time the fibers on the labial side of the root in the *apical third* will also be under strain, preventing the apex of the root from moving lingually.

**The Cellular Elements of the Periodontal Ligament.**—Fibroblasts and **Histiocytes.**— The fibroblasts are found everywhere between the fibers which they have formed and to which they belong. They are spindle-shaped or stellate connective tissue cells, having a more or less flattened nucleus and a body of granular cytoplasm, which is pressed out into thin projections between the fibers. The cells stain strongly with hematoxylin and the fibers pink with eosin (Plate VII). In this way the fibers are contrasted

PLATE VIII

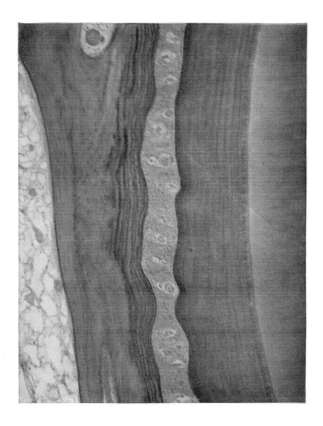

B.M.   L.B.   B.B. P.D.M Cementum Den-
-tin

Transverse section of the distal periodontal membrane at mid-root level of molar of 42 year old person. Note the bundle bone (B.B.) next to the periodontal membrane (P.D.M.) and the laminated bone (W.B.) between the bundle bone and the bone marrow (B.M.). The periodontal membrane shows the tissue spaces which contain blood vessels, nerves, and loose connective tissues and are surrounded by the principal periodontal fibers.

with the intervening cells. The fibroblasts decrease in number with age. They are large and numerous in the membrane of a newly erupted tooth and are comparatively small and few in the membrane around an old tooth. Histiocytes are found in the loose connective tissue between the bundles of principal fibers.

**Cementoblasts.**—The cementoblasts are the cells which form cementum. They cover the surface of the root everywhere between the fibers which are embedded in the tissue. While these cells perform the same function for cementum as the osteoblasts do for bone, they are quite different in form. They are always flattened cells, sometimes almost scale-like, and when seen from above are very irregular in outline. This irregularity is due to the projections of the cytoplasm around the fibers as they spring from the cementum, the edges of the cell being notched and scalloped to fit about them (Fig. 162). There is a central mass of granular cytoplasm which contains an oval and more or less flattened nucleus, from which the cytoplasm extends in projections passing partly around the fibers.

Fig. 162.—Cementoblasts (*c*) and periodontal fiber bundles (*b*) to which they are closely adapted. Section cut at a tangent to the surface of the root of a Macacus tooth. (Schour, in Cowdry's Special Cytology, courtesy of Paul B. Hoeber, Inc.)

In order to obtain an idea of the form of the cementoblasts, sections must be cut at a tangent to the surface of the root, and just missing the surface of the cementum. In this way the fibers are cut across and the cementoblasts are shown covering the entire surface between the fibers. These are shown in Fig. 162, in which the fibers are left perfectly clear in order to outline the cells more distinctly. In sections cut at right angles to the surface of the roots the cementoblasts are shown as more or less flattened, but no idea of the way in which they fit about the fibers can be obtained.

Cytoplasmic processes extend from the body of the cementoblasts into the matrix of the cementum. These correspond to the processes of the osteoblasts which occupy the canalicules of bone. They are, however, not nearly as numerous or as regular in their arrangement as the osteoblasts. In secondary cementum formation the cementoblasts become fastened down to the surface and enclosed in the matrix that is formed. They are then known as cementocytes.

**Osteoblasts.**—The osteoblasts of the periodontal membrane simulate those in other tissues. They cover the surface of the bone of the alveolar wall and lie between the embedded fibers. Even in the young subject they are not found evenly distributed. In the old subject they are generally absent or have been reduced to flattened scales, which are very difficult to demonstrate. Even in these cases areas of active bone formation will be found in which osteoblasts are present. The osteoblasts here lay down bone in exactly the same manner as occurs in attached portions of the periosteum. After a certain thickness of alveolar bone has been formed, resorption occurs from the sides of the bone marrow spaces. New Haversian Systems develop subsequently in the enlarged marrow spaces. This is illustrated in Fig. 160. In this way only sufficient alveolar bone is left to furnish an attachment for the fibers.

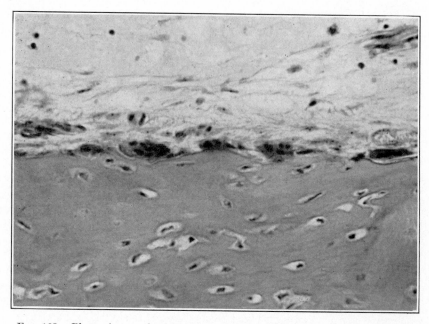

Fig. 163.—Photomicrograph of fundic portion of alveolar crypt of deciduous canine in figure 46. Note the five osteoclasts on surface of immature bone which is resorbing in response to the growing tooth germ. (× 338.)

**Osteoclasts.**—The osteoclasts of the alveolar bone are not constant elements. They appear and disappear in response to the same conditions which lead to their appearance and disappearance in other bones. They are large multinuclear cells, containing as many as forty nuclei (Fig. 163). They may appear upon the surface of the cementum, upon the surface of the alveolar wall, or within the medullary spaces of the bone. They are formed from connective tissue cells in the response to mechanical stimuli or in response to chemical changes of the bone tissue, for instance following necrosis of osteocytes.

The osteoclasts are tissue destroyers and are the active agents in the removal of any hard tissue. Their structure is the same regardless of whether they destroy the enamel, bone, cementum, or dentin. In order for them to act, their cytoplasm must lie in actual contact with the surface to be attacked. They do not first decalcify and then remove, but apparently by applying their cytoplasm to its surface the cells destroy the intercellular substance, forming hollows in the surface into which the cells sink. These hollows have been called *Howship's lacunæ*. The cells usually appear in groups and spread out over the bone or cementum to be attacked, but sometimes only two or three will be found at a point on the surface of the bone. Wherever bone or cementum or dentin are destroyed by the activity of the osteoclasts, the surrounding connective tissue proliferates and occupies its place.

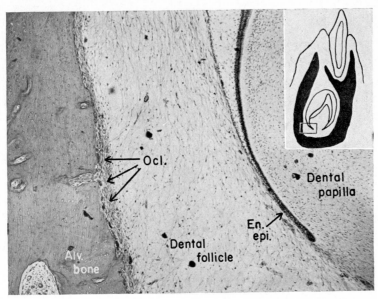

Fig. 164.—Osteoclasts (*Ocl.*) lining alveolar bone adjacent to developing permanent tooth germ. Enamel epithelium (*En. epi.*). Higher magnification of field indicated in insert. Two and one-half year old child.

It is probable that the osteoclasts destroy the organic substance by the action of a proteolytic enzyme and that the mineral salts are dissolved in the tissue fluid or engulfed by microphages.

**Epithelial Rests.**—Near the cementum in the periodontal membrane are found epithelial rests of Malassez, which are remnants of Hertwig's epithelial sheath. They may degenerate, become calcified, and give rise to cementicles, or, in inflammatory processes may lead to root cyst formation. While, like all the cellular elements, they are more numerous in young people than in old, they persist throughout life. They have been shown in the membrane from a man aged seventy years. It does not seem logical to suppose that embryonal débris that was useless to the organism would persist through life. Up to the present time, however, nothing has been discovered about these structures to throw any light upon their function. The possibility suggests itself that they may be related to the formation of cementum.

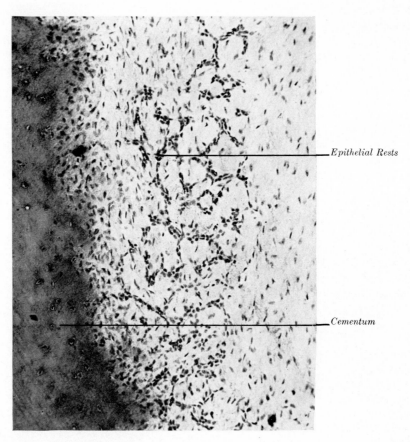

Fig. 165.—Tangential section of periodontal ligament showing network of epithelial rests from Hertwig's sheath. (Approximately × 200.)

The epithelial rests are composed of cords or rows of epithelial cells, surrounded by an extremely delicate basement membrane. In some cases there is a slight indication of a circular arrangement of connective tissue around them. The cords lie very close to the surface of the cementum, winding in and out among the fibers (Fig. 165). They anastomose and join with each other to form a network, the meshes of which are comparatively close in the gingival port on (Fig. 166) and comparatively wide in the apical portion, the cords becoming scarcer as the apex of the root is approached. They show a marked tendency to run out into the membrane and loop back, coming very close to the surface of the cementum.

The ends of the loops toward the cementum often show enlargements which in some cases apparently lie directly in contact with the cementum. There is no definite arrangement of the cells in these cords. In some places there will be a ring of irregular polyhedral or rounded cells which almost exactly resemble a simple tubular gland. In other places there is quite a definite outer ring of cells enclosing a central mass. The cells are made up of granular cytoplasm each containing an ovoid nucleus that is rich in chromatin.

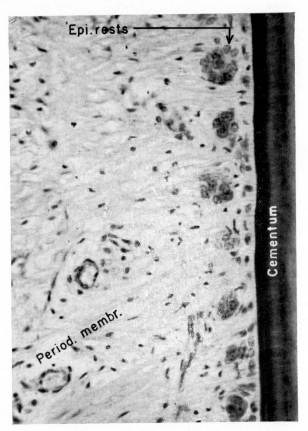

Fig. 166.—Row of epithelial rests (*Epi. rests*) near cementum border. Note direction of fibers of the periodontal membrane.

**Blood Vessels.**—The periodontal membrane has a rich blood supply. It consists mainly of twigs of the interdental and interradicular branches (also called perforating arteries) of the alveolar artery.

The alveolar artery, as shown in Figs. 168A and B gives off the following branches:

1. **Interdental or Interalveolar Arteries.**—On their way to the crest of the bony septa, these vessels send out numerous twigs which perforate the

alveolar bone proper in order to enter the periodontal membrane.  Terminal branches of the interdental arteries leave the alveolar crest and supply in part the interdental or papillary gingiva.

2. **Interradicular Arteries.**—These also send out twigs which perforate the interradicular alveolar bone and enter and supply the periodontal membrane.  They terminate in the periodontal Membrane of the bifurcation.

Thus the periodontal membrane of each root receives its blood supply from two adjacent perforating arteries.  In a single-rooted tooth the perforating arteries are derived from two neighboring interdental arteries. Individual roots of multi-rooted teeth receive their blood supply on one side from the interdental artery and on the other side from the interradicular artery (Fig. 168).

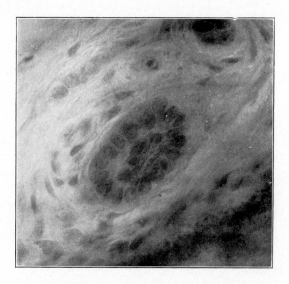

Fig. 167.—Epithelial rest.

3. **Dental Arteries.**—These course to each root and enter the pulp through the apical foramen.  They are therefore also called pulpal arteries.  In the apical region they send off small twigs which may participate in supplying the periapical tissue and anastomose with twigs of the perforating arteries.

The veins, lymphatics and nerves of the periodontal membrane follow the course of the arteries.  This bundle of structures is contained in fairly wide interdental and interradicular canals which are often visible in a roentgenogram.  They are noticeable especially in the anterior region of the jaws and can be termed interdental (Hirschfeld's) canals.

In the periodontal membrane itself the larger blood vessels, lymph vessels and nerves occupy the spaces between bundles of principal fibers.

The distribution of vessels and nerves is responsible for the peculiar spread of a gingival infection into the bone rather than into the periodontal

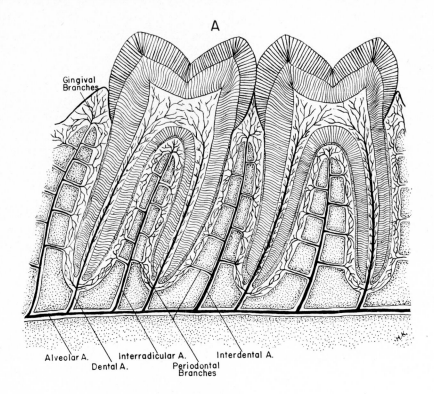

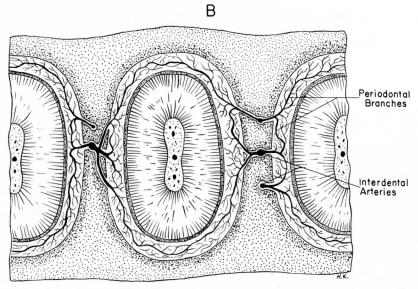

FIG. 168.—Diagram of the distribution of the branches of the Alveolar Artery. The artery and its branches are accompanied by veins, lymph vessels and nerves. A. Mesio-distal section. B. Cross-section. (Courtesy, H. Sicher.)

membrane.  The infection follows the path of least resistance in the loose connective tissue of the interdental canals.

**Lymphatic Vessels.**—The flow of the lymph follows closely the venous drainage.  The lymphatic capillaries in the papillæ under the epithelium on the labial or buccal and lingual surfaces of the gingiva pass to the collecting network in the submucous connective tissue outside the periosteum on the surface of the alveolar process.  The lymphatic capillaries of the periodontal membrane are collected in very fine vessels which extend in the interfibrous tissue of the periodontal membrane and follows the course of the veins through the canals of the alveolar bone proper of the septa. At the level of the apex of the root they receive lymphatics coming from the dental pulp and pass through the cancellous spaces of the bone to the inferior dental canal in the lower jaw and the infra-orbital canal in the upper. They emerge on the surface of the bone at the mental, or the infra-orbital foramina and end in the posterior or middle glands of the submaxillary chain, following the course of the facial artery.  A great amount of work remains to be done on the drainage of the teeth in different regions.  Little or nothing is known of the course of the vessels from the upper incisors, lower incisors and second and third molars.  Lymphatics from the lower incisors may pass to the submental glands.  Those from the upper incisors probably reach the surface of the bone below the level of the floor of the nose and join the vessel coming from the infra-orbital canal, though it is possible that some of them join vessels in the floor of the nose.  It is quite probable that lymphatics from the second and third molars pass to the glands of the parotid group.

**Nerves.**—The nerve supply of the periodontal ligament is very rich in myelinated nerve fibers.  They enter the periodontal membrane in company with the blood-vessels.  Their course is the same as that of the bloodvessels. The trunks entering in the apical space contain from eight to twenty medullated fibers.  Most of these enter the dental pulp.  The periodontal nerves are small branches of the interdental or interradicular nerves, generally following the course of the bloodvessels.

As they ascend gingivally they give off terminal branches which innerate the stroma of the periodontal ligament (Fig. 169).  Many trunks containing eight or ten fibers enter through the alveolar wall.  In this way a fairly rich plexus is formed, from which fibers are continually given off to be lost in the tissue.  Some of these have spindle-like endings (Fig. 170).  A few Pacinian corpuscles have been seen near the gingival border.  These are not generally found, however.  The nerves of the periodontal ligament give to it the sense of touch and pressure.  As has been noted previously, the hard tissues and the pulp have no sense of touch.  The contact of any substance with the surface of the tooth is reported to consciousness through the medium of the periodontal ligament.  The slightest touch of a delicate instrument produces a slight movement of the tooth which affects the nerves between the fibers.  The delicacy of this mechanism can be demon-

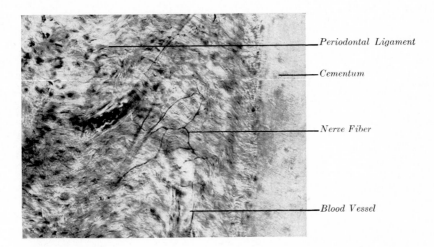

*Periodontal Ligament*

*Cementum*

*Nerve Fiber*

*Blood Vessel*

FIG. 169.—A section of the periodontal ligament of lower molar. Two nerve fibers are seen uniting to form a terminal arborization. From this network, delicate fibers arise which finally terminate in the area. (Courtesy Sol Bernick, Dental Clinics N. A., and W. B. Saunders Company.)

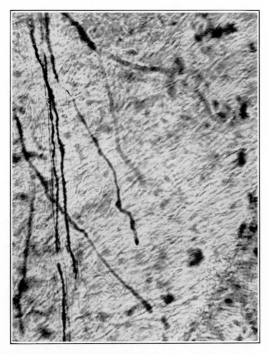

FIG. 170.—A section of the periodontal ligament from an upper central incisor. Note the spindle-like endings which are terminations of medullated nerves. (Courtesy of Sol Bernick, Dental Clinics N. A., and W. B. Saunders Company.)

strated by the following experiment: Lightly touch the surface of the enamel and the patient will tell you at once not only which tooth is touched, but whether a steel instrument or a wooden point or some soft material was used. If, however, the finger is placed uopn a surface of the tooth and firm pressure made in one direction, the contact of the point will not be recognized.

## HISTOPHYSIOLOGICAL REMARKS

**Functional Changes in the Periodontal Ligament.**—The forces of mastication tend to push the tooth more deeply into its socket. Since the oblique fibers are directed apically from the alveolar bone to the cementum, they support the load at their cemental ends. These stresses are in turn transmitted to the alveolar bone. The push of occlusion on the tooth is thus transmitted to a pulling force on the alveolar bone.

When the tooth first erupts, the alveolus is much larger than the root, and the fibers of the periodontal membrane are very long. The size of the alveolus is reduced by the formation of bone, and the size of the root is increased by the formation of successive layers of cementum on its surface (Fig. 171).

A histological examination of the periodontal membrane at any given level, indicates the direction in which the tooth is moving by the relaxed or taut condition of its fibers. In the relaxed condition the fibers present a wavy appearance, in the taut condition the fibers are straightened. In supporting stresses, the fibers are therefore not stretched but become elongated by straightening to perform their function. This mechanism explains how an inelastic fibrous tissue is capable of microscopic adjustment to stresses and permits the microscopic movement of the tooth in the alveolus.

Both the structure and the width of the periodontal ligament are determined by its functional condition. It is thickest at the alveolar crest, thinnest below the middle of the root and widens again towards the apex (Plate IX). When subjected to normal masticatory stress the width averages 0.20 to 0.25 mm. and its structure is normal as described above. If the tooth is subjected to increased functional stress due to the loss of adjacent teeth, the width increases to 0.28 to 0.35 mm. The structure becomes modified also, the fiber bundles becoming stronger and the loose connective tissue being greatly reduced. This picture is typical of functional hypertrophy.

If, on the other hand, the tooth lacks in functional stresses due to the loss of its antagonists, the average width is reduced to 0.10 to 0.15 mm. The fiber bundles atrophy and are replaced by loose, irregular connective tissue without definite functional orientation.

**Physiological Mesial Drift.**—The teeth normally tend to drift or wander toward the median line, because the contact points wear and flatten with age. Owing to this wandering, the fibers of the periodontal ligament on

# PLATE IX

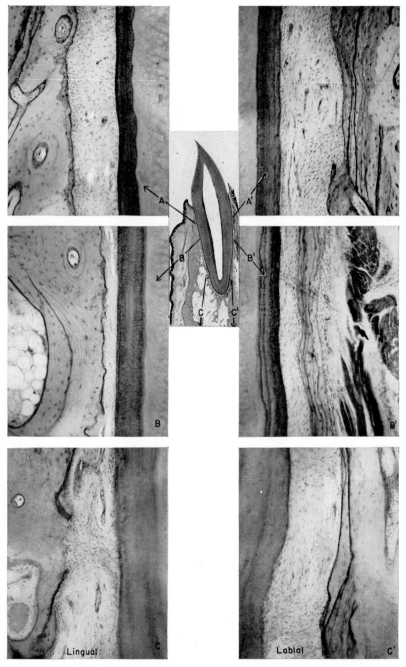

Plate showing the varying thickness of the periodontal ligament in a lower central incisor on the lingual and labial surfaces of the root.  A and A¹, near the alveolar crest; B and B¹, at the mid-root; C and C¹, near the apex.  Note the constriction of the periodontal membrane at the mid-root level (approximate width 60–90 microns) and its widening toward the cervical and apical areas (average width 200 microns).

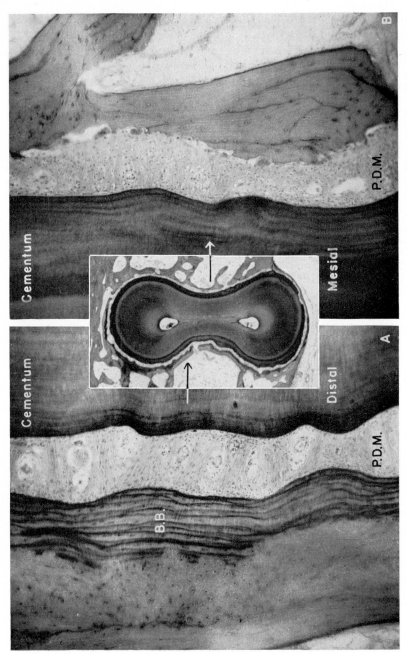

FIG. 171.—Transverse section through mid-root of a lower molar undergoing physiologic mesial drift. Note bundle bone apposition (B.B.) on side of tension in A, and bone resorption on side of pressure in B. Arrows indicate magnified fields and direction of tooth movement. Sections from jaws of 42 year old male. Higher magnification of mesial root of lower first molar in figure 146.

the distal side of the teeth are stretched, while those on the mesial are relaxed. The alveolar bone on the distal side is thus stimulated and shows active deposition. So many fibers are embedded on this side that the border has been called "bundle bone." This type of bone is quite thin or absent on the mesial side of the alveolus, where the bone is of the common lamellated type and often shows resorption (Figs. 149 and 171).

**Cementicles.**—Cementicles are calcified bodies located near the epithelial rests and are found in the adult periodontal membrane. Gottlieb has described cementicles which are a result of the deposition of cementum over

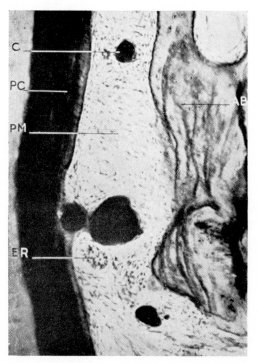

Fig. 172.—Cementicles in the periodontal membrane. PC, primary cementum; PM, periodontal membrane; ER, epithelial rests of the periodontal membrane; C, cementicles; AB, alveolar bone. Magnification × 140. (Kronfeld, Dental Histology.)

degenerating or dead epithelial cells. In other cases cementicles may form through a calcospherite formation or through the calcification of dead epithelial cells. Thus the cementicles, like the denticles, may be classified into true and false types and may be free, adherent or interstitial (Fig. 172).

**Clinical Considerations.**—In a sense, the periodontal ligament may be considered the most important tissue to the dentist, for the usefulness of the teeth and their comfort to the individual is dependent upon it. It makes no difference how perfect a crown may be, or how perfectly any damage which may have occurred to it has been restored; unless the periodontal ligament is in a healthy and fairly normal condition, the tooth will be useless, and the individual would be much more comfortable without it.

These structural facts are of the greatest practical importance, especially in the malleting of gold foil for young persons. Every operator has noticed the great difference in the feeling of the mallet upon different teeth. In one instance, it will ring under the steel mallet as if the tooth were resting upon an anvil; in another case, it feels as if the tooth were resting upon a cushion. In the former, all of the force of the blow is expended in the condensation of the gold. In the second, a large proportion is lost in the movement of the tooth. If the membrane is thin and the cementum and bone are interlocked, the tooth is firmly supported. If the membrane is thick and the fibers long, the blow is dissipated in the sag of the fibers. The tooth is jumping up and down in its socket. The force used is dissipated, the gold is not condensed, and in a very short time an acute inflammation is set up and the tooth becomes very sore to the blows. Serious damage thus may be done to the ligament.

In an acute inflammation of the periodontal ligament the tooth feels "high" because the ligament is enclosed by hard tissue and the swelling lifts the tooth in its socket.

## BIBLIOGRAPHY.

ARNIM, SUMTER S. and HAGERMAN, DAVID A.: "The Connective Tissue Fibers of the Marginal Gingiva," Jour. Am. Dent. Assn., *47*, 271–281, 1953.

BERNICK, SOL: Innervation of the Teeth and Periodontium, Dent. Clin. N. A., W. B. Saunders Company, July, 1959.

BLACK, G. V.: Periosteum and Peridental Membrane, Chicago, W. T. Keener, 1887.

COOLIDGE, E. D.: The Thickness of the Human Periodontal Membrane, Jour. Am. Dent. Assn., *24*, 1260, 1937.

KRONFELD, R.: Structure, Function and Pathology of the Human Periodontal Membrane, New York Jour. Dent., *6*, 112, 1936.

MALASSEZ, M. L.: Sur l'existence d'amas epitheliaux autour de la racine des dents, Arch. d. pyhsiol., *5*, ser. 3, 129, 1885.

ORBAN, B.: Contribution to the Knowledge of Physiologic Changes in Periodontal Membrane, Jour. Am. Dent. Assn., *16*, 405, 1929.

—————: Contribution to the Histology of the Dental Pulp and Periodontal Membrane, With Special Reference to the Cells of Defense of These Tissues, Jour. Am. Dent. Assn., *16*, 965, 1929.

# CHAPTER 15

# The Gingiva

**The Gingiva.**—The gingiva is that part of the firm oral masticatory mucosa which surrounds the necks of the teeth and covers the alveolar processes of the upper and lower jaws. It consists of the *free* and *attached* portions which are separated by the *free gingival* groove.

The thin border of the gingival crest surrounds the necks of the teeth and is called the *free gingiva*. It is freely mobile and extends to the bottom of the gingival sulcus. The free gingiva may be further subdivided according to anatomic location into the marginal and papillary zones that form the free edge of the marginal and papillary gingivæ, respectively (Fig. 173).

The *marginal gingiva* extends along the cervical level of the tooth at the labial and lingual surfaces. It tapers to a knife-like edge, the gingival margin, which normally is separated from the tooth surface by the shallow gingival sulcus.

The *papillary gingiva* is the portion of the free gingiva which fills the interproximal space between the two adjacent teeth. It is pyramidal in shape with the base resting over the crest of the interseptal alveolar bone and its apex tapering to the contact point. The papillary gingiva thus normally fills the embrasure bounded by the distal surface of the anterior tooth and the mesial surface of the adjacent and more posteriorly situated tooth. If the two teeth are crowded or overlap, the papillary gingiva is crowded accordingly and thus more susceptible to gingivitis. On the other hand, if there is no contact the papillary gingiva is reduced. In the case of a diastema the papillary gingiva is absent.

The *attached gingiva* is immovably anchored to the underlying cementum and alveolar process. It extends from the free gingival groove to the muco-gingival junction. Its surface shows a characteristic stippling resembling that of an orange peel.

The *free gingival groove* is a slight indentation which separates the attached from the free gingiva and is reinforced by a heavy epithelial ridge. It is situated at a level which corresponds to that of the bottom of the gingival sulcus (Plate X).

**Function.**—The chief function of the gingiva is to protect the underlying structures. This is achieved by the firm structure of the gingiva which is well adapted to resist masticatory forces and by its strong attachment to the tooth.

**Structure.**— *The epithelium of the gingiva.* The surface of the epithelium is smooth in the free gingiva and stippled in the attached gingiva. Except

( 230 )

PLATE X

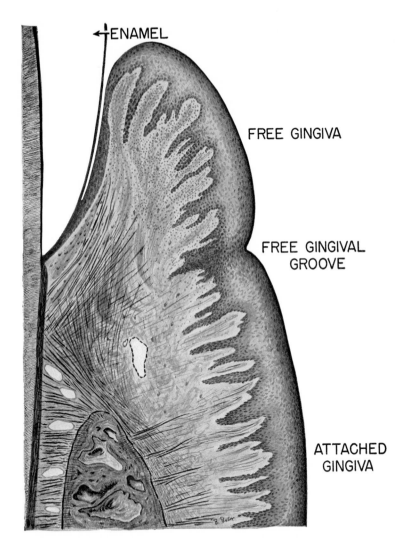

ENAMEL

FREE GINGIVA

FREE GINGIVAL
GROOVE

ATTACHED
GINGIVA

Drawing of longitudinal section of the free and attached gingiva separated by the free gingival groove. Note the free gingival, the alveolar crest, and the horizontal fibers.

## LEGEND FOR PLATE XI

Microphotographs of human gingiva showing range of Keratinization, ($\times$ 550). Figures 1, 3, 5, and 7 were stained with hematoxlyin and eosin; figues 2, 4, 6 and 8 were stained with Mallory. (Courtesy Weinmann and Meyer in J. Invest. Dermat.) Figs. 1 and 2: Region showing full keratinization. Figs. 3 and 4: Region showing parakeratosis. Figs. 5 and 6: Region showing incomplete parakeratosis. Figs. 7 and 8: Region showing nonkeratinization.

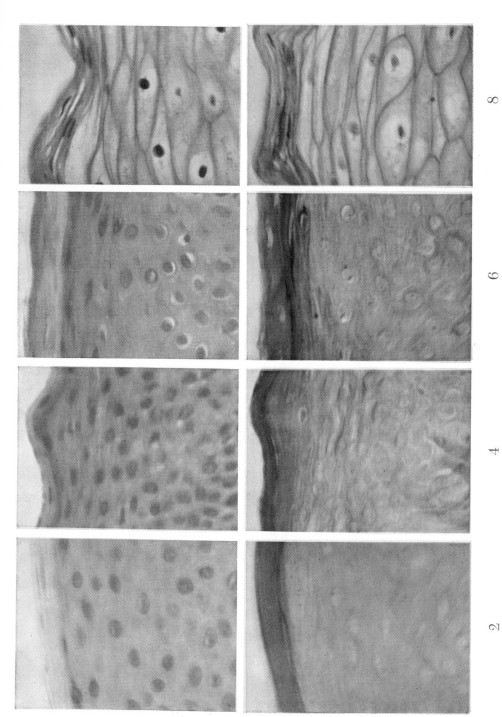

*Legend on opposite page*

for the gingival sulcus the epithelium is keratinized. This keratinizaiton, however, is not always complete, so that several superficial layers may consist of parakeratotic cells. Weinmann and Meyer have demonstrated that the normal variants in the degree of keratinization of the epithelial surfaces of the human gingiva range from nonkeratinization, incomplete parakeratosis, parakeratosis, and full keratinization (Plate XI). The granular layer is not always present.

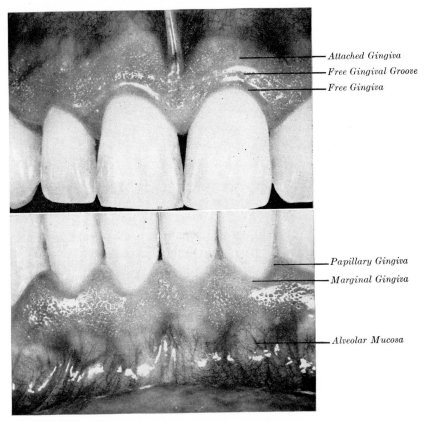

Attached Gingiva
Free Gingival Groove
Free Gingiva

Papillary Gingiva
Marginal Gingiva

Alveolar Mucosa

FIG. 173.—Photograph of gingiva of upper and lower anterior teeth. Note the stippling of the attached gingiva and the rich vascularization of the alveolar mucosa. (Courtesy, Maury Massler.)

The stratum spinosum is usually thin. According to Engel the cells show carbohydrate material (presumably glycogen) and alkaline phosphatase in their cytoplasm. The stratum germinativum consists as a rule of several layers and contains numerous mitotic figures (Fig. 175). The basement membrane is especially rich in glycoprotein. Alkaline phosphatase has been demonstrated in the gingival epithelium. In the gingival sulcus the epithelium presents a smooth boundary against the subjacent connective tissue except when inflamed.

*The Lamina Propria of the Gingiva.*—This connective tissue is composed of the papillary and reticular layers. Special adaptations of the gingiva to the masticatory function are evidenced in the junction between the lamina propria and the epithelium and in the interlacing fibrous network The epithelia-connective tissue boundary is characterized by large and numerous papillæ in which capillary loops reach close to the epithelium. These connective tissue papillæ interlock with the epithelium which is shaped into regular ridges (Fig. 174). The texture of the fibers which is fine in the young tends to increase in coarseness with age.

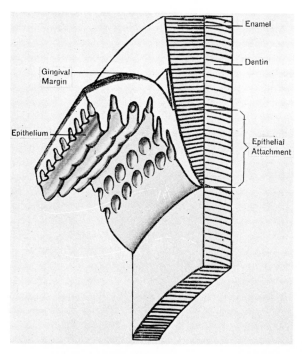

Fig. 174.—A diagrammatic representation of the free gingiva and epithelial attachment after the connective tissue had been removed. Note the pits in the epithelial attachment running almost parallel to the long axis of the tooth, and the pits in the sulci between the epithelial ridges at the gingival margin. (Courtesy, R. D. Emslie and J. P. Weinmann.)

In the attached gingiva, in particular, the predominant character of the lamina propria is that of an elaborate and densely interlacing fibrous matte. The collagenous fibers usually appear as coarsely and irregularly textured bundles. They arise from the cementum and the alveolar crest, and radiate to the papillary layers of the gingiva (Plate X). Elastic fibers are lacking.

At the level of the alveolar crest some of the collagenous bundles extend from the cementum directly over the crest and then incline apically between

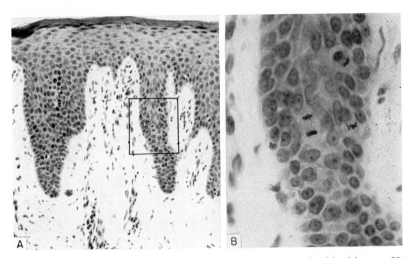

FIG. 175.—Photomicrographs of human attached gingiva obtained by biopsy. Note A, the surface keratinous layer, the prickle cell layer, and the boundary between the epithelium and the connective tissue; B, field indicated in A under higher magnification. Note the mitotic figures in the epithelium. (Courtesy of J. P. Weinmann.)

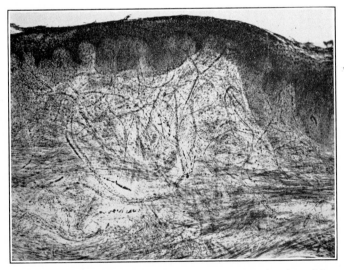

FIG. 176.—A section of the mucous membrane from the lingual surface of the mandible. Note the extensive network of nerves. (× 75.) (Courtesy of Sol Bernick, Dental Clinics N. A., and W. B. Saunders Company.)

the outer periosteum of the alveolar bone and the epithelium of the attached gingiva. This arrangement further strengthens the attachment of the gingiva.

The human gingiva is well innervated (Fig. 177). Some of the nerve endings are similar to those of the skin and others are of different forms.

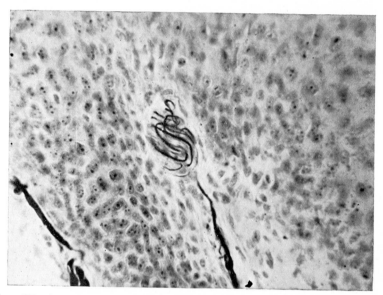

Fig. 177.—Nerve ending in a connective tissue papilla of human gingiva. (Courtesy of Gairns and Aitchison.)

Recent histochemical studies by Engel have revealed a glycoprotein structure in the connective tissue fibers and in the optically homogenous ground substance in which they are embedded. Wislocki and Sognnaes report a persistence of metachromatic ground substance and alkaline phosphatase and suggest their possible relation to the higher metabolic activity in the gingiva.

*Cellular Elements in the Connective Tissue of the Gingiva.*—The presence of plasma cells and lymphocytes is not uncommon in the clinically normal gingiva, especially near the gingival sulcus. In the free gingiva where the fibers are more finely textured, the cellular elements, predominately fibroblasts, are increased in number.

Wislocki and Sognnaes demonstrated large numbers of mast cells in the human gingiva in contrast to their absence in the pulp. The significance of these findings is not known.

*The Alveolar Mucosa.*—The transition from gingiva to alveolar mucosa is quite abrupt at the mucogingival junction and clearly visible because of the change in color. The gingiva is pale pink in color. The alveolar mucosa is red and glossy, and is covered by a thinner epithelium. A hornified layer is absent and the papillæ are few and low. At the junction an independent submucous layer of loose connective tissue commences, allowing the mucous membrane, which is rich in elastic fibers, to move freely over the underlying periosteum and bone.

The gingiva exhibits remarkable powers of rapid healing. It is well supplied with nerves which are not very sensitive, in this way allowing it to withstand the forces of mastication without discomfort. In spite of this resistance to abuse, it will become hypersensitive through continual irritation, a fact which must be remembered in the construction of artificial dentures. Should they bind too hard or move too freely, extreme pain and discomfort will result. Should the denture be extended beyond the gingiva onto the oral mucosa which has no stratum corneum, the more delicate mucous membrane will be readily injured.

## THE EPITHELIAL ATTACHMENT

The epithelial portion of the gingiva which is in direct contact with the surface of the tooth is called the epithelial attachment. It normally extends from the bottom of the gingival crevice toward the cemento-enamel junction and often passes the latter. It is characterized by a uniform width of stratified squamous epithelium which resembles closely that of the oral cavity. The superficial cell layers next to the enamel are so arranged that their long axis is parallel to the tooth surface. The cells of the remaining layers gradually change in their arrangement so that the layers adjoining the connective tissue surface are columnar in form and at right angles.

The boundary between the epithelial attachment and the underlying connective tissue is normally smooth and not interrupted by connective tissue papillæ. This ideal condition is not common because of the frequency of inflammatory conditions in this region, and projections of the epithelial attachment are frequently found to extend down between the papillæ of the connective tissue. These projections may be especially long and cells of inflammation are often found in the adjacent connective tissue. One of the important functions of the supporting tissues about the necks of the teeth is to resist and remove infection. The epithelium, the capillaries, the lymphatics and the cellular elements and fibers of the connective tissue are so arranged as to respond immediately to an invasion of pathogenic organisms, and to ward off a possible ensuing infection.

If the epithelial attachment atrophies, the enamel that is in direct contact with the connective tissue may be covered by cementum or may be resorbed. The epithelial attachment protects the enamel against such an occurrence.

**The Gingival Sulcus.**—The gingival sulcus is the trough-like depression that results from the tearing at the gingival crest of the epithelial attachment within the most superficial layers next to the enamel cuticle. It is thus bounded on one side by the dental cuticle and on the other side by the epithelium of the sulcus. The apical end is called the bottom of the gingival sulcus, and is limited by the level of the intact epithelial attachment (Fig. 178). In an ideal condition the sulcus is absent or very shallow. Should the gingival sulcus deepen it will become a gingival pocket and may play an important role in development of periodontal disease.

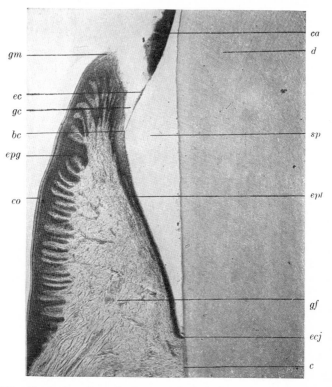

Fig. 178.—Gingival portion: *bc*, bottom of gingival crevice; *c*, primary cementum; *ca*, salivary calculus; *co*, stratum corneum of gum epithelium; *d*, dentin; *ec*, enamel cuticle; *ecj*, cemento-enamel junction; *epg*, epithelium of gum tissue; *ept*, epithelial attachment; *gc*, gingival sulcus; *gf*, gingival group of periodontal membrane fibers; *gm*, gingival crest; *sp*, space formerly occupied by enamel lost in decalcification. (54 ×.) (From Schour in Cowdry's *Special Cytology*, courtesy of Paul B. Hoeber, Inc.)

**Downgrowth of Epithelium.**—The occlusal eruptive movement of the teeth continues throughout life in compensation for occlusal wear. Usually the crown and later even the root become exposed to the oral cavity by a recession of the gingiva. During this process the epithelium is detached from the surface of the crown and proliferates along the surface of the cementum. The progressive exposure of the crown and later of the root by gingival recession and the peeling off of the epithelial attachment is termed passive exposure. The changing relation of the epithelial attachment to the tooth permits the establishment of four stages of passive exposure (Fig. 179).

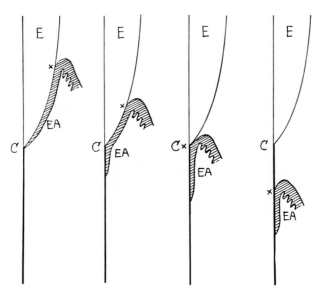

Fig. 179.—Diagram illustrting the four stages of passive exposure of the tooth. I. The epithelial attachment (EA) is confined to the enamel (E); II. EA is attached to the enamel and cementum; III. EA is confined to the cementum but the bottom of the gingival sulcus (X) is just at the cemento-enamel junction (C); IV. EA has grown down and part of the root surface is exposed. Orban, Oral Histology and Embryology (Courtesy of C. V. Mosby Company.)

## DENTAL CALCULUS

**Definition.**—Calculus is the calcified organic matter deposited upon the clinical crown in and above the gingival crevice (Fig. 178).

**Method of Formation.**—The manner of calculus formation is not completely understood. The consensus is that the first step in the formation of calculus consists in the deposition of an adherent film of organic matter upon the teeth. This primary deposit is composed of desquamated epithelial cells of the oral mucosa, food débris, salivary mucin and globulins, and various microörganisms. This film is readily removed in its early stages by correct brushing.

The second step consists of the calcification and consequent hardening of this film. Calcium salts derived from the salivary fluids are deposited within the organic matter in a calcospherite formation, in the manner described for calcification of the dentin. Black has shown by dietary experiments on himself and on his students that the formation of salivary calculus is directly proportional to the ingestion of protein. He explains this on the basis of an increased salivary globulin content which, when deposited, acts as a nidus for the formation of calcoglobulin.

The possible role of bacteria in the formation of calculus presents an interesting problem for investigation.

**Chemical Analysis.**—Chemical analysis gives the following average composition:

| | |
|---|---|
| Calcium phosphate | 70 per cent |
| Calcium carbonate, calcium fluoride and magnesium phosphate | 10 per cent |
| Organic matter and water | 20 per cent |

Clinically it has been observed that very hard calculus contains a higher percentage of inorganic salts while soft, chalky calculus contains a higher percentage of organic matter and water.

**Distribution.**—Since the formation of calculus is dependent on products of the salivary glands, it will be found only on the clinical crowns of the teeth. It is most frequently seen opposite the openings of the salivary glands, that is, on the lingual surfaces of the lower anterior teeth (opposite the openings of the submaxillary and sublingual glands) and on the buccal surfaces of the upper molars (opposite the opening of the parotid gland).

**Types.**—Calculus has been divided clinically into two types on the basis of location and color. Supragingival or salivary calculus appears above the gingival crest and ranges in color from a white to a very light yellow. Subgingival or serumal calculus is found within the gingival crevice and ranges in color from a dark brown to black.

The etiology of both types of calculus may be the same. Certain further differences exist clinically. The salivary calculus forms much more quickly than serumal calculus and is found in large amounts opposite the openings of the salivary ducts. Serumal calculus forms much more slowly and in comparatively small amounts in the gingival crevice of any of the teeth. Its hidden position makes it more difficult to locate and its consistency is more compact and harder than salivary calculus.

It is difficult to define calculus as a pathological deposition, since it is present in almost every mouth, and in small amounts and early stages it causes no harmful effects. Nevertheless, calculus is a common etiological agent of gingivitis.

## GINGIVITIS

The exposed position of the gingivæ and the multitude of irritating factors which are normally present in the oral cavity subject the tissue to constant insults which call forth a defensive response—inflammation. This condition is recognized by the presence of lymphocytes, histiocytes and polyblasts in the subepithelial tissue, and is termed gingivitis. It is most frequently caused by:

1. Irritation produced by the excessive formation of calculus.
2. Local irritation due to lack of oral hygiene.
3. Irritation due to loss of contact point or malposition of teeth.
4. Improperly contoured dental restorations.

Special types of gingivitis have been described in association with pregnancy, diabetes, menstruation and chemical poisoning.

BIBLIOGRAPHY.

BIBBY, B. G.: Formation of Salivary Calculus, Dental Cosmos, *77*, 668, 1935.

EMSLIE, R. D., and WEINMANN, J. P.: The Architectural Pattern of the Boundary Between Epithelium and Connective Tissue of the Gingiva in the Rhesus Monkey, Anat. Rec., *105*, 35, 1949.

GAIRNS, F. W., and AITCHISON, J.: A Preliminary Study of the Multiplicity of Nerve Endings in the Human Gum, Dent. Rec., 180–193, 1950.

GOLDMAN, H. M.: The Topography and Role of the Gingival Fibers, Jour. Dent. Res., *30*, 331, 1951.

HODGE, HAROLD C., and LEUNG, S. W.: Calculus Formation, Jour. Periodont., *21*, 211, 1950.

KING, J. D.: Experimental Investigations of Parodontal Disease; V. Capillary Microscopy as a Clinical Aid to Assessment of Gingival Health and Disease, Dent. Rec., *67*, 1, 1947.

ORBAN, B.: Clinical and Histologic Study of the Surface Characteristics of the Gingiva, Oral Surg. Oral Med. and Oral Path., *1*, 827, 1948.

————: Histology and Physiology of the Gingiva, Jour. Am. Dent. Assn., *44*, 624, 1952.

WEINMANN, J. P., and MEYER, J.: Types of Keratinization in the Human Gingiva, Jour. Invest. Derma., *32*, 9, February, 1959.

WENTZ, F. M., MAIER, A. W., and ORBAN, B.: Changes and Sex Differences in the Clinically "Normal" Gingiva, Jour. Periodont., *23*, 13, 1952.

WISLOCKI, G. B., and SOGNNAES, R. F.: Histochemical Reactions of Normal Teeth, Am. Jour. Anat., *87*, 239, 1950.

# CHAPTER 16

# The Oral Cavity

## MUCOUS MEMBRANE

THE mucous membrane of the oral cavity is composed of a layer of stratified squamous epithelium supported upon a tunica propria, which is usually described as composed of two parts—the papillary and the reticular layers (Fig. 180). The epithelium and the tunica propria make up the mucous membrane proper, which is supported upon a submucous connective tissue layer.

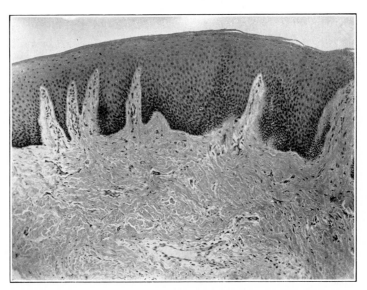

Fig. 180.—Stratified squamous epithelium and lamina propria of the attached gingiva covering the alveolar process. Note thin hornified layer. × 100.

**The Epithelium.**—The stratified squamous epithelium is provided with a horny or corneous layer only in the portions having a masticatory function. (Fig. 180). The horny layer consists of dead cells which have lost their nuclei and whose cytoplasm has been converted into keratin or horny material.

These scale-like remains are closely packed into a protective layer. There is no distinct stratum lucidum separating the dead from the living cells as there is in the skin. In the deeper portions the cells possess oval or rounded nuclei and become larger and more polyhedral as the basement membrane is approached. The cells of the deepest layer next to the basement membrane are tall and approach the columnar form, but are not much greater in height than width. The polyhedral cells in the middle portion of the layer show distinct intercellular spaces across which the cytoplasm extends in intercellular bridges. Isolated cells from this region show the broken bridges projecting from their surface, and for this reason have been called "prickle cells."

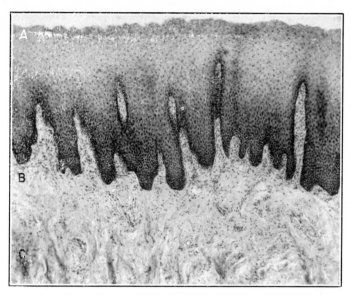

Fig. 181.—Photomicrograph of the oral mucosa of the cheek of a 2-year-old boy. × 75. Note the lack of hornification. *A.* Stratum germinativum; *B.* Lamina propria; *C.* Submucosa. (Courtesy, Dr. O. Kampmeier.)

The epithelium lining the gingival sulcus and that covering loosely attached portions is without the horny layer, and the cells are larger and more loosely placed. In these positions the epithelial layer is usually thinner than in the attached portions of the membrane (Fig. 181).

**Tunica Propria.**—The connective tissue layer of the mucous membrane interlocks with the epithelial layer by means of the papillary layer which is composed of very delicate connective tissue fibers. The papillæ are usually about half as tall as the thickness of the epithelium, and about one-third as wide as they are tall. The height and character of the papillæ vary greatly, however, in different positions. In the red border of the lip they are very tall and narrow, and approach very close to the surface of the epithelium. Over the gingiva and the palate they are much shorter and wider and do not extend more than half-way through the epithelium. These papillæ contain loops of capillary blood-vessels and in some special nerve endings are found.

**Reticular Layer.**—The reticular layer joins the papillary layer with no line of demarcation, and is composed of the same kind of tissue, the fibers being arranged in a delicate network. Occasionally in the tunica propria are found ducts from mucous glands which lie in the deeper layers.

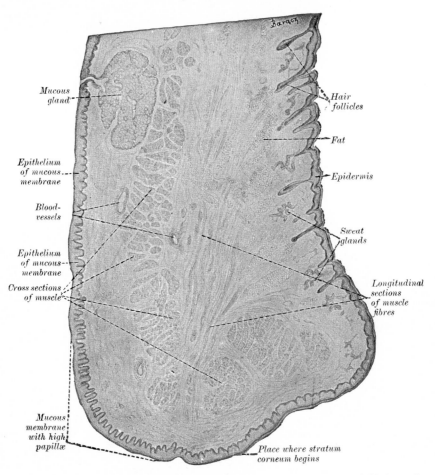

*Mucous gland*

*Hair follicles*

*Fat*

*Epithelium of mucous membrane*

*Epidermis*

*Blood-vessels*

*Sweat glands*

*Epithelium of mucous membrane*

*Cross sections of muscle*

*Longitudinal sections of muscle fibres*

*Mucous membrane with high papillæ*

*Place where stratum corneum begins*

Fig. 182.—Section through the upper lip of a two-and-a-half-year-old child. (14 ×.)

**Submucosa.**—The submucosa varies from a very firm dense collagenous tissue to a loose soft elastic tissue according to the function of the mucosa. It will be described in greater detail as the different areas are discussed. It contains two plexuses of blood-vessels both more or less parallel with the surface. The outer is composed of small vessels forming a small-meshed network, the deeper of large vessels more widely separated. Lymphatic vessels everywhere follow the course of the blood-vessels.

**Glands.**—The submucosa contains a great many small acinous glands. These are distributed widely over the tongue and membrane of the cheek and lip (Fig. 182). They are branched acinous glands, sometimes simple and sometimes compound. The body of the gland is in the submucosa, though it may extend into the underlying muscle. Some are serous and others mucous, while many of the larger ones are mixed. The secretion of these glands is probably much more important than has been supposed.

**Nerve Endings in the Mucosa.**—Sensory nerve endings of two types are found in the mucous membrane. *Krause's end bulbs* are found in many of the papillæ, and other nerves terminate in free endings lying between the epithelial cells.

## CLASSIFICATION OF THE ORAL MUCOSA

The layers of the mucosa and submucosa vary with their function in different areas of the oral cavity. The mucosa may be classified as follows (Table 8):

1. **Masticatory Mucosa.**—Firmly fixed to hard structures.
    *A.* Simple—gingiva and palatine raphæ.
    *B.* Cushioned—hard palate.
2. **Lining Mucosa.**
    *A.* Firmly fixed to underlying muscle. Soft palate, lips and cheeks, inferior surface of tongue.
    *B.* Loosely attached to underlying bone, fascia, or muscle—Alveolar mucosa, vestibular mucosa (Fornix), floor of the mouth.
3. **Specialized Mucosa of Dorsum of Tongue.**
    *A.* Masticatory—firmly fixed to muscle—anterior portion.
    *B.* Lining—firmly fixed to muscle. Posterior portion.

The gingiva is considered in Chapter 15.

### THE HARD PALATE

The mucous membrane of the hard palate is covered with stratified squamous epithelium and characterized by the presence of five or six transverse folds, palatine rugæ, which vary in number and prominence in different individuals and at different ages.

The rugæ are best developed in fetal life but are still well formed in the new-born. Their development in later life is retarded and in the adult they may be absent entirely. According to Lund they are not simple elevations of mucous membrane but contain as their base a connective tissue nucleus called "ruga nucleus" which consists of a tissue of embryonic character, rich in cells and interwoven with very delicate connective tissue fibers. He believes that their disappearance in later life is due to the decrease of sub-mucous fat tissue rather than to the shrinkage of the "ruga nucleus."

The rugæ may have a mechanical function in the suckling age but are rudimentary in man probably because of the soft nature of his food (Keith).

The epithelium of the hard palate has a corneated layer and is indented by numerous connective tissue papillæ. In the new-born the lamina

TABLE 8.—CLASSIFICATION OF ORAL MUCOSA*

| Clinical Classification | Physiological Characteristics | Histologic Characteristics | | | Attachment | | Remarks | Clinical Application |
|---|---|---|---|---|---|---|---|---|
| | | Epithelium | Lamina Propria | Submucosa | Type | Underlying Structure | | |
| I. MASTICATORY MUCOSA A. Simple 1. Marginal gingivae 2. Attached gingivae | Immobile. | Hornified | Fused into single layer thick, dense, compact, non-elastic. | | Firm | Bone or tooth structure. | In edentulous jaw, the alveolar crest is covered by simple masticatory mucosa. | 1. Denture construction must take into consideration the different resiliency of cushioned and simple masticatory mucosa. Wounds in masticatory mucosa do not gape because of the lack of elastic tissue. Suturing difficult in masticatory mucosa because of firm attachment. Injections into masticatory area are difficult because of the firmness of the tissue. |
| B. Cushioned 1. Anterior zone of hard palate 2. Posterior zone of hard palate | Resistant to pressure and stress. | | Thick, dense, non-elastic | Bands of thick collagenous. Spaces filled with: 1. Fat cells. 2. Glands. | | Bone | The palatal raphe and mucosa of palatine torus belong to the simple masticatory mucosa. | |

( 246 )

| | Characteristics | Epithelium | Lamina propria | Submucosa | | Attachment | Clinical Considerations |
|---|---|---|---|---|---|---|---|
| II. Lining Mucosa<br>A. Firmly attached<br>1. Soft palate<br>2. Cheeks or lips<br>3. Inferior surface of tongue. | Mobile. Serve as lining. Quick change in surface area possible. | Non-hornified. | Thin, dense, elastic. | Fused to fascia.<br>1. and 2. Strands of dense connective tissue. Spaces filled with glands or fat.<br>3. Thin. | Firm | Muscle (cheek or soft palate). | II. Injections for anesthesia should be made in these areas. Preferred sites for surgical incisions if final sutures are contemplated.<br>Hemorrhages and inflammation spread easily and can assume great proportions without causing as much pain as in firmly fixed areas of the mucosa, as in the alveolar gingivæ. |
| B. Loosely attached<br>1. Vestibular mucosa<br>2. Alveolar mucosa (labial and mandibular lingual)<br>3. Sublingual mucosa. | Capable of great mobility and rapid absorption. | | Thin, dense, elastic. | Loose connective tissue. | Loose | Bone or muscle. | |
| III. Specialized Mucosa<br>Dorsum of tongue. | Mobile. Resistant to pressure and friction. | Partly hornified. Papillæ. | Dense, elastic. | Fused to fascia<br>Strands of dense connective tissue. | Firm | Muscle. | III. Degree of hornification varies with general body state. Coated—smooth.<br>III. Includes Anterior masticatory area (filiform, fungiform and vallate papillæ) Posterior lymphatic area (lingual lymph follicles). |

*Adapted from Orban and Sicher.

propria contains epithelial "rests" (Epstein pearls) similar to those found in the gingivæ. They were originally mistaken for glands but are epithelial strands which extend along the entire posterior section of the raphé.

These epithelial rests arise from epithelium which was included during the closure of the palate. After birth, the epithelial strands atrophy and become resorbed, and in the course of the third year disappear entirely.

Lund differentiates four regions in the hard palate: fibrous marginal zone, fibrous median zone, fat tissue zone, and glandular zone (Fig. 183).

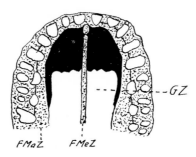

Fig. 183.—Schematic representation of the four zones in the hard palate. Black area, fat tissue zone; *GZ*, glandular zone; *FMaZ*, fibrous marginal zone; *FMeZ*, fibrous median zone. (After Lund.)

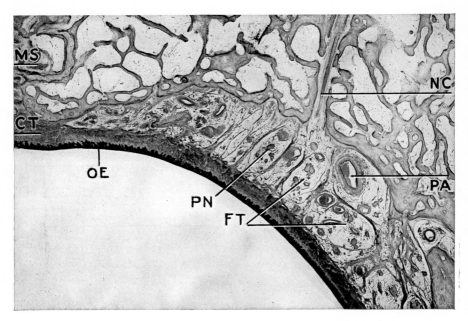

Fig. 184.—Area between maxillary ridge and maxillar suture. *PA*, palatine artery; *PN*, palatine nerves; *FT*, fat tissue; *CT*, fibrous connective tissue overlying the maxillary suture; *MS*, maxillary suture; *NC*, nutritional canal in the bone; *OE*, oral epithelium. (Pendleton, Jour. Am. Dent. Assn.)

The fibrous zones are the simple firmly attached masticatory mucosa described in the chapter on the gingiva. The fat zone is cushioned and firmly attached masticatory mucosa. In the submucosa the heavy collagenous strands connecting the lamina propria to the periosteum surround small lobules of fatty tissue. This cushioned area functions in distributing local pressures over a wider area in the same way as the skin over the palms and soles. In the posterior cushioned zone of the hard palate the submucous fat tissue is replaced by the purely mucous palatine glands (Figs. 184 and 185).

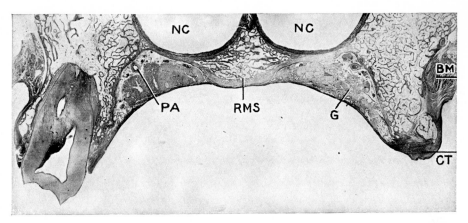

Fig. 185.—Frontal section through an upper jaw in the third molar region. The upper left third molar is intact; the right side of the maxilla is edentulous. *NC*, nasal cavity, *BM*, buccinator muscle; *CT*, fibrous connective tissue; *G*, mucous glands of palate; *RMS*, bony ridge of maxillary suture; *PA*, palatine artery. (Pendleton, Jour. Am. Dent. Assn.)

## THE SOFT PALATE

The soft palate consists of the palatine aponeurosis and the levator palati muscle and is covered by mucous membrane. The oral surface consists of stratified squamous epithelium which is indented by high connective tissue papillæ. These papillæ end in slightly club-shaped thickenings which, when studied in oblique sections, suggest the presence of taste-buds. Von Ebner and Schaffer question their presence. The lamina propria is relatively thin and contains scattered lymphoid cells. Elastic fibers running chiefly in a sagittal direction form a layer which marks the boundary between the mucous membrane proper and the submucosa and is called the *supraglandular layer*. The submucosa of the oral surface is continuous with the perimysium and is characterized by coarse connective tissue bundles, a rich supply of adipose tissue, and strong bundles of elastic fibers which run from the mucous membrane deep into the muscle bundles. The submucosa also contains a large glandular layer which is 3 to 4 mm. thick and becomes smaller toward the uvula. The glands are purely mucous and form a continuation of similar glands of the hard palate. Their twisted ducts point toward the uvula, penetrate the elastic layer where they are surrounded by a well developed elastic net, and open between the papillæ. They are lined by one or two layers of columnar cells which are filled with mucus.

The nasal surface consists of typical "respiratory" mucous membrane. Goblet cells are scattered among the pseudo-stratified columnar ciliated epithelium. There is a well developed basement membrane below which lies a lymphoid layer. The mixed glands which are characteristic of the respiratory tract are found in the mucous membrane. The lamina propria is separated from the muscles by a dense layer of long elastic fibers, the *infraglandular layer*.

The dorsal surface of the uvula presents a transitional zone which is covered with stratified squamous epithelium but contains the mixed glands characteristic of the nasal mucous membrane. Only irregularly arranged elastic tissue is found at the tip of the uvula. The latter has a very rich blood and lymph supply. This helps to explain the edema of the uvula, which often has a rapid onset (Schaffer).

## THE MAXILLARY SINUS

The mucous membrane of the maxillary sinus resembles that of the nasal fossa, but is thinner and more delicate. It is covered with a layer of pseudo-stratified epithelium which is invaded by lymphoid cells and contains scattered goblet cells. The cilia beat toward the ostium. A delicate basement membrane is sometimes present. The tunica propria consists of loose collagenous bundles and very few elastic fibers. It is moderately vascular and contains serous and mucous glands which are few in number but increase near the opening into the nasal fossa. The tunica propria blends with the periosteum without the intervention of a submucosa.

In those cases where the roots of the upper bicuspids or molars come into close proximity with the floor of the sinus, infection of the teeth may spread to the maxillary sinus.

## THE LIPS AND CHEEKS

The lip fold consists of a base or middle layer of muscle which is covered externally with the cutaneous portion and internally with the mucomembranous portion. The change from the skin to the mucous side is marked by a transitional portion which is called the vermilion zone. The middle layer is made up of voluntary striated muscle (chiefly the muscularis orbicularis oris) which is interwoven with single bundles of connective tissue. It is nearer to the mucomembranous than to the skin part.

*The cutaneous portion* is covered with a uniformly thick low stratified squamous epithelium which has a very thin corneated layer. The connective tissue papillæ, which are flat and far apart, are penetrated by elastic fibers. The lamina propria also contains hair follicles. The submucosa is less compact and contains sebaceous and sweat glands, and thin strips of muscle.

The *transitional* portion presents an epithelium which lacks any keratinization. The connective tissue papillæ are more frequent, extend deeper into the epithelium, and toward the mucous part become so high (especially in children) that they penetrate four-fifths of the epidermis. They possess a rich supply of large blood-vessels. The above histological structures, together with the rich subcutaneous blood supply cause the red color of this portion of the lip. Free sebaceous glands, smaller than those found in the cutaneous portion, are frequently found near the angles of the mouth. Bolk explains their presence on a phylogenetic basis, because the lips and cheeks were originally formed by an invagination of the external hair-covered integument.

The *mucomembranous* portion of the lip functions as a lining of the oral cavity, and is firmly attached to the muscle fascia. The epithelium is noncornified (Fig. 181). The connective tissue papillæ are irregular. The lamina propria has only a few elastic fibers and contains the typical labial glands which are of the mixed type with pure mucous, pure serous, and mixed acini. They are more numerous in the lower lip. Sometimes they produce flat, uneven projections in the mucous membrane which, according to v. Lenhossék, may aid the self-cleaning of the teeth. The deeper layers contain adipose tissue and may be regarded as belonging to the submucosa. In the region of the frenulum labii superioris and inferioris the epithelium is thinner and the papillæ are smaller and less frequent. The lamina propria is not prominent and contains relatively many blood-vessels and many fine irregularly coursing elastic fibers.

The submucosa is thin and elastic and affords a firm connection of the mucosa to the fascia of the underlying muscle. The glands lie between the bundles of connective tissue fibers. This arrangement allows for free mobility of the lips and cheeks in chewing but the firm attachment prevents the mucosa from falling into folds and being caught between the teeth.

The lining of the cheeks is continuous with and identical to that of the lip.

## ALVEOLAR MUCOSA, VESTIBULAR MUCOSA AND FLOOR OF THE MOUTH

Since stratified squamous epithelium is flexible but not elastic, the areas of mucosa connecting the firmly attached lining and masticatory zones are loosely attached to allow movement between the latter. These areas, the labial and lower lingual alveolar mucosa, the vestibular fold, and the floor of the oral cavity proper are normally out of direct range of masticatory forces. The epithelium is thin and non-cornified and the interdentations of the epithelium with the connective tissue are few and shallow. The submucosal connections to the underlying bone or muscle are of the loose areolar connective tissue type.

## THE TONGUE

The tongue is composed of a mass of voluntary muscle fibers arranged in complicated interlacing bundles, covered by the mucous membrane. The mucous membrane of the dorsal surface has been classified as specialized mucosa. It differs in function from other areas in that it is the mobile counterpart of the hard palate against which it presses during chewing and swallowing. The most striking characteristics of the mucous membrane of the tongue (Fig. 186) are: (1) The thinness of the submucosa, which holds it closely to the mass of muscle and allows very little movement of it;

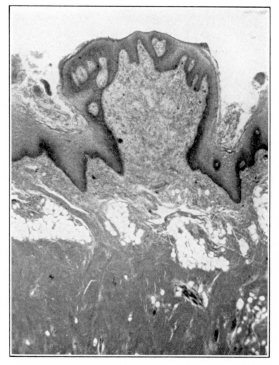

Fig. 186.—Fungiform papilla of the human tongue. 41 ×.

(2) the submucosa in the dorsal surface contains no glands, though there are among the muscle fibers glands whose ducts pass through the submucosa; (3) the presence of the projecting papillæ upon its dorsal surface (Fig. 186). The tongue is imperfectly divided vertically on the median plane by a band of connective tissue forming the median raphé or septum, which causes the depression at the central line of the dorsal surface.

**The Muscles.**—The muscles of the tongue include two groups—the extrinsic and the intrinsic. The extrinsic muscles comprise the genioglossus, the hyoglossus, and the styloglossus. All these muscles are paired and extend from either the skull or the hyoid bone into the tongue. The intrinsic muscles comprise fibers of different course, the lingualis. A transverse section through the body of the tongue in the central portion shows a complicated network of muscle fibers running in three directions—longitudinally, transversely, and vertically. The longitudinal fibers are arranged around the outer portion, forming a cortical layer about 5 mm. thick. These constitute the chief bulk of the lingualis, and are supplemented by fibers from the styloglossus. The vertical fibers are mostly deeply placed in the central portion on either side of the raphé. They are derived chiefly

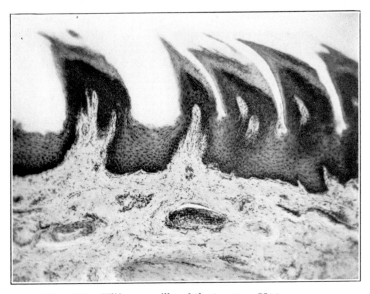

Fig. 187.—Filiform papillæ of the tongue. 80×.

from the genioglossus and radiate toward the dorsal surface. The transverse fibers are entirely from the lingualis except for a few from the palatoglossus. They arise from the septum and interlace with the longitudinal and vertical fibers. They break up into strands running between the longitudinal fibers of the cortical portion, and spread out to a submucous insertion.

The complicated movements of the tongue are accomplished by the contractions of these sets of muscles. When the longitudinal fibers are relaxed and the transverse fibers contracted the tongue is rolled and extended. When the transverse fibers are relaxed and the vertical fibers contracted the tongue is flattened.

**The Papillæ.**—The roughness of the dorsal surface of the tongue is caused by projections of the cornified epithelium and its tunica propria (the papillæ of the tongue). These projections are not to be confused with the connective tissue papillæ in the tunica propria of the mucous membrane. They are of three kinds—the *filiform* and *fungiform* papillæ, which are found over the entire dorsal surface, and the *circumvallate* papillæ, which are limited in number and confined to the posterior portion. The filiform are much the more numerous, especially near the tip of the tongue. They are from 0.5 to 2.5 mm. in height and often end in brush-like strands of epithelial cells.

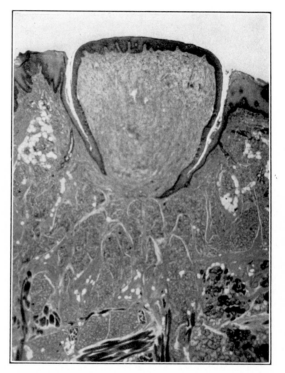

Fig. 188.—Circumvallate papilla of the human tongue.  27 ×.

The fungiform papillæ, because of the thinness of their epithelium, form the red points on the surface of the tongue, especially near the edges. They are low and rounded in form, from 0.5 to 1.5 mm. in height, and are named from their mushroom-like appearance. Fig. 186, a section from the human tongue, shows the form of these papillæ. The circumvallate papillæ usually number nine or ten, and are arranged in a V-shaped line near the base of the tongue, with the apex extending backward. They are from 2 to 3.5 mm. in height and from 2 to 3.5 mm. in width. They are surrounded by a deep trough, so that the upper surfaces of the papillæ are not much higher than the general level of the membrane. The ducts of the small serous glands of von Ebner open into the trough. Their secretion rinses the depression and eliminates particles of food.

**The Taste-buds.**—These are found chiefly on the sides of the circumvallate papillæ (Fig. 188), though they are occasionally found in the epithelium of the fungiform papillæ and the soft palate, and on the superior surface of the epiglottis. They are always entirely embedded in the epithelium and extend through its entire thickness. These structures are ovoid in form, with the rounded end toward the connective tissue and the pointed end at the surface, where a small opening, the taste-pore, communicates with the mouth cavity (Fig. 189). Most of the cells are elongated and spindle-shaped, and arranged like the layers of an onion. Four varieties may be recognized. The sustentacular cells form the outer layer and are in contact with the epithelial cells. They are elongated, with an oval nucleus near the center. The inner sustentacular cells are rod-shaped,

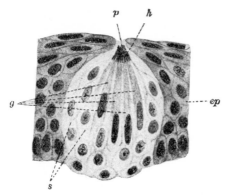

Fig. 189.—A section of a taste-bud: *p*, pore; *g*, gustatory cells; *ep*, epithelial cells; *s*, sustentacular cells; *h*, bristles of the gustatory cells. (Schaefer.)

more slender in form, and with a nucleus at the base. The neuro-epithelial cells are elongated spindle-shaped cells at the center of the taste-bud. The nucleus is at the base of the cell, and from the opposite end a stiff bristle-like process extends through the taste-pore.

The basal cells are irregular in form with large oval nuclei; they communicate with each other and the sustentacular cells by cytoplasmic bridges. They form the base of the taste-bud.

Beyond the lateral borders of the dorsum of the tongue the inferior surface is covered by a thin smooth lining mucous membrane which is firmly fixed to the underlying muscle. It blends at the floor of the mouth with the loosely fixed mucosa which is so thin that certain substances, as drugs, are absorbed readily through it to the blood stream.

## THE TONSILS

In the posterior part of the tongue and the wall of the pharynx is found adenoid tissue in the form of *solitary follicles* lying in the tunica propria and invading the epithelium. This adenoid tissue forms an organ which Waldeyer has called the lymphatic pharyngeal ring. This tissue is divided into three main masses—that lying in the base of the tongue forming the lingual tonsil, that associated with the palate and lying between the pillars of the fauces and forming the palatine tonsil, and that situated in the pharynx or pharyngeal tonsil.

**The Lingual Tonsils.**—These are situated in the base of the tongue between the circumvallate papillæ and the epiglottis. They are rounded masses of adenoid tissue composed of solitary follicles lying mostly in the tunica propria, and causing clearly visible projections of the surface. In the center of each mass is a deep depression forming a blind pouch, known as the crypt (Fig. 190). This crypt is lined with stratified squamous epi-

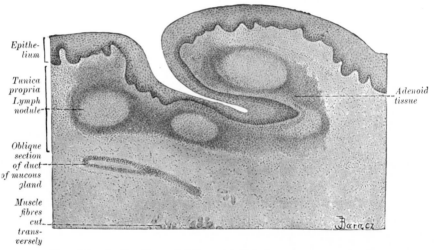

FIG. 190.—Section through a lingual follicle in man: *x*, crypt. (50 ×.)

thelium like that of the adjoining mucous membrane except that at various places the lymphocytes have pushed their way through the epithelial cells, and escape on the surface.

**The Palatine Tonsils.**—These lie at the base of the tongue between the the anterior and posterior pillars of the fauces. They are much larger than the lingual tonsils and are composed of from ten to twenty follicles and a number of crypts. The epithelium covering them is pierced in many places by encroachments of the adenoid tissue. The crypts always contain many lymphocytes (Plate XII). These are what are ordinarily called the tonsils, the inflammation of which is termed tonsillitis.

**The Pharyngeal Tonsil.**—It is located on the back wall of the pharynx above the level of the palate. Its structure is similar to that of the palatine tonsil. The crypts are five to six in number and are often clothed with ciliated epithelium. Into them open the ducts of mixed glands which form a distinct layer under the follicle. Here also is a migration of lymphocytes

# PLATE XII

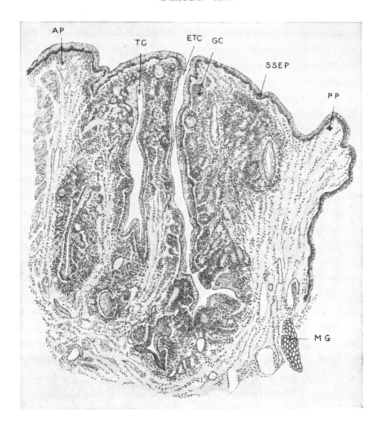

Human palatine tonsil.  (After Rauber-Kopsch.)

AP.    anterior pillar of the fauces
ETC.   entrance into tonsillar crypt
GC.    germinal center of lymph follicle
SSEP.  stratified squamous epithelium

MG.    mucous gland
PP.    posterior pillar of the fauces
TC.    tonsillar crypt

through the epithelium. It is the hypertrophy of these which forms the adenoids so often found in children.

## THE MAJOR SALIVARY GLANDS

On the assumption that the student has studied the salivary glands previously, a brief summary is presented for review purposes.

The smaller serous and mucous glands which provide the saliva for the oral cavity have been located in the areas in which they occur. These probably secrete constantly to maintain the moist environment of the mucous membrane. The bodies of the larger glands, the parotid, the submaxillary (submandibular) and the sublingual, lie outisde the mucosal wall and their secretions, important in digestion, are carried to the lumen of the oral cavity through their main ducts.

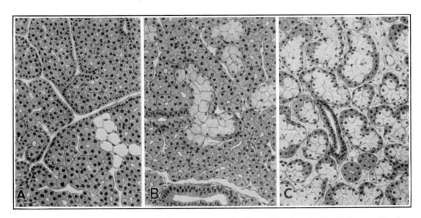

Fig. 191.—Semidiagrammatic drawings of *A.* Parolid gland; *B.* Submandibular gland; and *C.* Sublingual gland (Courtesy Ciba Pharmaceutical Products.)

The parotid is divided into lobes and lobules by the septa from its capsule. Through this connective stroma travel the blood and nerve supply and the duct system. The parenchyma is composed, in man, of serous alveoli with occasional fat cells present (Fig. 191) The main duct opens into the oral cavity opposite the upper second molar tooth.

The encapsulated submaxillary gland has a structural arrangement similar to the parotid. In man it is mainly serous but some mucous alveoli are present. The mucous alveoli are frequently capped by demilunes of serous cells (Fig. 191). The main duct (Wharton's) opens into the mouth beneath the tongue.

The sublingual gland appears, usually, as a collection of lobules without any distinct capsule. The parenchyma is of the mixed variety, as is the submaxillary, but in this case most of the alveoli are of the mucous type. Serous demilunes occur widely but few purely serous alveoli are found. The gland empties through a series of ducts (Fig. 191).

17

## BIBLIOGRAPHY.

KAISLERING, C.: Mundhöhle, in Henke, F., and Lubarsch, O.: Handb. d. spez. path. Anat. und Hist., Berlin, Julius Springer, 1928.

LUND, O.: Histologische Beiträge zur Anatomie des Munddachs and Paradentiums, Vrtljschr. f. Zahnheilk, *40*, 1, 1924.

MAXIMOW and BLOOM: A Textbook of Histology, Chapter XVI on Oral Cavity and Associated Structures, Philadelphia., W. B. Saunders Company, 1942.

ORBAN, B., and Sicher, H.: The Oral Mucosa, Parts I and II, J. Dent. Educ., 10, 94 (Dec.) 1945, *10*, 163, (Feb.) 1946.

OSTLUND, SITG G. SON: The Effect of Complete Dentures on the Gum Tissues, Acta Odontologica Scandinavica, *16*, 1958.

PENDLETON, E. C., and GLUPKER, H.: Research on the Reaction of Tissues Supporting Full Dentures, J. A. D. A., *22*, 76, 1935.

SCHAEFFER, J. P.: The Mucous Membrane of the Nasal Cavity and the Paranasal Sinuses, in Cowdry, E. V.: Special Cytology, New York, Paul B. Hoeber, Inc., vol. *1*, 1928.

# CHAPTER 17

# The Lymphatics of the Oral Region

## GENERAL CONCEPTION OF THE LYMPHATIC CIRCULATION

THE student generally finds difficulty in getting any clear idea of the lymphatic circulation. It seems best, therefore, to make a most simple and elementary statement of this most important circulatory system as a basis for a study of the lymphatic vessels. Life at present can be understood only in terms of a single cell. Every living cell must be bathed in fluid from which the cytoplasm receives the material for its constructive processes and to which it gives up its waste products or the results of catabolism. Just as the single-celled protozoan floating in a pond of water, so each cell of every tissue of the body can be considered as bathed in a fluid—*the lymph.* The epithelium of all external and internal surfaces makes a bounding layer which prevents the loss of the fluid. If a slight cut or abrasion is made on the skin, removing the outer layer of dried cells and not breaking the blood capillaries, there will appear the exudation of a drop of yellowish fluid on the surface. This fluid immediately coagulates and prevents further loss until the continuity of the surface is restored. In this simple way we may demonstrate the presence of the intercellular fluid or lymph.

For the health and nourishment of the cells this fluid must be in circulation or the cells would be poisoned by their own products of catabolism. In a very general way the blood circulatory system may be said to be the means of bringing oxygen to the tissues and the lymph circulatory system the means of supplying the material for metabolism.

The fluid of the blood passes through the cells of the capillary walls into the intercellular and tissue spaces, and in that sense may be considered the source of the lymph. The passage of the blood plasma through the capillary walls is not simply a matter of transfusion or osmosis, but is a vital function of the cells of the capillary walls. The intercellular lymph is not the same as the plasma of the blood in the bloodvessels, for from it the cytoplasm of the tissue cells have taken up material and to it they have given products of metabolism.

The fluid from the intercellular and tissue spaces is collected by a system of vessels, *the lymphatic vessels,* and returned to the blood circulation through the thoracic duct emptying into the left subclavian vein. On the right a very short, lymphatic duct, not more than 10 to 12 mm. in length, empties into the right subclavian vein. Very frequently no right lymphatic duct

( 259 )

exists, the jugular and subclavian trunks opening independently into the right subclavian vein.

Formerly it was supposed that the smallest of the lymph vessels or lymph capillaries opened directly into the intercellular and tissue spaces, but it has become more and more evident that this is not correct but that the lymphatic vessels form a closed system opening only into the subclavian veins. The intercellular fluid passes into the lymph capillaries through their wall by a vital process. A diagram of the lymphatic vessels and their relation to the blood circulation is shown in Plate XIII.

It is undoubtedly true that the blood capillaries also may take up fluid from the tissue as well as give up fluid to it and it is certain that they take up products of metabolism from the tissue cells. But as a beginning and elementary idea the statement may be made that the plasma of the blood passes out of the capillaries, bathes the cells, giving up material to them and receiving products from them, and is returned to the blood circulation through the lymphatic vessels.

In comparing the two systems in Plate XIII several things can be noted: (1) The blood passes from the heart, through the arteries to the capillaries and back to the heart in the veins; and is a closed system all the way. The lymph is collected from the tissue spaces by the lymphatic capillaries, passes through collecting trunks to the glands, where it passes through the capillaries again and on to the blood circulation through the subclavian vein. (2) The blood circulation is the oxygen carrier, the lymphatic circulation the food and waste carrier. (3) The blood circulation is rapid, the lymph circulation slow.

**Lymphatic Nodes or Glands.**—Along the course of the lymphatic vessels are placed structures, lymphatic nodes or glands in which the fluid must come in contact with masses of active cells for the purpose of preventing infection carried in the current from reaching the blood circulation and so the entire body. For the structure of the lymph nodes and their relation to the lymphatic vessels the student is referred to text-books of histology and anatomy.

## PARTS OF THE LYMPHATIC SYSTEM

To have a conception of this system, the fluid that circulates, the cells it carries, the vessels through which it goes, and the tissue or special structures through which it passes in its course, they must be studied in their relation to each other.

1. Lymph.
2. Leukocytes (cells found in the lymph).
3. Lymph vessels.
4. Lymphatic glands (lymph nodes).

**Lymph.**—The lymph is a slightly viscous liquid, sometimes with slightly yellowish color, no or very slight odor, slightly alkaline reaction, and specific

# PLATE XIII

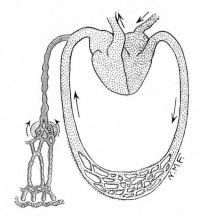

General scheme of the lymphatic system

gravity of 1.012 to 1.022. Krause states that the entire quantity of lymph is equal to one-third of the body weight. Five and one-half liters have been collected from the thoracic duct from man in twenty-four hours. The quantity is dependent upon tissue activity.

From the most fundamental conception of it the lymph must be slightly different from the plasma of the blood, and its chemical composition must be variable. It is slightly less alkaline and contains less fibrin than the blood plasma.

**Leukocytes.**—The term leukocytes includes cells that are found in the blood, lymph, and connective tissues, and is synonymous with white blood corpuscles.

The leukocytes are soft cytoplasmic masses with no cell wall, nearly colorless, extensible, and of varying refraction. They are heavier than lymph or plasma and lighter than red corpuscles. They are viscous, adhering to a glass slide and sticking to the walls of vessels, resisting the current which carries them along, so that they accumulate when the current slackens.

They possess all the biological properties of primitive cells, mobility, sensibility, absorption, secretion and reproduction. Such important functions as the absorption of foreign matter and bacteria are dependent upon these primitive functions.

Leukocytes have been classified by their form, size, the character of the nucleus and the granules found in the cytoplasm.

**Lymphatic Vessels.**—Lymphatic vessels were discovered by the ancient Greeks and were known by Aristotle (384–322 B.C.), but the knowledge was lost and they were rediscovered by Nicholas Massa in 1532 A.D. In 1563 Eustachius discovered the thoracic duct.

It was formerly believed that the lymph in the intercellular spaces drained into the interfibrous spaces in the connective tissues, that these became lined with endothelial cells and that the lymph capillaries opened into them. It has been more and more apparent that the lymphatic vessels present a system closed at the periphery, and opening into the subclavian vein at the opposite extremity. This does not in any way change the action of the system. The taking up of the lymph from the tissue spaces cannot be thought of as a simple process of filtration but as a vital function of the cells forming the closed ends of this terminal or collecting plexus of the lymphatic capillaries. The entire system of the lymph vessels may be more clearly understood if it is thought of as made up of the following parts (1) The network of origin or terminal plexus of the lymphatic capillaries which take up the lymph from the tissues and organs. (2) A few vessels *collecting trunks* drain a comparatively large area of the collecting capillary network and carry the lymph from the network to the first lymphatic gland. (3) In the gland or node it again breaks up into capillaries, but leaves the gland through one vessel, the efferent vessel. (4) Larger and less numerous efferent ducts which carry the lymph from one node to another or from the last node to the venous system.

The structure of the vessels is different in the different parts but may be described in general by saying that the capillaries and small collecting vessels are lined by a single layer of exceedingly delicate endothelial cells and the larger trunks show three layers similar to the walls of the veins but more delicate in structure (Figs. 192 and 193).

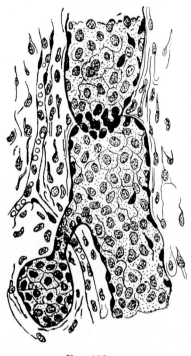

As a general statement the network of origin is in the subepithelial connective tissue. The collecting and transporting trunks are found in the connective tissue and are either superficial or deep, as they are above or below the fascia. The superficial vessels are usually more highly developed.

The total capacity of the network of origin is very great, being equal to

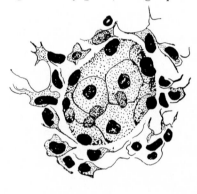

FIG. 192                          FIG. 193

FIGS. 192 and 193.—Lymphatics in involution. Fig. 192, lymphatic vesicle continuity with neighboring trunk; Fig. 193, isolated vesicle. (After Ranvier.)

or greater than that of the veins, but the capacity is greatly reduced in the collecting and efferent ducts, so that the entire system is representative of a cone, with the base in the network of origin and the apex in the opening into the subclavian veins.

There are two entirely independent systems of the lymphatic vessels, one emptying into the right subclavian vein through the right lymphatic duct, draining the right side only as far as the level of the diaphragm, and the other into the left subclavian vein through the thoracic duct, draining all of the rest of the body. The area of the body drained by each system is represented in the diagram in Fig. 194.

**The Network of Origin.**—The delicate vessels which form the network of origin are often called the lymphatic capillaries. They resemble the blood capillaries only in that their walls are formed by a single layer of endothelial cells. They are of extremely variable form, depending upon the character of the tissue in which they are found. They form a very rich anastomosing network of very delicate vessels, some idea of the structure of which can be had from Fig 195. A few very delicate vessels collect the lymph from this network and carry it to the collecting trunks. The capillaries are without valves but the collecting vessels are abundantly supplied with them (Fig. 193), which causes their characteristic beaded appearance. Stained with silver nitrate the cells are more easily outlined than those of the blood capillaries, showing cells 30 to 40 microns long. Their edges are wavy forming lines like the sutures of the skull. Their nuclei are oval and project into the cavity of the vessel, especially when they are not distended. The diameter of these vessels may be from 30 to 60 microns, which is much greater than that of the blood capillaries.

**The Collecting Trunks.**—The walls of the collecting vessels are made up of three layers: (1) The endothelium. (2) A layer of involuntary muscle. (3) An adventitious layer of white elastic connective tissue. They are like the walls of the veins, but more delicate, less destructible and more resilient to pressure.

**Lymphatic Glands or Lymph Nodes.**—For the structure of the lymph nodes the student is referred to text-books of histology. They are by no means constant either in number, size or position.

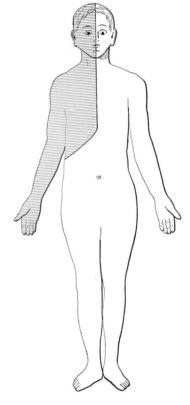

FIG. 194

In order to understand the lymphatics of the dental region it is necessary to make a brief statement of the principal groups of the head and neck and the regions which they drain.

**The Lymphatics of the Head and Neck.**—The lymphatic glands of the head and neck may be described as arranged in six groups, forming a glandular collar or circle at the junction of the head and neck from which two vertical chains extend under the sternomastoid muscle and along the large blood-vessels and nerves extending to where the neck joins the thorax. These main vertical chains are flanked by lesser auxiliary chains (Fig. 196).

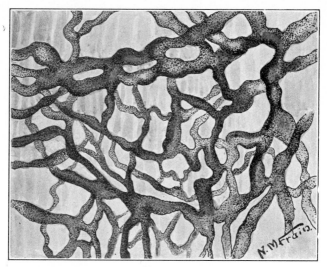

Fig. 195

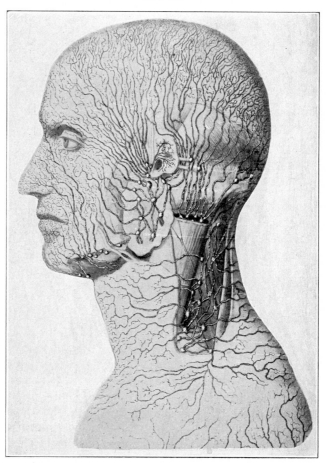

Fig. 196.—Lymphatics of the head and neck.

The glandular collar is composed of (1) the *suboccipital group;* (2) the *mastoid group;* (3) the *parotid* and *subparotid group;* (4) the *submaxillary group;* (5) the *submental group;* (6) the *retropharyngeal group.*

1. The *suboccipital group* usually contains two glands. They receive afferents from the occipital portion of the scalp. Their efferents terminate in the highest glands of the substernomastoid group of the vertical chain.

2. *The Mastoid Group.*—There are usually two, one behind the other, and are united by two or three trunks. They lie on the mastoid insertion of the mastoid muscle. They receive afferents from the temporal portion of the scalp, from the external surface of the auricle, except the lobule, and the posterior surface of the external auditory meatus. Their efferents empty into the superior glands of the submastoid group after traversing the superior insertion of that muscle.

3. *The Parotid Group.*—This group is made up of (1) the subcutaneous glands, which are often absent; (2) the glands contained in the parotid space; (3) the subparotid glands.

The glands of the parotid space are situated on the external surface of the gland or in its external substance. The superficial ones are usually two or three in number. The deep ones are scattered through the entire substance of the gland and are usually grouped along the external jugular vein and the external carotid artery. One constantly occupies the lower part of the space and is attached close to the angle of the jaw in contact with the cervical fascia. They receive afferents from the external surface of the auricle and external auditory meatus, from the tympanum, from the skin of the temporal and frontal region, the eyelid and root of the nose. They perhaps also receive vessels from the nasal fossa and the posterior part of the alveolar border of the superior maxilla. Their efferents empty into the substernomastoid group.

The subparotid glands are placed between the parotid and the pharynx in the lateropharyngeal and poster or subglandular space. They are in contact with the internal carotid and the internal jugular. They are the starting-point of the lateropharyngeal abscess (Quaine). They receive afferents from the nasal fossa, nasal pharynx and Eustachian tube. Their efferents pass to the glands of the deep cervical chain.

4. *Submaxillary Glands.*—These glands, three to six in number, are the most important from the dental standpoint. They form a chain stretching along the inferior border of the mandible from the insertion of the anterior belly of the digastric to the angle of the jaw. They are found in the junction of the cutaneous and bony surface of the submaxillary gland on which they rest. The largest and most constant of the chain is found at the point where the facial artery crosses the border of the mandible. They receive afferents from the nose, the cheek, the upper lip and external part of the lower lip, the anterior third of the lateral border of the tongue and almost the whole of the gums, alveolar process and teeth of both upper and lower arch. Their efferents descend on the cutaneous surface of the submaxillary

gland, across the hyoid bone and terminate in the glands of the deep cervical chain, over the bifurcation of the carotid artery or much deeper, where the omohyoid crosses the internal jugular vein.

5. *The Submental Glands.*—These glands are extremely variable in number and position. Usually one to four in number they are found in the triangle between the anterior bellies of the digastric muscle and the hyoid bone. They receive afferents from the chin, the central portion of the lower lip, the tip of the tongue and the anterior portion of the alveolar process and the lower incisor teeth. The latter is probably not constant.

6. *The Retropharyngeal Group.*—These glands are placed behind the pharynx at the junction of the posterior and lateral surfaces, at the apex of the lateral masses of the atlas. Usually two in number they are in relation with the posterior wall of the pharynx and the anterior surface of the rectus capitis anticus major and externally with the constrictors of the pharynx. They are about two centimeters from the median line. They receive afferent vessels from the mucous membrane of the nasal fossæ and the cavities connected with it, the nasal pharynx, Eustachian tube and perhaps the tympanum. Their efferent vessels empty into the superior glands of the internal jugular chain.

*Descending Cervical Chains.*—These extend from the glandular collar through the neck to the thorax. The most important chain is the deep cervical chain, one on each side, under the sternomastoid muscle and in the subclavian triangle. The smaller are the external jugular chain, the two anterior cervical chains superficial and deep, and the recurrent chain.

The deep cervical chain (Fig. 196) is one of the largest and most important relays in the body. It contains fifteen to thirty glands. It is made up of two groups: (1) the upper or substernomastoid group, and (2) the lower or subclavian triangular group. Only the first group will be considered.

*Substernomastoid Glands.*—1. External Glands: Behind and external to the internal jugular vein. Afferent vessels are received from the occipital and mastoid glands and from cutaneous lymphatics from the posterior part of the head and neck.

2. Internal Glands: Rest on the internal jugular or along its external border. At different points in the chain, glands of special importance are found; for instance: (*a*) Beneath the posterior belly of the digastric, the principal terminus for lymphatics from the tongue and gum about the lower teeth on the lingual. (*b*) Where the omohyoid crosses the internal jugular. Afferent vessels: These glands form the second relay for lymphs from the (*a*) retropharyngeal and (*b*) parotid and subparotid.

3. Submaxillary.

4. Submental glands.

5. The superficial and deep anterior cervical chain and the recurrent chain. They receive direct afferents from: (*a*) the majority of the vessels from the tongue; (*b*) part of the nasal pharynx and larynx; (*c*) the vault of the palate and soft palate; (*d*) the cervical portion of the esophagus; (*e*) the nasal fossæ; (*f*) the larynx and trachea; (*g*) the thyroid body.

*The Network of Origin in the Dental Region.*—The lymphatic network of origin is absolutely continuous over the whole of the face, eyelids, conjunctivæ, lips and the mucous membrane of the lips, cheeks, gums and gingiva. Every papilla of the connective tissue under the epithelium contains such networks of vessels. It is difficult for the elementary student to get any conception of the fineness, delicacy and intercommunicating anastomosis of this network. From this network a few collecting vessels lead to the afferent trunks going to the first glands. There is therefore a more or less definite drainage for a given area, though the network of origin is continuous.

**Lymphatics of the Lips.**—In the lips there are two networks: one in the subcutaneous layer of the outer surface and one in the sub-mucous layer of the internal surface. These communicate freely at the border of the lips.

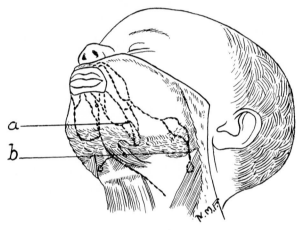

FIG. 197

Each network is drained by a few collecting trunks, which receive lymphatic vessels from the muscular layers that are less developed. The subcutaneous collecting vessels of the lower lip, two to four in number on each side, frequently cross and anastomose at the median line. Those from the middle portion pass to the submental glands. Those from the region of the oral commissure reach the most anterior of the submaxillary glands (Fig. 197). The submucous collecting vessels, two or three on each side, pass obliquely downward and outward to the region of the facial artery and end in the submaxillary glands. They do not cross or anastomose at the median line. There are two submucous and two or three subcutaneous collecting vessels in the upper lip. They all pass obliquely downward and outward, usually to the middle gland of the submaxillary chain. One of these may enter the most external of the collecting trunk from the lower lip.

**Lymphatics of the Mucous Membrane of the Mouth and Gingiva.**—In the mucous membrane of the mouth and gingiva the network of origin forms an exceedingly close network.

*From the outer surface of the mandible* the collecting vessels form a wreath of interlacing vessels at the reflection of the mucous membrane from the bone to the cheek. The vessels increase in size as they pass distally and finally penetrate the cheek and end in the submaxillary glands, especially the last one.

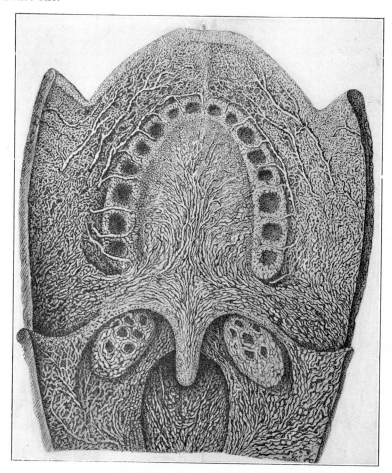

Fig. 198.—Lymphatic vessels of the palate. (After Sappey.)

*From the inner surface of the mandible* a similar wreath of collecting vessels is formed at the reflection of the tissue from the bone to the floor of the mouth and tongue. From the anterior part, lingual to the incisors, the vessels pass, with those from the tip of the tongue to the submental glands. From the lateral portion they unite with lymphatics from the anterior part of the lateral surface of the tongue and pass to the glands of the submaxillary chain. From the region of the second and third molars they probably join the lymphatics from lateral portions of the base of the tongue in the region of the tonsil and pass to the large gland of the deep cervical chain, placed under the posterior belly of the digastric.

*Outer Surface of the Maxilla.*—From the outer surface of the upper arch the collecting vessels pass to a wreath of large vessels at the reflection from the bone to the cheek. These increase in size as they extend distally. At the level of the molars they pierce the cheek, join the facial artery and terminate in the posterior glands of the submaxillary chain (Fig. 198). On the lingual the collecting vessels first pass obliquely backward and toward the median line of the palate, then backward and upward at the junction of the hard and soft palates. They pass in front of the anterior pillar of the fauces, pierce the superior constrictor of the pharynx and end in the large gland of the deep cervical chain under the posterior belly of the digastric.

**Lymphatics of the Periodontal Ligament.**—The lymphatic capillaries in the papillæ under the epithelium on the labial or buccal and lingual surfaces of the gingivæ pass to the collecting network in the submucous connective tissue outside the periosteum on the surface of the alveolar process (Fig. 198). The lymphatic capillaries from the papillæ under the epithelium lining the gingival space are collected in very fine vessels which pierce the ligamentum circularæ very close to the surface of the cementum and extend in the interfibrous tissue of the periodontal membrane accompanying the bloodvessels. At the level of the apex of the root they receive lymphatics coming from the dental pulp and pass through the cancellous spaces of the bone to the inferior dental canal in the lower and the infraorbital canal in the upper. They emerge on the surface of the bone at the mental foramen, or the infraorbital foramen and end in the posterior or middle glands of the submaxillary chain, following the course of the facial artery (Fig. 196). A great amount of work remains to be done on the drainage of the teeth in different regions. Little or nothing is known of the course of the vessels from the upper incisors, lower incisors and second and third molars. Lymphatics from the lower incisors may pass to the submental glands. Those from the upper incisors probably reach the surface of the bone below the level of the floor of the nose and join the vessel coming from the infraorbital canal, though it is possible that some of them join vessels in the floor of the nose. It is quite probable that lymphatics from the second and third molars pass to the glands of the parotid group.

**Lymphatics of the Dental Pulp.**—For many years the dental pulp was said to be devoid of lymphatics and all attempts to inject vessels in the dental pulp failed. In 1909 Schweitzer reported successful injections of the dental pulp, and in 1914 Dr. Kaethe Dewey and the author repeated Schweitzer's results and succeeded in injecting lymph capillaries of the submaxillary lymph glands in the dog by injections into the dental pulp and followed the course of the vessels continuously from the pulp to the glands (Fig. 113). There is much work to be done in this field before our knowledge will be at all complete regarding both the perivascular lymph sheath and the independent lymph vessels. The vessels begin at the surface of the pulp and follow the course of the bloodvessels to the apical foramina, where they join the lymphatics of the periodontal membrane. Their course from this point has already been followed.

**Lymphatics of the Tongue.**[1]—The lymphatics of the tongue are very highly developed and have been thoroughly studied. There are two networks of origin: one superficial in the mucous membrane and one deep in the muscular body of the tongue. Their efferent vessels unite in the submucosa.

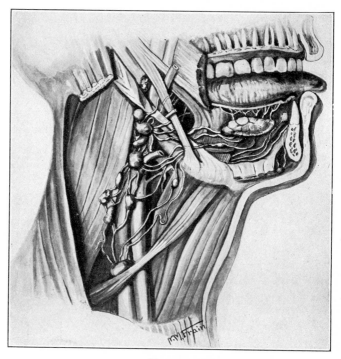

Fig. 199

The collecting trunks are divided into four groups: (1) Anterior apical. (2) Lateral marginal. (3) Posterior or basal. (4) Median or central.

1. *Anterior Apical Trunks.*—These vessels, two on each side, run along the frenum to the posterior surface of the mandible. Here they separate (Fig 199): (1) One runs downward and backward between the geniohyoglossus and the mylohyoid crosses the great cornu of the hyoid bone behind the anterior belly of the digastric and along the external border of the omohyoid to the gland of the deep cervical chain where this muscle crosses the internal jugular vein. (The general statement is that the more anterior the

---

[1] See page 270, The Lymphatics, by G. Delamere, P. Poirer and B. Cuneo. Edited by Cecil H. Leaf.

origin in the tongue the lower the gland in the deep cervical chain to which it goes.) (2) The second trunk passes to the submental gland.

2. *The Marginal Trunks.*—These vessels collect from all the mucous membrane from the tip of the tongue to the V-shaped groove on the dorsal surface. They are eight to twelve in number: (1) One group, the external (three or four), pierce the mylohyoid and pass around the inferior border of the mandible to the glands of the submaxillary chain. (2) The internal (five or six). These vessels run downward and backward on the muscles of the tongue and all end in glands of the deep cervical chain.

3. *Basal Trunks.*—These vessels (seven or eight) arise from the region of the circumvallate papillæ and are the largest and most important vessels of the tongue. They form a medial and lateral group and all terminate in the large gland of the deep cervical under the posterior belly of the digastric.

4. *The Central Trunks.*—These vessels arise from the middle part of the dorsal network of the body of the tongue. Instead of running outward they descend in the middle line between the two geniohyoglossi and end in the glands of the deep cervical chain.

## BIBLIOGRAPHY.

Fish, E. W.: Circulation of Lymph in Dentin, Proc. Roy. Soc. Med. London, 1924–1925, *18* (Odont. Sect.), 35, 1925–1926, *19* (Odont. Sect.) 59.

Magnus, G.: Ueber der Nachweis der Lymphgefässe in der Zahnpulpa, Deutsch. Monatschr. f. Zahnheilk., 1922, *40*, 661.

Noyes, F. B., and Dewey, K.: The Lymphatics of the Dental Region, Jour. Am. Med. Assn., *71*, 1179, 1918.

Noyes, F. B.: Lymphatics of Dental Region, Jour. Am. Dent. Assn., *15*, 1911, 1928.

Sappey: Anatomie, physiologie et pathologie des vaisseaux lymphatigques consideres chez l'homme et les vertebres, Paris, 1874.

Schweitzer: Ueber die Lymphgefässe des Zahnfleisches under der Zähne bei Menschen und Säugetieren, Arch. f. mikr. Anat., *69*, 807, 1907; *74*, 927, 1909.

Solower, E. A.: Zur Frage über das Vorhandensein von Lymphgefässen in der Zahnpulpa, Anat. Anz., *64*, 73, 1927.

# CHAPTER 18

# The Eruption of Teeth

**Introduction.**—A tooth may have successfully passed through the various stages of formation and calcification and yet be unable to perform its normal function if its eruptive processes have been disturbed. Eruption is therefore a very essential phase in the sum total of tooth development.

Very little is known about eruption. This chapter is an attempt to consider some of the histological changes which may be recognized in various stages of the eruptive process. It is hoped that a histological analysis will contribute a little to the final understanding of the mechanism of eruption and the eventual prevention of malocclusion.

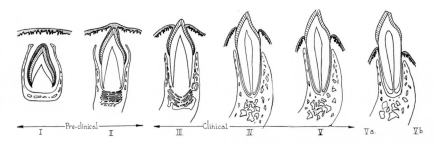

Fig. 200.—Diagrammatic representation of the stages in eruption.
(After Gottlieb and Orban.)

**Definition.**—Eruption is the process through which the forming tooth comes into its final occlusion. This process involves the migration of the crown of the tooth from its intraosseous location to reach and maintain its full clinical position within the oral cavity.

While the movement of the tooth in relation to the bone is termed active eruption, the exposure of the erupting crown and later of the root by recession of the gingiva has been called passive exposure. The latter involves also the peeling of the epithelial attachment from the enamel and in advanced stages the downgrowth of the epithelium along the cementum (Fig. 179).

The normal growth of the jaws is essential for the normal eruption of the teeth. As the mandible by its condylar growth moves away from the maxilla, space is obtained into which the alveolar processes of both jaws grow and into which upper and lower teeth erupt.

( 272 )

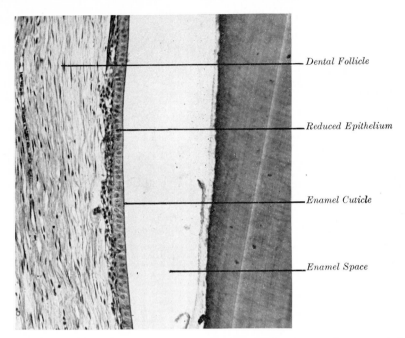

Dental Follicle

Reduced Epithelium

Enamel Cuticle

Enamel Space

FIG. 201.—Photomicrograph of dental follicle surrounding crown of unerupted deciduous canine. The loose connective tissue becomes more condensed next to the reduced enamel epithelium which covers the enamel. The arrangement of the fibers is longitudinal and parallel to the enamel surface.

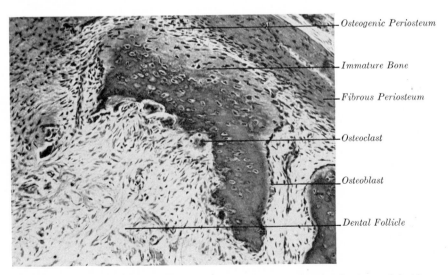

Osteogenic Periosteum

Immature Bone

Fibrous Periosteum

Osteoclast

Osteoblast

Dental Follicle

FIG. 202.—Higher magnification of section of crest of labial alveolar bone of deciduous canine shown in Figure 46. The tooth is moving upward in the crypt with resorption of bone by osteoclasts which developed from the dental follicle. On the outer surface the bone is of immature type and growing rapidly to maintain thickness. Note the fibrous protective layer and the osteogenic layer of periosteum. ($\times$ 200.)

18

The various stages in the growth of the jaws complicate the picture of active eruption. Some of the changes in the positions of the teeth were discussed in the chapter on "Postnatal Growth of the Jaws and Their Relation to the Teeth." The *active* changes in the position of the teeth will be described in terms of a constantly changing histological picture (Fig. 208). It must always be borne in mind, however, that other changes in position occur during the active eruption of the teeth.

## STAGES IN ERUPTION

For the purpose of simplification, active eruption may be divided into the following stages:

**Stage I—Preparatory Stage (Opening of the Crypt).**—Active eruption apparently begins at about the time of the completion of the crown, when the enamel and the corresponding dentin are formed. The tooth germ is at this time enclosed within a bony crypt, and the following histological events can be recognized (Fig. 203):

TABLE 9.—PHASES IN THE ERUPTION OF TEETH.

Preclinical (intra-osseous)   Active   Stages I and II of eruption.

Clinical (intra-oral)   { Active   Stages III, IV and V of eruption.

   Passive   Recessive of investing tissues.

(*a*) *The enamel epithelium secretes its final product*, the enamel cuticle, and becomes reduced to a stratified squamous epithelium. The reduced epithelium over the growth centers becomes thickened except at the cervical area where the ameloblasts retain their columnar form (Fig. 201).

(*b*) *Hertwig's Epithelial Sheath*, which arises from the union of the outer and inner odontogenic epithelium at the peripheral margins, begins its proliferative activity. Its presence stimulates and guides the formation of the dentin and possibly cementum of the root.

(*c*) *The Dental Sac* at this stage shows first an irregular circular arrangement of its fibers around the tooth germ, and later a stage of greater differentiation characterized by a coarse inner and outer layer of fibers.

(*d*) *The Bony Crypt* in which the tooth germ is embedded becomes resorbed at the roof, thus presenting a wide opening through which the crown of the tooth can pass. The permanent teeth are completely enclosed within a bony crypt, the gubernaculum at the occlusal aspect being the only communication with the outside (Figs. 206 and 223). Osteoclasts are found to be very active along the inner wall of the roof of the crypt (Fig. 202).

The bony crypts of the deciduous teeth never completely enclose the tooth germ and are always open at their occlusal aspects where only outer walls are found. The teeth of an infant can be easily felt within the jaw before they erupt.

(*e*) *The Path of Eruption* is toward the oral cavity, the deciduous teeth following a more vertical path than the permanent teeth. The long axes of the deciduous teeth come to lie in a more vertical position in the jaws. The permanent teeth, which erupt from a position lingual to the deciduous teeth, come to lie more obliquely.

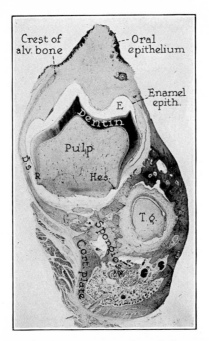

FIG. 203.—A bucco-lingual decalcified section through the mandible of a six-months-old child in the region of the lower first deciduous molar. Intra-osseous Stage II of preclinical eruption is just beginning. *E*, Enamel space; *Hes.*, Hertwig's epithelial sheath; *D.s.*, dental sac; *R*, beginning of root formation; *T.g.*, permanent tooth germ; *cort. plate*, cortical plate of mandible. (From Schour and Kronfeld.)

**Stage II—Migration of the Tooth Toward the Oral Epithelium.**—(*a*) The root forms under the guidance of Hertwig's epithelial sheath. The latter disintegrates as soon as the adjacent dentin has formed, but continues to grow at the free end and stimulates the formation of the deeper levels of the radicular dentin. According to Orban the end of Hertwig's epithelial sheath constitutes a relatively fixed point, the elongation of the root causing active migration of the crown occlusally.

(*b*) As the root becomes longer and the roof of the crypt resorbs further to allow for the exodus of the crown of the tooth, bone deposition occurs which closely embraces the formed portion of the root. The formation of the alveolar socket is subservient to the position of the tooth, the socket being constructed about the root of the tooth in whatever stage it may be. The alveolar crest during this time is thin and lies occlusally to the level of the cemento-enamel junction (Fig. 205).

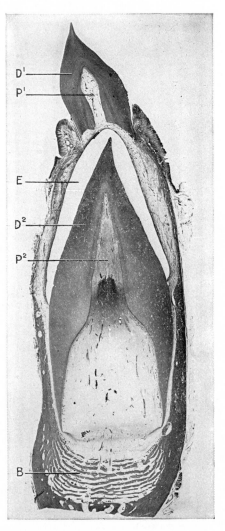

Fig. 204.—Labio-lingual section of a lower deciduous and permanent cuspid; aged eight years. The permanent tooth is in Stage II of eruption. Note the parallel arrangement of trabeculæ of spongiosa (*B*) at the apical base of the permanent tooth indicating active eruption. *P*¹, pulp of deciduous cuspid; *D*¹, dentin of deciduous cuspid; *E*, enamel space of permanent cuspid; *D*² dentin of permanent cuspid; *P*², pulp of permanent cuspid. (Kronfeld's Histopathology.)

(c) At the floor of the crypt horizontal bone trabeculæ are apposed and undergo active reconstruction in the direction of occlusion (Fig. 204). Histological examination of a single trabecula shows active resorption on the side away from and apposition on the side facing the tooth. This process continues through Stages III and IV and is indicative of a rapid rate of eruption. The fact that the rate of eruption is faster than the rate of root elongation calls for the filling in of the fundus with the horizontal trabecular of immature bone (Fig. 210).

(d) The dental sac shows a rearrangement of its circular fibers into the three distinct layers of the primitive periodontal membrane, the inner-cemental fibers, the outer alveolar fibers, and the plexus intermedius. The inner layer of the primitive periodontal membrane forms the early primary cementum and embeds the cemental fibers. The plexus intermedius is a complex of intermediate fibers arranged in such a manner as to allow for the active migration of the tooth, yet having the inner and outer fibers embedded within cementum and alveolar bone respectively. At this stage the tooth is very loosely held within its alveolus and is easily removed (Fig. 205).

(e) The permanent tooth germ develops in the same bony crypt with the deciduous tooth until it reaches the stage when its crown is almost complete. At this stage,

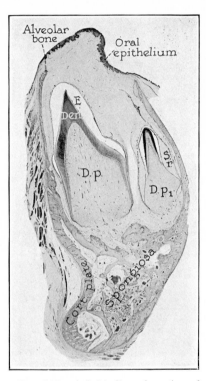

Fig. 205.—A labio-lingual section of the mandible of a six-months-old infant in the region of the lower lateral deciduous and permanent incisors. Preclinical eruption of the deciduous tooth has commenced (eruption Stage II). Enamel formation is completed and root formation has begun. Note that the permanent tooth germ still lies within the bony crypt of the deciduous tooth. *E*, enamel space; *Den.*, dentin; *D.p.*, dental papilla of deciduous tooth; *D.p.₁*, dental papilla, and *S.r.*, stellate reticulum of permanent tooth germ.

a complete separation occurs in the form of an intervening ledge of alveolar bone, and the permanent tooth germ comes to lie within its own crypt. This crypt does not share in the occlusal movement of the deciduous teeth at this time so that it eventually comes to lie lingually and apically to the tip of the root of its deciduous predecessor.

(*f*) The connective tissue lying in the path of the erupting tooth becomes more fibrous and compressed. It finally becomes anemic and disappears as the reduced enamel epithelium approaches the oral epithelium. The final phase of this stage can be observed macroscopically as a bulging and blanching of the overlying gum tissue.

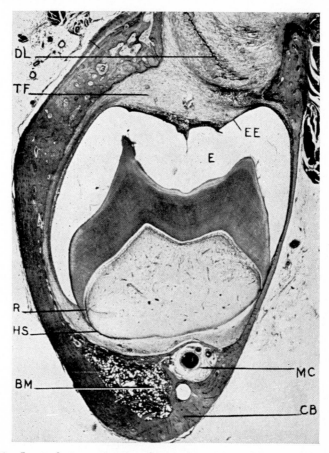

Fig. 206.—Lower first permanent molar at three years. The enamel formation is completed; the enamel was mature and was therefore dissolved by the acid except for some minute traces. The surface of the crown is covered by the united enamel epithelium. Root formation has just started. *E*, enamel; *EE*, enamel epithelium; *R*, beginning formation of the root; *HS*, Hertwig's sheath; *TF*, tooth follicle; *DL*, dental lamina; *MC*, mandibular canal containing nerve and artery; *BM*, bone marrow; *CB*, compact bone of mandible. Magnification × 8. (Kronfeld, Dental Histology.)

**Stage III—The Emergence of the Crown Tip (the Beginning of Clinical Eruption).**—(*a*) The thickened summit of enamel epithelium unites with the oral epithelium, the center atrophies, forming a tiny perforation, and the tip of the crown emerges through the opening into the oral cavity. The union of the oral and enamel epithelia around the tooth results in the first appearance of the gingival margin.

(*b*) The attachment apparatus, under the stimulus of oral pressures (tongue, suckling or mastication) becomes more firm and attaches the tooth more strongly. The periodontal fibers become more solidly fixed in the cementum and now begin to transmit the oral forces to the bony walls of the alveolus. There the periodontal fibers become more firmly embedded by the apposition of new bone.

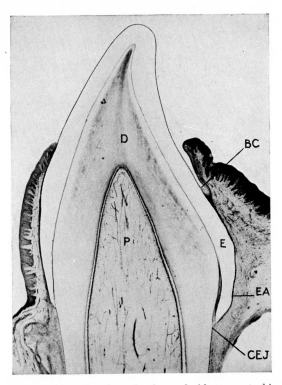

Fig. 207.—Labio-lingual section through a lower deciduous central incisor; aged nine months. The outline of the acid-soluble (mature) enamel is indicated by a black line. This tooth is clinically partially erupted and is about to experience its first occlusal contact (Stage IV). Approximately one-half of the height of the enamel on the labial and lingual sides of the crown is still in organic union with the gingival tissue. *P*, Pulp; *D*, dentin; *E*, enamel; *CEJ*, cemento-enamel junction; *EA*, epithelial attachment; *BC*, bottom of gingival crevice. (× 15.) (Kronfeld's Histology.)

(*c*) The alveolar crest begins to show a more dense character, although it still lies occlusal to the cemento-enamel junction. The floor of the alveolus still shows the stratification of the trabeculæ.

The attachment apparatus, while constantly being stimulated and strengthened through oral forces, has not yet acquired the firmness of its mature functional state.

The forces of the lips from the outside, and the action of the tongue from the inside tend to mould the erupting teeth into a symmetrical arch. The root has not yet completed its formation, and should the tongue and lip action be misdirected a malformation may result and further eruption will be "abnormal."

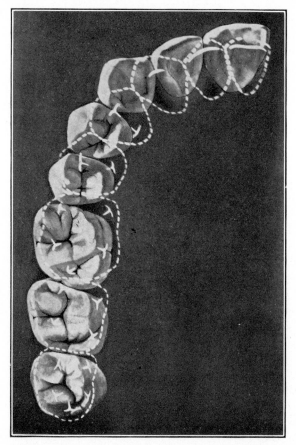

Fig. 208.—Occlusal surface of the maxillary permanent teeth of a young adult, with the outlines of the opposing teeth superposed in occlusion (Friel, courtesy of Int. Jour. Orthodontia).

The period between the initial emergence of the crown and the time it meets its antagonist in full occlusion is significant, because this interval constitutes a most susceptible period of the tooth toward malocclusion.

**Stage IV—First Occlusal Contact.**—Most of the teeth meet their antagonists before they are in full occlusion or have completely erupted. This early contact provides, through mechanical means, a guide to the perfect alignment and intercusping of the antagonistic teeth by mutual direction through their inclined planes.

Even after their complete eruption the teeth exhibit great powers of adjustment, shifting to accommodate themselves to changes which occur in their relationships with neighboring or antagonistic teeth. At this stage, about two-thirds of the anatomical crown of the deciduous teeth and about one-third of the anatomical crown of the permanent teeth lie below the gingival crest.

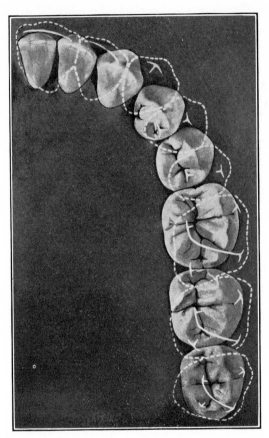

Fig. 209.—Occlusal surface of the mandibular permanent teeth of a young adult. with the outlines of the opposing teeth superposed in occlusion (Friel, courtesy of Int. Jour. Orthodontia).

(*a*) The clinical crown during this period is comparatively small. The gum and gingival tissues are closely adherent to the surface of the teeth and fill the interproximal spaces completely.

(*b*) The rate of eruption is considerably retarded by the action of the contact between opposing teeth.

(*c*) The slowing of the rate of eruption allows the reconstruction of the trabeculæ at the floor of the alveolus by lamellated bone. The thin alveolar crest becomes thickened and strong, and comes to lie below the cemento-enamel junction (Fig. 207).

(*d*) The entire supporting apparatus becomes strengthened in response to the greater stresses applied to the tooth by constantly increasing functional forces.

(*e*) Abrasion begins and the enamel cuticle is soon worn off at the summit of the crown.

(*f*) During the stages III and IV of clinical eruption, the crown is gradually exposed by a recession of the gingiva (passive exposure).

**Stage V—Full Clinical Occlusion.**—Full clinical occlusion persists for the greater functional lifetime of the tooth. At the beginning of this stage the roots are not yet completed. But later, the root reaches its complete length and most of the secondary cementum is deposited. The attachment apparatus is now subjected to the optimum amount of oral stresses, and exhibits the normal adult structure described in the previous chapters.

The harmonious functional relationship between the upper and lower permanent dentition is shown in figures 208 and 209.

### POSTERUPTIVE CHANGES

1. **The Deciduous Teeth.**—After the deciduous dentition is in full functional occlusion, there follows a long interval preparatory to the appearance of the permanent teeth. During this period the following events occur:

(*a*) The eruption of the permanent teeth in the stages outlined above.

(*b*) The progressive resorption of the deciduous teeth seems to occur mainly under the eruptive influences of the successional teeth. Should resorption of either tooth or alveolar bone be incomplete the succeeding tooth may be deflected from its normal path and erupt into a position of malocclusion. Occasionally the root of a deciduous tooth may be amputated by an erupting tooth and the fragment will be left behind in the jaw. It may or may not be subsequently exfoliated.

(*c*) A spacing of the anterior deciduous teeth is a frequent but not an invariable precursor to the normal eruption of the permanent teeth. To be sure, the jaws must grow to accommodate these larger permanent teeth, but such teeth do not all erupt at the same time. The steady growth of the alveolar process in an occlusal and outward direction gradually enlarges the arch throughout the period of eruption, so that each pair is accommodated as it appears.

(*d*) The shedding of the deciduous teeth is the final result of the resorptive process and occurs just prior to the emergence of the succeeding teeth into the oral cavity.

2. **The Permanent Teeth.**—Eruption is not terminated when the permanent teeth are in full clinical occlusion. With age the epithelial attachment tends to grow apically, and the clinical crown continues to become larger and finally surpasses the size of the anatomical crown. The bottom

PLATE XIV

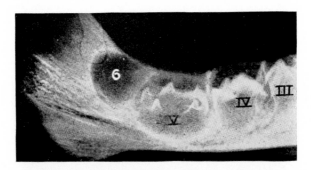

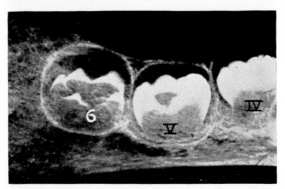

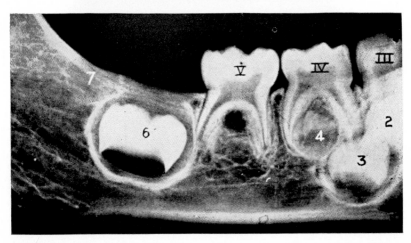

Radiographs of mandible. *Top*, of a newborn; *center*, at nine months; *bottom*, at two years. The primary teeth are marked with Roman and the permanent with Arabic numerals. (Kronfeld, Dental Histology.)

# PLATE XV

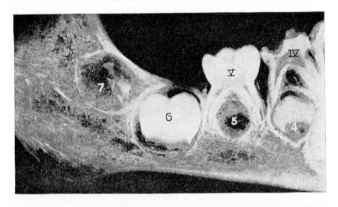

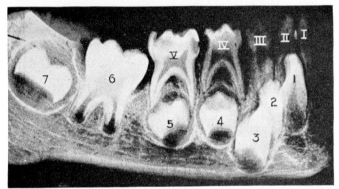

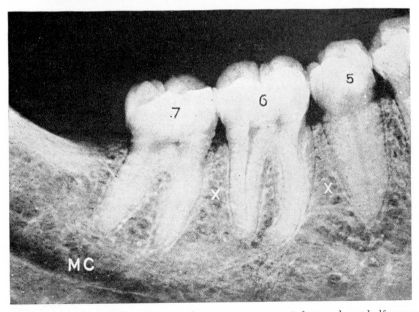

Radiographs of mandible. *Top*, at three years; *center*, at four and one-half years; *bottom*, at thirty-five years. The primary teeth are marked with Roman and the permanent one with Arabic numerals. (Kronfeld, Dental Histology.)

of the gingival crevice and the deepest point of the epithelial attachment thus pass apically below the cemento-enamel junction (passive exposure). Thus the height of the clinical crown is adjusted. At the same time the tooth continues to erupt actively in compensation for the loss of tooth substance by attrition. This occurs in part by apposition of cementum at the apex and of bone at the fundus of the socket.

Eruption and passive exposure during the functional period of the tooth are delicately correlated and balanced. This equilibrium is however frequently disturbed by periodontal diseases.

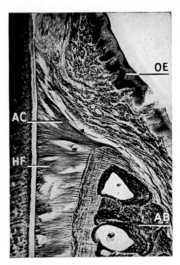

Fig. 210.—Actively growing alveolar crest on the lingual side of an upper second premolar. Silver staining. *AB* Alveolar bone; *AC*, alveolar crest fibers; *HF*, horizontal periodontal membrane fibers; *OE*, oral epithelium of attached gingiva. (Kronfeld's Histopathology.).

## THE CHRONOLOGY OF ERUPTION

The teeth appear in the oral cavity in groups. The lower deciduous central incisors emerge at approximately seven months of age, followed by a period of two months when no teeth appear. The upper incisors and lower laterals appear next (nine months) followed, after a few months, by the first four deciduous molars (fourteen months). The canines appear after a four month interval (eighteen months) and are the only deciduous teeth which erupt between teeth already in position. The second deciduous molars appear four to six months after the canines. At this time (two years), although the crowns are fully erupted, the roots of the deciduous dentition are still incomplete. The roots are completed about the third year (Table 2).

The time of eruption is as a rule earlier in girls than in boys. This fact is in harmony with the earlier maturity of the female.

## THEORIES CONCERNING THE MECHANISM OF ERUPTION

The growth of the jaws plays a significant part in the eruption of the teeth. Some investigators, Brash in particular, have even ascribed the most important rôle in eruption of the growth of the jaws, and regard the teeth as being entirely passive agents in the process of eruption. While there is no doubt that a considerable portion of the eruptive process involves active movements of the tooth incident to jaw growth, there is also little doubt that the tooth also moves by its own growth. The evidence available indicates that the process of eruption is dependent on the normal growth of the jaws, especially the growth of the condyle, and an active inherent movement of the tooth itself.

On the basis of the various histological changes that may be observed, different theories have been advanced to explain the mechanism of active eruption. No one theory has yet been able to explain all the factors involved in the eruptive process. However, each may contribute toward a better understanding of the process as a whole.

1. **Pressure From the Elongation of the Roots.**—The simplest explanation of the entire process would be that the increase in the length of the root pushing against the resistance offered by the floor of the bony crypt results in the movement of the crown toward the oral epithelium. Orban regards the proliferative end of Hertwig's sheath as a fixed point from which the development of the root proceeds peripherally.

This theory fails to explain why teeth sometimes erupt in the absence of root formation; and why teeth may sometimes have their root completed and yet remain within the jaw for a considerable time only to erupt at a later date. Also, in certain dermoid cysts, the teeth erupt in the absence of a bony base. Another objection to this theory is that normally the distance traveled by the crown of the tooth often greatly exceeds the amount of root added, as is the case in the canine. (A concomitant apposition of bone at the fundus of the alveolus might explain this fact).

2. **Pulp Pressure Theory.**—Constant suggested that the blood pressure is the impelling force in eruption. He pointed out that the vascular supply of the pulp and the tissues beneath the tooth is greater than that above it. It is also possible that the force evolved during the constriction of the pulp by the forming dentin contributes to the forces of the blood-pressure. F. B. Noyes points out that, "The force exerted by the growing tooth is the result of the multiplication of cells in the tooth germ, and is exactly comparable to the forces exerted by multiplication of cells in any position. For instance, the force exerted by the multiplication of the cells in a rootlet of a plant is sufficient to force pebbles aside and make an opeining through hard packed earth. How this force is generated has been a matter of much speculation and investigation. It shows some points of similarity with the swelling of wood fibers when water is added. It apparently is related to

osmosis and has direct relations to blood-pressure. It is certainly a very complicated matter, with chemical affinities at the bottom of it."

Tomes considers the pressure theory inadequate, since the movement of the erupting tooth is not always in the direction of its long axis.

While there seems to be no doubt that the tooth has an inherent capacity to erupt, the mechanism of this active eruption presents a complex problem that awaits further investigation. Experimental evidence has shown that the pituitary gland plays a very significant rôle in the regulation of eruption. The removal of the hypophysis in rats results in a progressive retardation and final cessation of eruption. The appositional growth is interfered with to a much lesser degree. This may indicate that the eruptive process, although interrelated with the growth process, involves much more than growth. Clinical evidence confirms the retardation of eruption in hypopituitarism. The possibility of an endocrine control of eruption is not remote.

Other experimental evidence (fluorosis, rickets) shows that there is a close correlation between the general growth processes of the body and the eruption of the teeth. In those cases where growth was found to be severely retarded, a positive correlation appeared in the delayed eruption of the teeth.

## BIBLIOGRAPHY.

BRASH, J. C.: The Growth of the Alveolar Bone and Its Relation to the Movements of the Teeth, Including Eruption, Int. Jour. of Orthod., *14*, 197, 283, 487, 1928.

BRODIE, A. G.: Present Status of Knowledge Concerning Movement of the Tooth Germ Through the Jaw, Jour. Am. Dent. Assn., *21*, 1830, 1934.

CATTELL, P.: The Eruption and Growth of the Permanent Teeth, Jour. Dent. Res., *8*, 279, 1928.

GOTTLIEB, B., and ORBAN, B.: Zahnfleischentzündung und Zahnlockerung, Berlin, 1936, Berlinische Verlagsanstalt.

MASSLER, M., and SCHOUR, I.: Studies in Tooth Development: Theories of Eruption, Am. Jour. Orthod. and Oral Surg., *27*, 552, 1941.

ORBAN, B.: Growth and Movement of the Tooth Germs and Teeth, Jour. Am. Dent. Assn., *15*, 1004, 1928.

SCHOUR, I.: The Hypophysis and the Teeth. II. Effects of Replacement Therapy on the Eruption and the Histologic Changes of the Teeth of the Hypophysectomized Rat, Angle Orthod., *4*, 142, 1934.

SMITH, M. C.: Effect of Fluorine on Rate of Eruption of Rat Incisor. Correlation With Growth and Bone Development of Body, Jour. Dent. Res., *14*, 133, 1934.

WEINMANN, J. P.: Bone Changes Related to Eruption of the Teeth, Angle Orthod., *11*, 83, 1941.

# CHAPTER 19

# The Temporomandibular Joints

**Introduction.** — The temporomandibular joints are an integral part of the masticatory apparatus. The right and left articulations must be considered together since movement in one necessitates movement in the other. They are highly specialized in that the articulating surfaces of the mandible and the temporal bones are not covered by hyaline cartilage as are most of the other joints but by an avascular dense fibrous tissue which may contain some cartilage cells. The interposed articular disc divides the articular space into an upper compartment for the gliding movement and a lower compartment for the hinge movements and thus provides a double joint function on each side (Fig. 211). The reason for the fibrous covering lies in the embryologic development of the mandible. The latter is at first widely separated from the temporal bone by a connective tissue and gradually grows upward and backward to an articulating contact with the temporal bone. This separation persists as the disc and fibrous coverings.

**Bony Structures.** — The temporomandibular joints are the articulations between the articular tubercle of the right and left temporal bones and the condyles of the mandible (Figs. 211 and 212). The substance of the tubercles and the condyles is spongy bone. The trabeculæ join in the adult the thin compact cortical layer at nearly right angles in adaptation to the masticatory forces. The bony roof of the articular fossa is quite thin. The bone marrow in both the condyle and tubercle is hemopoietic even in the adult.

**Covering of Articular Surfaces.** — The connective tissue covering the articular tubercle is calcified immediately next to the bone. The fibers in this area are irregularly arranged. In the outer layer the fibers are densely arranged and parallel to the surface, where the fibroblasts are flattened and give the appearance of an endothelium. It contains chondrocytes which are either isolated or in small groups (Figs. 214 and 215) and is thus as a rule a type of fibro-cartilage.

The covering of the condyle is also fibro-cartilage but unlike in the tubercle it is separated from the bone by hyaline cartilage which serves as an active growth center till about 20 years of age. Remnants of this cartilage persist even in the adult. Except for the marginal surfaces, the articular fibrous tissue is, like hyaline articular cartilage, avascular. This is an adaptation to the bearing of pressure exerted in all articulations.

**Articular Disc.** — The articular disc is composed of dense connective tissue

( 290 )

(Figs. 211, 213 and 214). The coarse bundles of collagenous fibers interlace to form a three dimensional feltwork. Blood vessels and nerves are seen only in the peripheral parts of the disc. It fuses with the fibrous capsule on its anterior circumference. At its posterior margin it is connected to the

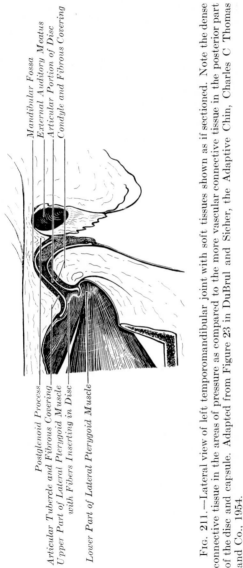

*Mandibular Fossa*
*External Auditory Meatus*
*Articular Portion of Disc*
*Condyle and Fibrous Covering*

*Postglenoid Process*
*Articular Tubercle and Fibrous Covering*
*Upper Part of Lateral Pterygoid Muscle*
*with Fibers Inserting in Disc*
*Lower Part of Lateral Pterygoid Muscle*

Fig. 211.—Lateral view of left temporomandibular joint with soft tissues shown as if sectioned. Note the dense connective tissue in the areas of pressure as compared to the more vascular connective tissue in the posterior part of the disc and capsule. Adapted from Figure 23 in DuBrul and Sicher, the Adaptive Chin, Charles C Thomas and Co., 1954.

capsule by the retrodiscal pad of loose connective tissue which is well vasculated and innervated. The disc is directly attached to the medial and lateral pole of the condyle. Isolated flattened fibroblasts are present at the surfaces.

**Fibrous and Synovial Capsule and Fluid.**—The fibrous capsule consists of dense connective tissue of variable thickness (Figs. 211 and 212).  A regular arrangement occurs only in the reinforced lateral wall of the articulation, *i.e.* in the fan-shaped temporomandibular ligament.

The synovial membrane is a thin layer of loose connective tissue which has a rich blood supply.  It is present only where there is no pressure and

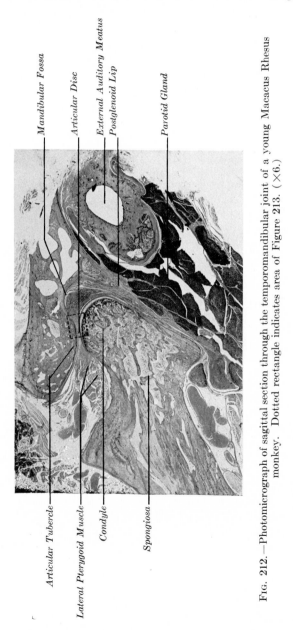

Fig. 212.—Photomicrograph of sagittal section through the temporomandibular joint of a young Macacus Rhesus monkey.  Dotted rectangle indicates area of Figure 213. (×6.)

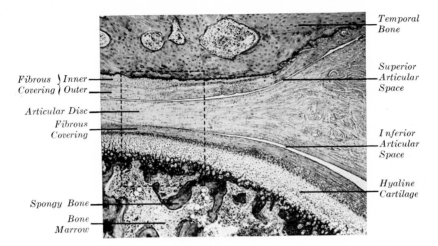

Temporal
Bone

Superior
Articular
Space

Inferior
Articular
Space

Hyaline
Cartilage

Fibrous } Inner
Covering { Outer

Articular Disc

Fibrous
Covering

Spongy Bone

Bone
Marrow

FIG. 213.—Photomicrograph of articulating surfaces of temporomandibular joint. Higher magnification of corresponding field from Figure 212. Dotted rectangle indicates area of Figure 214. (×70.)

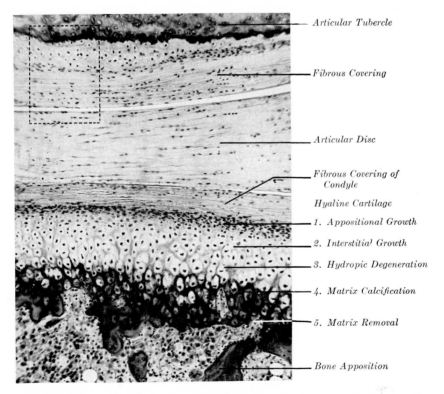

Articular Tubercle

Fibrous Covering

Articular Disc

Fibrous Covering of
Condyle

Hyaline Cartilage

1. Appositional Growth

2. Interstitial Growth

3. Hydropic Degeneration

4. Matrix Calcification

5. Matrix Removal

Bone Apposition

FIG. 214.—Photomicrograph of section of condyle showing stages in its growth. Higher magnification of corresponding field from Figure 213. Dotted rectangle shows area of Figure 215 (×190).

becomes folded when the jaws are closed. The synovial fluid serves as a lubricating and nutritive agent for the avascular tissues of the articulation. It is clear, viscous and slightly yellowish. Its electrolyte content is similar to that of the blood plasma and there is a constant exchange between the synovial fluid and the blood plasma. It contains free cells, most of them macrophages which remove the tissue debris from the articular cavity caused by the normal wear of the articulating surfaces.

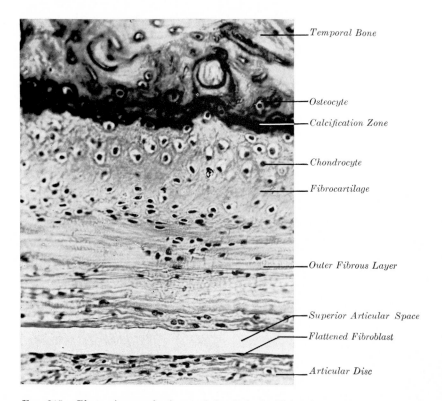

Temporal Bone

Osteocyte

Calcification Zone

Chondrocyte

Fibrocartilage

Outer Fibrous Layer

Superior Articular Space

Flattened Fibroblast

Articular Disc

Fig. 215.—Photomicrograph of part of the Articular Tubercle and the upper surface of the disc. Higher magnification of corresponding field from Figure 214 (×400.)

**Development of Mandibular Condyle.**—In the developing mandible, the mandibular condyle is first indicated as a connective tissue condensation in the posterior portion. Later, chondrocytes and hyaline cartilage develop in the mesenchyme of this area as a secondary cartilage growth center. Once this cartilage has appeared it takes over as a model tissue in the growth of the mandible. As it grows backward and slightly upward it approaches the temporal bone and together with it forms the temporo-mandibular joint. During this growth process, the intervening connective tissue between the temporal bone and the future site of the condyle persists and later becomes the fibrous tissue covering of both the developing and adult condyle and the disc.

**Condylar Growth.**—The condylar cartilage is principally comparable to epiphyseal cartilage because its proliferation and replacement by bone is the main factor in mandibular growth. However, the condylar cartilage cannot be likened directly with either epiphyseal or articular cartilages at the cranial base. Epiphyseal and cranio-basal cartilages are interposed between bony parts. Articular cartilages have a free surface facing the next bone.

The mandibular condyle is unique in the fact that it is covered by connective tissue in the deepest layers of which new layers of hyaline cartilage are added by the differentiation of the fibroblasts. Its growth is appositional, in contrast, the epiphyseal articular and cranio basal cartilages proliferate by interstitial growth.

The growth of the mandibular condyle presents an orderly sequence of steps which occur in its three basic structures—the layer of fibrous tissue; the layer of hyaline cartilage; and the spongy bone (Fig. 214). Starting with the inner and outer layer of the fibrous covering which is in direct contact with the lower surface of the interarticular disc, we see a densely cellular transitional layer in which young mesenchymal cells and fibroblasts proliferate and differentiate into chondroblasts. These become chondrocytes and are responsible for the zone of appositional growth of hyaline cartilage.

The replacement of the growing condylar cartilage by bone proceeds in the same manner observed in the epiphyseal, articular and basal cartilages. The chondrocytes gradually swell by intracytoplasmic and intranuclear edema. The intercellular substance of the cartilage calcifies and becomes destroyed and resorbed by osteoclasts and chondroclasts. Osteoblasts then deposit bone on the border of the calcified cartilage spicules and form the primary spongiosa of the condyle.

## BIBLIOGRAPHY

SARNAT, BERNARD G., *et al.*: *The Temporomandibular Joint*, Springfield, Illinois, Charles C Thomas, 1951.

WEINMAN, J., and SICHER, H.: "Histophysiology of the Temporomandibular Joint," Ch. II in Sarnat, B. G. *The Temporomandibular Joint*, 41–48. Springfield, Illinois, Charles C Thomas, 1951.

# CHAPTER 20

# The Deciduous Teeth

**The Importance of the Deciduous Teeth.**—The deciduous dentition has a much greater biological importance than has been generally recognized. In addition to their masticatory function, the deciduous teeth, by their presence in the dental arch maintain the space for the correct alignment of the successional teeth and stimulate the normal development of the jaws.

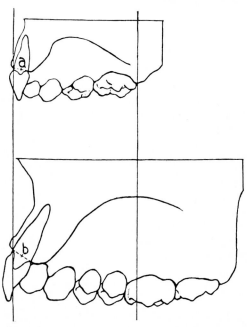

Fig. 216.—Drawing of a sagittal section through the permanent and deciduous maxillary incisors. The labial surface at the cervical margin is oriented in the same plane. Note that the deciduous incisor stands almost straight vertically while the permanent incisor has a distinct labial inclination. Note also that the line passing through the distal of the deciduous second molar passes through the mesial cusps of the first permanent molars. This indicates the fact that the permanent premolars have a smaller mesiodistal diameter and have allowed the first permanent molar to drift mesially. (Friel, Int. Jour. Orthodontia.)

Premature loss or extraction of any deciduous canine or molar will often cause malposition or malocclusion. An infection of deciduous teeth may lead to injury of the enamel organ of its successor. There is no justification for the neglect of the deciduous dentition because of its shorter life-span. Preventive dentistry should be instituted as early as possible.

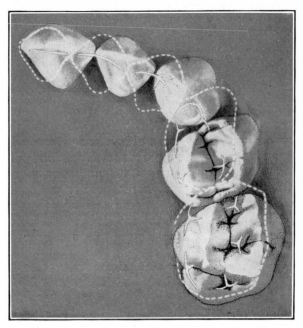

Fig. 217.—Occlusal surface of the maxillary deciduous teeth, with the outlines of the opposing teeth superposed in occlusion. Three years of age. (Friel, Int. Jour. Orthodontia.)

Fig. 218.—Occlusal surface of the mandibular deciduous teeth, with the outlines of the opposing teeth superposed in occlusion. Three years of age. (Friel, Int. Jour. Orthodontia.)

## GENERAL DIFFERENCES BETWEEN THE DECIDUOUS AND PERMANENT TEETH

Microscopic examination of the deciduous teeth shows that their morphology in general, with the exception of the deciduous first molar, resembles that of the corresponding permanent teeth. A detailed description of the deciduous first molar belongs in a text of dental anatomy. There are, however, a number of general differences between the deciduous and permanent teeth.

1. **Size.**—The deciduous teeth are smaller. The thickness of the enamel and dentin is approximately one-half that of the permanent teeth.

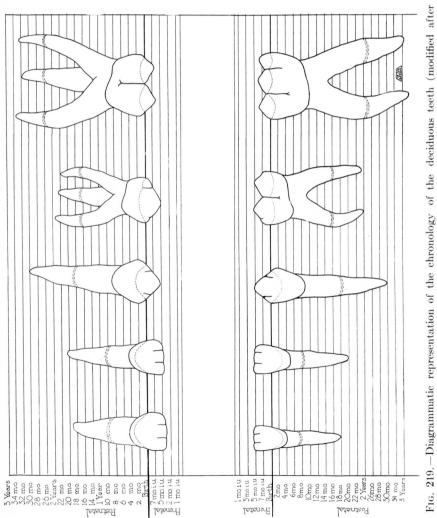

Fig. 219.—Diagrammatic representation of the chronology of the deciduous teeth (modified after McBeath). The dotted line on the crown indicates the position of the neonatal ring. Eruption begins when the crown is fully formed and is completed at the approximate time indicated by the dotted area on the roots of the teeth.

2. **Shape of Crown.**—The bucco-gingival ridge is very prominent. It ends abruptly at the cemento-enamel junction and produces a markedly bell-shaped crown with a constricted neck. The buccal and lingual inclines are relatively flatter than in the permanent teeth.

3. **Shape of Roots.**—The roots of the deciduous molars are flatter and diverge to allow for the underlying developing crowns of the permanent successors. In the anterior teeth they are longer in proportion to the crown than is the case in the permanent teeth.

4. **Color.**—The enamel in the deciduous teeth is whiter in appearance.

These morphological differences as well as differences in microscopic structure will be discussed in greater detail.

## ENAMEL

**Thickness of the Enamel.**—The thickness of the enamel is in general one-half the thickness of that of the corresponding permanent teeth. The lingual enamel of the anterior teeth is much thinner than the labial (Fig. 221).

**The Prenatal and Postnatal Enamel.** —Since the enamel of the deciduous

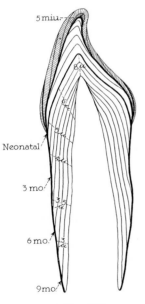

Fig. 220

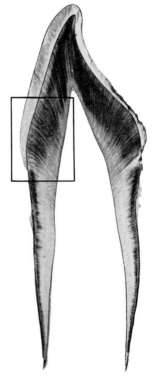

Fig. 221

Fig. 220.—Diagram of the incremental appositional pattern of the upper deciduous central incisor. The chronology and rate of formation is indicated. *miu.*, Months *in utero.* (Schour and Massler.)

Fig. 221.—Ground section of upper deciduous central incisor. See Figure 222 for higher magnification of field within rectangle. (×9.)

teeth begins to form *in utero* and is completed within the first year of post-natal life, the enamel may be classified into two zones, prenatal and post-natal. These zones are sharply demarcated by a line or ring of arrested growth which has been termed the neonatal ring of the enamel (Fig. 221). The latter is therefore an accentuated stria of Retzius of known origin. The prenatal enamel is more homogeneously and densely calcified than the postnatal tissue. It very seldom contains any striæ of Retzius, and enamel hypoplasias are relatively rare. This may be correlated with the fact that it is formed and calcified in a period (*in utero*) that is characterized by exceptionally good protection and nourishment.

The striæ of Retzius are readily found in the postnatal enamel and may be correlated with the postnatal experiences of the child. They are less prominent in number and pigmentation than those observed in the permanent teeth. The postnatal enamel, however, appears in most cases distinctly darker than the prenatal enamel (Fig. 221).

**Distribution of Prenatal Enamel.**—A review of the chronology of the formation and calcification of the enamel shows that the major portions of the incisors and one-half of the canine are prenatal in origin. The occlusal surface of the first and the areas immediately over the growth centers of the second deciduous molars also consist of prenatal enamel.

The distribution of the prenatal enamel is analogous to the cuspal enamel in the permanent teeth but extends over a much wider area. The structural characteristics and appearances are similar.

**Color.**—The external surface of the enamel of the anterior teeth, consists for the most part of the nearly paper white prenatal enamel. The posterior teeth which are composed for the most part of postnatal enamel still present a much whiter appearance than the corresponding permanent teeth because of the lesser frequency and pigmentation of the striæ of Retzius. These factors give to the deciduous teeth their characteristic white appearance.

*Color in Teeth.*—The light incisal color seen invariably in *all* the deciduous teeth is correlated histologically with the fact that this region invariably is composed of enamel that is bluish-white and translucent in appearance. The gingival portion of the enamel invariably contains more striæ of Retzius than the incisal portion. The bands of Retzius, in addition, become pigmented with age through the ingress of coloring matter from the oral fluids. Since the striæ are shorter and more exposed to the surface in the gingival levels than in the occlusal region, they are always more pigmented. The color grades from a white at the incisal to a yellow at the gingival and by the overlapping of the incremental zones, gives the *intermediate* shades of color seen in the intermediate regions.

The underlying dentin also plays a rôle in the color of the tooth. The incisal edge is made more translucent in appearance than the rest of the tooth by virtue of the fact that no dentin (which is opaque and yellowish in appearance) intervenes between the labial and lingual portions of the enamel. Light is thus more highly refractive through the incisal edge. As the gingival level is approached, the enamel becomes thinner, allowing the yellow color of the dentin to become more and more apparent.

These histological facts have important clinical applications. The esthetics of teeth in dentures, porcelain crowns and synthetic fillings are controlled by the color as well as the form of the tooth. Esthetics will be preserved only insofar as the color harmony seen in histological structures is observed.

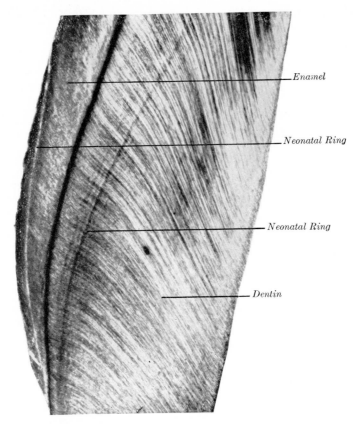

*Enamel*

*Neonatal Ring*

*Neonatal Ring*

*Dentin*

FIG. 222.—Photomicrograph of ground section of upper human deciduous incisor showing the neonatal ring in the enamel and dentin. Note two distinct prenatal rings in the dentin which register disturbances in intra-uterine metabolism. (×56.)

**Enamel Rod Directions.**—The histological picture of the enamel rod of the deciduous teeth presents the same characteristics as those described for the permanent teeth. There is, however, a difference in the direction of the enamel rods, which is an important consideration in cavity preparations. Like the permanent teeth, the enamel rods at the incisal edge and cusps tend to lie parallel to the long axis of the tooth; and as they approach the cemento-enamel junction they incline gradually toward the perpendicular plane, but do not quite reach it, since the crown is shorter than that of the permanent tooth. Thus, unlike the permanent teeth, the enamel rods in the gingival one-third of the tooth do not incline apically but tend to remain inclined slightly toward the incisal or occlusal surface.

**Dentino-enamel Junction.**—The dentino-enamel junction of the deciduous molars presents a markedly S-shaped contour with the concave portion at the occlusal half and the convex portion at the gingival half (Fig. 224).

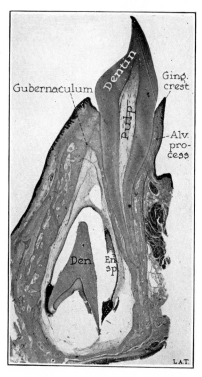

FIG. 223

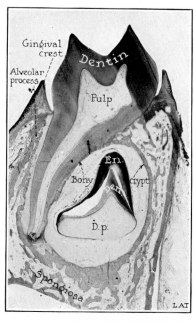

FIG. 224

FIG. 223.—Decalcified section through deciduous central incisor and permanent successor of a two-and-a-half-year-old child. *Den*, dentin of permanent tooth; *en sp.*, enamel space of permanent tooth; *alv. process*, alveolar process of deciduous tooth; *gingocrest*, gingival crest. The gubernaculum is the dense connective tissue which connects the follicle of the tooth germ with the overlying mucosa.

FIG. 224.—Decalcified section through the deciduous first molar and permanent first premolar of a two and a half year old child. *D.p.*, dental papilla; *Den.*, dentin; and *En*, organic enamel matrix of permanent tooth germ.

The convex portion is so prominent as to give the enamel surface a characteristic bell shape. This is particularly accentuated on the buccal surface, producing the typically prominent bucco-gingival ridge of enamel. The shapes of the cusps toward the central sulcus also present an accentuated S-shaped appearance. The contour of the dentino-enamel junction offers an ideally shaped retentive base for the overlying enamel.

## DENTIN AND PULP

**Contour and Width.**—The width of the dentin is approximately one-half that in the corresponding permanent teeth. The pulpal outline in the fully formed tooth is parallel to, and almost equi-distant from, the peripheral surface of the dentin. The pulpal horns extend for a relatively longer distance into the crown. This factor must be kept in mind during operative procedures. The pulp canals characteristically are wide and present open apical foramina. This may be correlated with the fact that the resorption of the deciduous tooth often begins before the roots have completed their formation and calcification.

**Structural Characteristics.**—The prenatal dentin occupies a portion under the dentino-enamel junction which corresponds, in its incremental formation, to the overlying prenatal enamel. Its calcification is denser and more homogeneous than the postnatal dentin. Owen's lines of contour are rarely found in this region. The postnatal dentin is demarcated from the prenatal zone by an accentuated Owen's line of contour which corresponds to the neonatal ring in the enamel and which has been named the neonatal ring in the dentin (Figs. 220–222).

While the deciduous teeth show a layer of mantle dentin which corresponds to that observed in permanent teeth, the submantle interglobular layer is absent. However, incremental layers of interglobular dentin are often present and are associated with the cycles of growth, weaning, or various childhood diseases (parathyroprivic tetany, and other endocrine disturbances).

The direction of the dentinal tubules in deciduous teeth follows the same general plan as observed in the permanent teeth, except in the region of the cemento-enamel junction. Here the tubules are more horizontally placed so that the incremental pattern which runs at right angles to the dentinal tubules does not present the sharply S-shaped appearance seen in permanent teeth.

## RESORPTION OF DECIDUOUS TEETH

**Chronology.**—The resorption of the deciduous teeth begins approximately when root formation is completed. This occurs at about two years of age for the incisors and at about three years for the canines and molars. This process produces the necessary space for the succeeding permanent tooth.

The developing permanent teeth are a stimulus for the resorption of the deciduous teeth, although the latter may occur without the former. The permanent tooth lies lingual and somewhat apical to the deciduous predecessor. As the permanent tooth moves occlusally during its eruption it stimulates resorption of its predecessor.

Resorption is not a continuous but an intermittent process. Periods of activity alternate with periods of rest during which reparative processes take place. It does not begin at one point and spread continuously over the entire surface of the root. If it did so, all of the periodontal fibers would be severed and the tooth would drop out with at least a considerable portion of the root. The process seems to progress in the following manner: At a point on the side of the root near the apex, facing the permanent successor where the growth of the erupting tooth produces pressure, osteoclasts appear in the membrane in considerable number, displacing the cementoblasts,

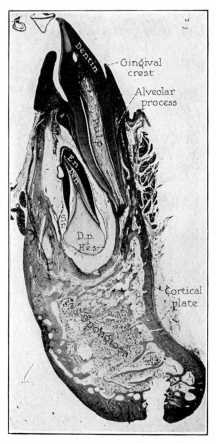

Fig. 225.—Decalcified section through the deciduous and permanent incisors of a nine months old child. *En*, Enamel; *Den*, dentin; *S.r.*, stellate reticulum; *D.p.*, dental papilla; *H.e.s.*, cervical epithelial loop of permanent tooth germ.

and arranging themselves in groups on the surface of the root. These dissolve away the cementum and sink into the tissue, perhaps cutting into the dentin for a short distance. By this excavation the pressure is relieved, the osteoclasts disappear, cementoblasts are formed in the embryonal connective tissue, and the deposition of cementum begins in the excavation, reattaching the fibers in this area. As the rebuilding progresses, at a point a little farther occlusally, osteoclasts appear and begin a new excavation.

In this manner the process continues. When the resorption stops at the second point, it begins again at the first, cutting much deeper into the dentin, thus continuing back and forth.

The amount of cementum apposed in the reparative process is much less than the amount of resorbed tissue. This process progresses until all of the dentin may be destroyed, leaving the hollow crown, and even then new-forming cementum to maintain the attachment will be found around the

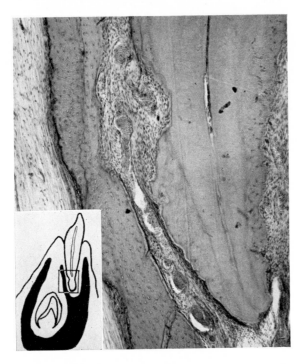

Fig. 226.—Physiologic resorption of permanent incisor in advance of erupting permanent successor. Note vascularity and temporary repair with new cementum. Higher magnification of field indicated in insert.

circumference of the root. In this way it will be seen that the function of the tooth is maintained until its successor is ready to take its place in a very short time. The crown of the deciduous tooth remains functional by peripheral attachment, the inside continues to be hollowed out so that the tip of the crown of the permanent successor actually comes to lie above the gingival level and often appears in the oral cavity at the time of shedding (Fig. 227).

The importance of this arrangement will be more fully appreciated after a study of the relation of the teeth to the development of the face. This patchwork performance goes on in the same way in the bone of the alveolar process, and its study is one of the most interesting phases of the relation of the teeth to the development of the face. Without a clear conception of this it is impossible to understand how the teeth, after their roots are fully formed, can move through three dimensions of space and maintain their function all the time.

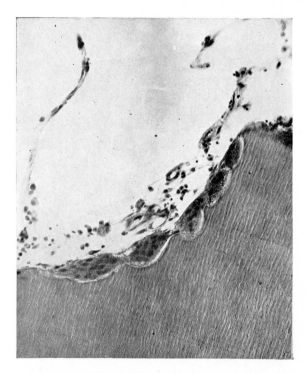

Fig. 227.—Osteoclasts resorbing the dentin of a primary tooth. The osteoclasts appear to form a continuous sheath of cytoplasm.

## HISTOPHYSIOLOGICAL REMARKS

**Submerged Deciduous Teeth.**—Ankylosis of the resorbed surface of the deciduous tooth with its alveolar bone may occur during the reparative process. When such ankylosis persists and extends over large areas, the deciduous tooth remains entirely or partially submerged and prevents the normal eruption of the permanent successor (Fig. 228). F. B. Noyes has made an intensive study of submerged teeth and advocates their removal when the eruption of the permanent teeth cannot take place.

**Resorption of Permanent Teeth.**—While the resorption of the deciduous teeth is a normal physiological process, resorptive processes in permanent teeth are pathological. Kronfeld lists the following groups of permanent teeth which are occasionally subjected to resorptions: pulpless, replanted, impacted teeth in close proximity to tumors and cysts of the jaws, teeth exposed to excessive occlusal trauma, and idiopathic conditions.

**The Pattern and Rate of Growth of Teeth.**—Three unique morphological and physiological characteristics permit a quantitative and qualitative analysis of the growth pattern of the enamel and dentin:

1. Their rhythmic manner of their appositional growth.

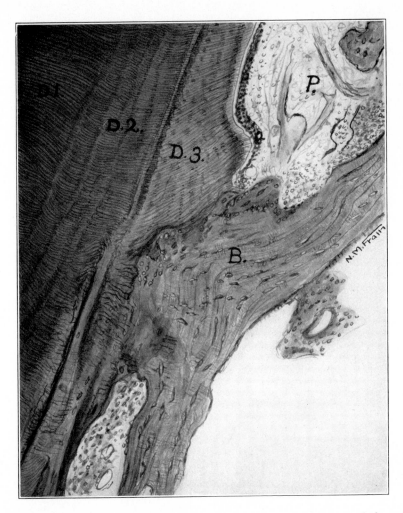

Fig. 228.—Field of deciduous molar showing ankylosis. *P*, A corner of the pulp showing a layer of odontoblasts and new predentin at the left, osteoblasts at the right. $D^1$, $D^2$, $D^3$, three periods in dentin formation. *B*, Tissue of bone-like structure. (Noyes, courtesy of Angle Orthodontist.)

2. Their extreme sensitivity to fluctuations in metabolic processes, particularly calcium metabolism, during their calcifying stage.

3. The permanence of the hard tooth tissues and their freedom from calcium withdrawal.

Histological examination reveals a pattern and gradient of growth in the form of normal incremental rings which is characteristic for each tooth type. These rings, which record the ontogenetic and chronological history of the particular tooth, recur in a constant 16 $\mu$ incremental rhythm in the enamel and dentin of all the species studied from rat to man.

Vital staining with alizarine and injections of sodium fluoride show that the 16 $\mu$ incremental rhythm is a twenty-four-hour phenomenon in the lower species studied, and a four-day phenomenon in the macacus rhesus monkey and man. The rate of growth of enamel and dentin in humans averages approximately 4 $\mu$ each twenty-four hours, but this is not constant in all regions of the tooth. A gradient exists that conforms with the anatomy of the tooth and is correlated with the age of the formative cells and the antero-posterior position of the tooth. Figure 220 shows an analysis of the growth pattern and growth gradient of the upper central deciduous incisor.

Histological analysis of teeth following various constitutional disturbances shows that each particular dysfunction produces a characteristic record which is superposed on the basic pattern in the form of accentuated incremental rings of arrested growth or disturbed calcification. The neonatal ring, for example, reflects the physiological readjustments incident to birth.

**Clinical Problems.**—The formation of secondary dentin in response to abrasion or caries, the ease with which the deciduous teeth abrade, and their incidence of caries, present problems necessitating further research.

### BIBLIOGRAPHY.

BAKER, C. R.: The Deciduous Molars and Their Relation to the Development of the Jaws, Int. Jour. Orthodont., *3*, 253, 1917.

FRIEL, E. S.: Occlusion, Observations on Its Development From Infancy to Old Age, Int. Orth. Cong. (First) Trans., *138*, 159, 1926. Also, Int. Jour. Orth., *13*, 322, 1927.

KRONFELD, R.: The Resorption of the Roots of Deciduous Teeth, Dental Cosmos, *74*, 103, 1932.

MORNINGSTAR, C. H.: Effect of Infection of the Deciduous Molar on the Permanent Tooth Germ, Jour. Am. Dent. Assn. and Dental Cosmos, *24*, 786, 1937.

NOYES, F. B.: Submerging Deciduous Molars, The Angle Orthod., *2*, 77, 1932.

SCHOUR, I.: The Neonatal Line in the Enamel and Dentin of the Human Deciduous Teeth and First Permanent Molar, Jour. Am. Dent. Assn., *23*, 1946, 1936.

SCHOUR, I., and MASSLER, M.: Growth Pattern and Chronology of Upper Deciduous Central Incisor, Jour. Dent. Res., *16*, 350, 1937.

STOLLER, A. E.: A Study of the Direction of the Enamel Rods in Deciduous Molars, Master's Thesis, Northwestern University, College of Dentistry, 1937.

# CHAPTER 21

# Postnatal Development of the Face and Oral Cavity[1]

**Introduction.**—**Growth and Development.**—In the same way that differentiation of specialized tissues is the prominent feature of the fetal period, so growth and its accompanying development predominate after birth. Increase in size is accompanied by attainment of characteristic form and function, which we call development. This represents progress toward the matue or adult state. Expressed in other words, it is the process of realizing the potentiality of the unit. Following the differentiation of specialized cells and their arrangement in tissues which are associated in particular organs, the characteristic morphology of body structures is accomplished by unequal growth of these tissues. We may for convenience designate growth as increase in size, and development as progress toward maturity. Actually growth is often a mechanism in the accomplishment of the gross manifestations of development.

**Growth Forces.**—In studying the growth and developmental progress of the individual it has been convenient to distinguish certain forces which contribute to the process. These factors seldom if ever permit complete isolation and must therefore be recognized as being of a reciprocatory and interdependent nature. One or another frequently predominates at a particular time.

*Actual Growth Force* may be considered as that force which is produced by the increase in number and size of the cells and the amount of intercellular substance. The actual pressures produced by the growth of plant and animal tissues may be very great. The splitting of rocks and displacement of soil occasioned by growing vegetation is a familiar phenomenon. In the animal body the reactivity of vital tissues to pressure stimuli effecting changes in form, seldom permits the generation of forces comparable to those developed when the resisting substance is of inanimate character. They are none the less real and are of great significance in the mechanism of growth and development.

*The Inherent Growth Force* is a term which has been applied to the tendency possessed by each individual structural unit to develop a form characteristic of the species and the individual. A mandible tends to become a mandible even though it be removed from the animal to which it belongs

---

[1]This chapter was originally prepared by Harold J. Noyes, D.D.S., M.D., Dean of the University of Oregon Dental School.

and is grown in an implanted position in another animal. Each bone, each tooth, as well as each muscle and gland, has a growth-pattern which it tends to fulfil. The extent to which each ultimately fulfils this potentiality is dependent upon the nature and degree of coördination in the growth and development of the whole being and upon the environment to which the units are subjected, both collectively and individually.

*Functional Growth Force* is that growth and developmental impulse which arises through use and activity. Each structural unit expresses an important growth motive from the inherent growth force and generates also an actual growth force. There is, in addition, an appreciable contribution to both size and detail of form supplied by the performance of function. Thus the implanted mandible never attains the size of the normal mandible. Moreover, the arm of a blacksmith assumes a size and a minute bony architecture which would not have been attained had he chosen the occupation of a clerk. Even like portions of the same body illustrate minor differences in response to the degree and nature of their use. For example, right and left hands or forearms and likewise the right and left halves of the jaws are frequently asymmetrical due to differences in the degree of function.

How much of this functional growth force is affected by the blood vascular system through the relative volume and rate of circulation and to what extent the activity of the cellular units themselves contributes is debatable. It is certain that the blood supply is important.

## THE NEONATAL PERIOD

Birth marks a profound change in the environment of the developing individual. Because of the magnitude of this adjustment and the hazards which are encountered, pediatricians have given special attention to the first two weeks after birth and designated the interval as the neonatal period. Harris points out that "in neonatal life, as a result of the catastrophic changes involved at birth an arrest of growth concomitant with the loss of weight in the first week of life is of such frequency as to be almost a normal feature." Important changes take place in the heart and blood-vessels to meet postnatal circulatory conditions. Also function of the gastro-intestinal tract is initiated as the infant must now digest and assimilate food for himself. This critical time of adjustment is attended by the largest mortality rate of any growth period.

**The Head.** — The head is the largest portion of the body at birth and is consequently most subject to injury and distortion (moulding) during delivery. The fontanelles are open. The anterior one is large and the posterior is closing. The cranial sutures have not united.

**The Face.** — The face occupies a relatively insignificant position beneath the anterior part of the cranium to which at this time it bears the ratio

# LEGEND FOR PLATE XVI.

## Lateral Views of Human Skulls.

*A*, Skull at eight months. The deciduous centrals are clinically erupted but the laterals are not yet through the gums. The developing first permanent molar has been lost from its crypt. Note the angulation of the ramus to the body of the mandible in this and the succeeding figures.

*B*, Skull at one year. The deciduous incisors are clinically erupted.

*C*, Skull in the second year. The deciduous first molar and canine are almost completely erupted. Note the development of the roots and the relation of the crypt of the second deciduous molar to the inferior alveolar canal. Note also the stage of development of the permanent first molar and canine.

*D*, Skull in the fourth year. The deciduous dentition is completely erupted and functional. Note the permanent teeth in their crypts.

*E*, Skull in the seventh year. The first permanent molars have clinically erupted.

*F*, Left side of skull shown in *E*. Note the relation of the permanent premolars to the roots of the deciduous molars.

*G*, Front view of skull shown in *E* and *F*. Note the relation of the developing permanent anterior teeth to each other and to the roots of the deciduous teeth. Note the beginning of clinical eruption in the lower permanent central incisors, which have not yet experienced first occlusal contact.

*H*, Skull in the eighth year. The upper deciduous incisors are shed and the permanent successors are at the beginning of clinical eruption (the toothless age). Note the crown of the second permanent molar and the position of the permanent canine.

# LEGEND FOR PLATE XVII.

## Lateral Views of Human Skulls.

*I*, Skull in the eleventh year. Mixed dentition. The permanent incisors and first molars and the deciduous molars are clinically erupted. The second molars are about to appear in the oral cavity to be followed by the premolars.

*J*, Left side of skull shown in *I*. The deciduous canine and deciduous first molars were lost during preparation. Note the position and the length of the permanent upper cuspid and its distance from the orbit. The permanent lateral is dystrophied and shows a typical "peg" shape.

*K*, Skull in the thirteenth year. The deciduous lower second molar remains unshed. Note the relation of the roots to the underlying premolars. The second permanent molar is in clinical eruption. Note the crypt of the third molar from which the developing tooth has been lost.

*L*, Skull of a young adult about fifteen years of age. The crown of the third molar lies within its crypt.

*M*, Skull of adult. The permanent dentition is in full clinical occlusion and the roots are completed. Note the distance from the apices of the teeth to the lower border of the mandible and the floor of the nose and orbit.

*N*, Edentulous jaws. Note the loss of the alveolar process and the position of the mental foramen.

In this series, trace the formation and eruption of the deciduous and permanent dentitions. Note the angulation of the ramus to the body of the mandible; the posterior growth of the ramus of the mandible; the increase in the height of the maxilla and mandible; and the relative positions of the deciduous and permanent teeth.

PLATE XVI

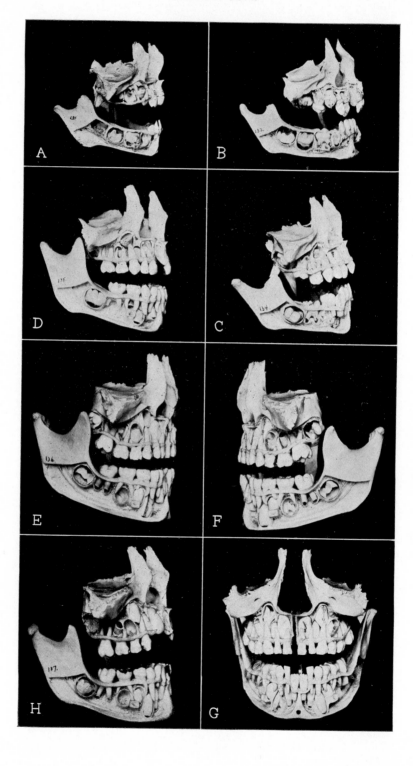

PLATE XVII

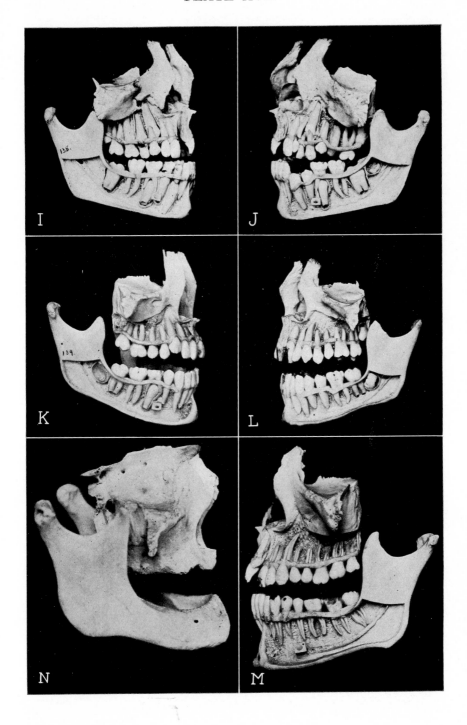

of 1 to 8. The lower half of the face is least developed in vertical height which gives the characteristic infantile appearance (Fig. 229).

**The Maxillæ.**—The maxillæ are relatively greater in lateral extent than in height, due to the absence of erupted teeth and of their supporting alveolar process. The palatal vault is therefore shallow. The maxillary sinus has just begun to develop and the premaxillary-maxillary sutures are about to unite. The crypts of all the deciduous teeth and the first permanent molars occupy practically the entire body of the bone (Fig. 229).

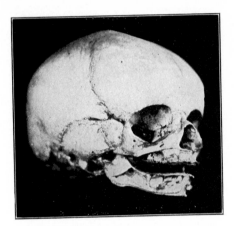

FIG. 229.—Skull at birth.

**The Mandible.**—The mandible is almost straight with very little angulation between the body and ramus (Fig. 237). As in the upper jaw, the tooth crypts occupy the bulk of the body of the bone which possesses somewhat heavier cortical plates than the maxillæ. The cartilaginous core (Meckel's cartilage) has been resorbed and replaced by bone. The suture at the symphysis unites soon after birth (Fig. 229).

**The Deciduous Teeth.**—The deciduous teeth are all in the process of formaformation and calcification, as indicated by Table 2. The metabolic changes during the neonatal period are permanently recorded in the enamel and dentin of the deciduous teeth that are formed and calcified at this time. This particular kymographic record is termed the *neonatal ring*. Severe birth injuries may cause hypoplasias of these tissues which are recognizable grossly.

**The Permanent Teeth.**—The permanent teeth, with the possible exception of the mesio-buccal cusp of the first permanent molars, have not yet begun to calcify. The crypts of the first permanent molars are well formed. The germs of all of the permanent teeth, except the bicuspids, upper lateral incisors and third molars have been differentiated and are in an early stage of development.

**The Soft Tissues.**—The soft tissues are differentiated and relatively well developed. The tongue is completely formed and active. The oral mucous membrane is in the process of rapid growth. It is thin and easily traumatized over the crest of the alveolar process. Nests of epithelial cells are commonly isolated by the rapid proliferation of the adjacent connective tissue. The multiplication of these epithelial groups produces the minute, ovoid, and slightly raised nodules often found along the medial raphé of the palate (Epstein's pearls).

**The Salivary Glands.**—The salivary glands have developed to the point where function is possible but still limited. The muscles of mastication and facial expression are fully differentiated, but their activity has not yet come under conscious control.

## PERIOD OF THE DECIDUOUS DENTITION

At approximately six months of age, depending somewhat upon the familial and racial pattern, the lower central deciduous incisors appear. The time interval from that event until the eruption of one of the first permanent molars at about six years may be considered as the deciduous dentitional period. This roughly represents the first half decade of the child's life and comprises infancy (first year of life) and early childhood (the pre-school age).

**General Growth and Development.**—The rate of growth in the first year is reduced materially and remains relatively constant for weight with an annual increase of about five pounds per year. Gain in length continues to decrease throughout the first six years, and is finally reduced to about 2 inches annually. Increase in both weight and length fluctuates among individuals. Variations in both are markedly accentuated by ill health. In other words, deviations from the child's normal state of health will influence growth and developmental processes, tending to produce irregular growth curves, while the maintenance of optimal health is inclined to even them. Interruptions in growth may be leveled by acceleration at a later age. Severe disturbances, however, are seldom completely compensated. Frequently weight lags behind height during periods of active growth when the food may fail to provide for these as well as the demands of activity. The efficiency of the body mechanism with respect to assimilation and metabolism has a direct bearing upon the quantity of food required.

There is a growth and developmental variation between the sexes even at this age. Boys at birth are as a rule somewhat heavier and longer. Girls, by a slightly more rapid growth rate, tend to level these differences by the fifth year. Both sexes about double their birth weight in the first five months and treble it at the end of the first year. Thereafter the rate of growth gradually decreases and the yearly gains are reduced in proportion to the total body bulk.

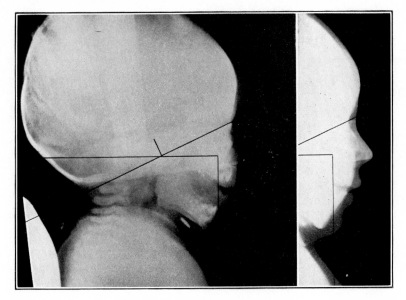

*A*

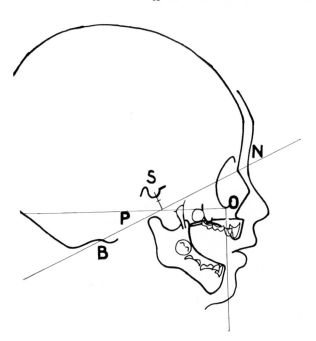

*B*

FIG. 230.—*A*, Cephalometric roentgenogram of a healthy three-months-old infant. (Courtesy of Dr. B. H. Broadbent, Bolton Foundation.)

*B*, Tracing of *A*. *B*, Bolton point; *N*, nasion; *O*, orbitalis; *P*, porion; *S*, sella turcica.

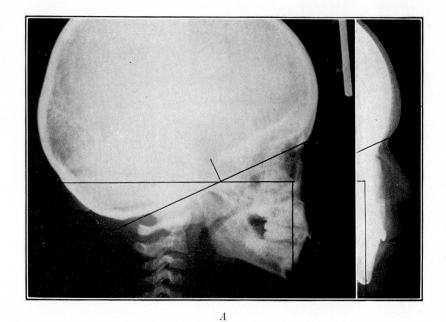

A

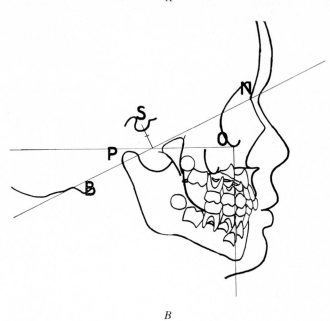

B

Fig. 231.—Cephalometric roentgenogram of a healthy four-years-old child. (Courtesy of Dr. B. H. Broadbent, Bolton Foundation.)

B, Tracing of A.  B, Bolton point; N, nasion; O, orbitalis; P, porion; S, sella turcica.

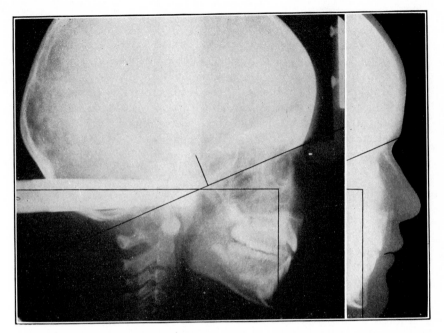

*A*

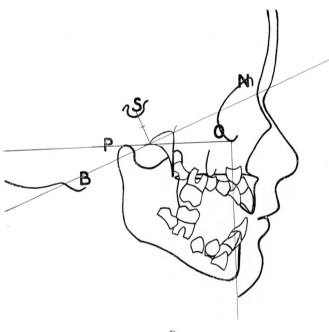

*B*

FIG. 232.—*A*, Cephalometric roentgenogram of a healthy six and a half-years-old child.  (Courtesy of Dr. B. H. Broadbent, Bolton Foundation.)

*B*. Tracing of *A*.  *B*, Bolton point; *N*, nasion; *O*, orbitalis; *P*, porion; *S*, sella turcica.

The deciduous dentitional period is a time of development and refinement of conscious control. The child is learning to use his body and his mind. This is essentially a matter of experiment, practice and discipline. Superimposed upon this great task he must, as well, orient his person to a very complex environment. Habits of physical and mental activity are acquired which grant him freedom to apply himself to purposeful endeavor. When one considers the magnitude and complexity of these demands, it is not surprising that deviations from perfect accomplishment occur. It is important from a dental point of view to attain a state of nutrition, develop habits of function and establish mental concepts which will build, use and appreciate the highest potentiality of the dental structures.

**The Head.**—The head in this period changes materially in proportion. The cranium is still growing, although by the sixth year it has approximated its eventual size. The borders of the cranial bones are approximated at the cranial sutures where subsequent growth continues. Following the early rapid growth of the cranium, which is concluded at about the six month, there is a pause until about the second year. From two to four years, however, there is active growth in the bones at the base of the skull, particularly the sphenoid. This increases the height of the vertex and parietal bones. In the later part of the deciduous and the first part of the mixed dentitional periods, contemporaneously with the growth of the face, the parietal and frontal regions are extended forward. This produces a change in angle which raises the forehead, allowing it to assume a more vertical position (Figs. 231, 232, and Plate XVI, *A–F*).

**The Face.**—The face occupies a more prominent position through increase in length and depth. The growth in the orbital framework has established approximately the width of the upper face. The maxillary sinuses have enlarged, the ethmoid spaces have now appeared and the frontal sinus is developing. The reflexes of facial expression have been established and the facial musculature exerts a positive effect upon the dental structures. Likewise detrimental habits or perversion of useful habits soon show their influence upon the denture, which is easily moulded during this period of rapid growth (Figs. 231 and 232).

**The Maxillæ.**—The maxillæ in these years grow in width, height and depth, though the two latter dimensions increase more rapidly than the first. The increase in height of the maxilla is effected mainly by the growth of alveolar bone.

The palate moves downward, making way for enlargement of the nasal space by resorptions upon its superior surface and additions to the oral vault. It is carried anteriorly with the body of the bone, and extended posteriorly as the palate and maxillary tuberosities develop. The nasopalatine canals diminish in diameter and the maxillary-premaxillary sutures unite (Plate XVI, *A–E*, and Plate XVII, *A–D*).

The maxilla thus grows to accommodate the demands of teeth, sinuses, oral and nasal cavities. There is a reciprocal influence between all of these structures. Moreover, this bone is particularly susceptible to general systemic influences on bone growth. It is perhaps because of the high degree of coördination of all factors required for normal growth and maturity that the maxilla is one of the most sensitive bones of the face to growth disturbances.

**The Mandible.**—The mandible increases proportionately in size. The angle between ramus and body becomes more acute, and the mental eminence more prominent (Fig. 237). The body, which supports the lower dentition, is carried forward by additions to the bone at the angle and along the posterior surface of the ramus. The antero-posterior dimension of the ramus is controlled by resorption along the anterior surface. As the deciduous teeth erupt and become functional, the growth of the alveolar process surrounding these teeth increases the height of the body of the bone.

The ultimate architecture of the bone is materially influenced by the muscular stresses to which it is subjected. The degree of angulation of the ramus and the body, the height of the symphysis and the detail of internal spicules as well as the thickness of cortical plates all reflect these influences. Increase in height in this bone as well as the maxilla is accomplished through the same mechanism, *i. e.*, the vertical growth of the alveolar process. Thus the mandible is moulded in response to the inherent, active and functional growth forces (Plate XVI, *A–F*).

A lack of harmony of the growth forces influencing both maxillæ and mandible is responsible for developmental imperfections common to this age range. Hereditary absence of tooth units, insufficient functional stimulation, or imbalance in the pressures exerted by the soft tissues of tongue and facial musculature, together with the hazard through the introduction of external pressures such as finger- or thumb-sucking may easily alter the form of the jaws and affect tooth position. The ultimate extent of damage is determined by the degree to which the changes are carried beyond the possibility of recovery when the perverting influence no longer exists.

**The Deciduous Teeth.**—The developing unerupted teeth are each encased in a crypt, the wall of which is formed by the cribriform plate (alveolar bone proper). The crypt walls are braced against themselves and the cortical plates of maxilla or mandible by spicules of cancellous bone surrounding medullary spaces. As the tooth develops within the crypt, pressure is exerted, pushing the crypt wall backward through the cancellous bone.

Usually between the sixth and ninth months after birth the teeth move occlusally, cutting through the soft tissues. The formation of cementum on the surface of the root and of bone on the wall of the crypt attach the connective tissue fibers and form the beginning of the periodontal membrane. As the tooth moves occlusally the bone grows up around it from the crypt wall, converting it into the wall of the alveolus.

The deciduous teeth are the only teeth erupted in this period. The age at which the teeth appear is subject to normal variation related to the growth and developmental pattern of the individual. Eruption may be

21

accelerated or retarded by systemic disturbances in the same way that other features of this pattern may be altered by deviations from optimum health. As a general rule, the lower dentition precedes the upper by a very short interval. The lower central incisors of the the first dentition commonly appear about the sixth month and are followed rapidly by the corresponding teeth of the upper arch. Observation of average children suggests a normal variation in cutting the first tooth from the fifth to ninth month; yet this represents too wide a range if the growth and developmental pattern of the individual child were known. It has been noted clinically that the relative age at which the first tooth is cut frequently forecasts the child's tendency to be early, late or average in dental eruption. The age of eruption does not bear an invariable relation to the extent of calcification before the teeth appear. In other words, the age of eruption and age of calcification are affected in different degree and by diverse influences. It is probable that as our knowledge of growth of the child is refined, our standards of normal variation for the particular individual will be shortened and the significance of dental age will be more useful.

The lower lateral incisors appear soon after the upper centrals (eight to ten months) and are in turn followed by the upper laterals. There is then an interval of two to three months before the lower first deciduous molars erupt. Subsequently the cuspids and second deciduous molars take their clinical position.

By the time the child has reached two years, his deciduous dentition is complete and functioning. The roots are not entirely formed until the third year. Under masticatory stresses the deciduous teeth wear more rapidly than those of the permanent dentition. This is particularly true when the lateral masticatory movements of the mandible are emphasized and the chewing is vigorous. In sucking, the mandible is raised and lowered largely in a vertical direction. This habit having been established early tends to persist. It is usually some time after the completion of the deciduous dentition that the lateral grinding movements are utilized. There are many factors which influence the attainment of these lateral movements. The height of the cusps, the form of the dental arches, and the character of the food all assist or hinder the establishment of lateral movements. Many children do not develop them until late in the mixed dentitional period and some never use but a very slight lateral movement. This establishes a carnivorous type of mastication which fails to develop the greatest efficiency

---

LEGEND FOR PLATE XVIII

Frontal View of Human Skulls.

These skulls were photographed in the same relative size, to show the amount and direction of growth with the development of the full permanent dentition. *A*, Eight months; *B*, one year; *C*, second year; *D*, fourth year; *E*, eighth year; *F*, thirteenth year; *G*, fifteenth year; *H*, adult.

# PLATE XVIII

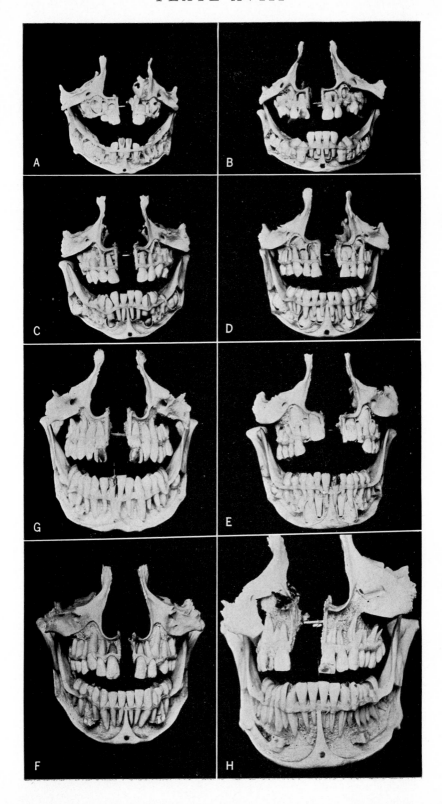

of the dental mill. For this reason training in the development of proper masticatory habits at this time will result in immense benefit at a later date. By the end of the deciduous dentitional period the growth of the permanent teeth supplies a very important active growth influence. This is particularly noticeable in the incisor region where, if it is experienced before the first teeth are lost, these teeth are separated, causing the spacing commonly observed in children of this age. If this growth spurt occurs after shedding of the temporary teeth, spacing may not be evident.

Commonly the appearance of the first permanent molar terminates the deciduous dentitional period. When the jaws are slightly retarded in development, the lower central incisors may be lost before the molars appear. Either event marks the beginning of the mixed dentitional period.

**The Permanent Teeth.**—The permanent teeth continue to develop within the jaws. The crypts of bicuspids and second molars encase the respective tooth germs which begin to calcify, the first bicuspid at about the age of two, the second bicuspid at the age of two and a half, and the second molar at the age of three years (Figs. 231 and 232). The pressures exerted by cellular multiplication and activity cause the bone of the crypts to respond and affect enlargement and alteration in form. These changes occasion remodeling of the bracing trabeculæ in the alveolar process and the body of the upper and lower jaws (Table 2, Logan and Kronfeld).

Before the lower last deciduous and first permanent molars erupt the crypt walls are pushed downward by the development of the tooth root until the inferior dental nerve lies between the floor of the crypt and the cortical plate of the lower border of the mandible. In this way pressure may be produced to cause reflex nervous symptoms which sometimes precede eruption.

**The Alveolar Process.**—The growth of the alveolar process is closely correlated with the development of the dental units and the growth pattern of the individual. It is modified by alterations due to the abnormalities in the development of the teeth themselves.

The alveolar process grows in response to the demands for support of the deciduous dentition. The changes occurring within the crypts of the permanent teeth contribute materially to the height of both maxillæ and mandible. The change in dimension and proportion is in a large measure responsible for the change in facial appearance so characteristic of this age. Measurements from the mental foramen to the crest of the alveolar process in the mandible taken from a new-born skull and compared with that of a six-year-old child show clearly the increase in height (Plate XVI, *A–F*).

## THE MIXED DENTITIONAL PERIOD

The time from the appearance of the first permanent tooth, at approximately six years of age, until the shedding of the last deciduous tooth, about the age of twelve, marks the interval frequently referred to as the mixed dentitional period. At no time is coördination of growth and development, freedom from disease, and the stimulus of function more important. The occluding surfaces of the teeth are contoured by cusps, marginal ridges and fossæ. As these irregular surfaces of opposing teeth in the upper and lower jaws are approximated by the process of eruption the very narrow margin of a cusp apex or a marginal ridge may determine normal or abnormal tooth relationship. Once contact of the occluding surfaces of antagonists has been established each tooth influences the position of the other as pressures are reciprocated. Moreover each of the dental units through contact with adjacent teeth contributes to a similar interchange of pressures within its respective dental arch. The stimulus of function applied to normal inter- and intra-dental arch contacts promotes normal growth. When abnormal tooth relationship prevails the force of function serves to accentuate and lock the teeth in abnormal relationship. The supporting tissues react readily to detrimental influences which alter the form and architecture of the bone and produce the deformities of malocclusion.

**General Growth and Development.**—General growth and development in this period often exhibit greater variation due to environment, activity and disease. Gains in height and weight are somewhat greater for girls than boys. This is more noticeable in the last two years because of the earlier evidences of adolescent changes in the female. The early period of puberty is characterized by gains in height while weight increase is more noticeable in the latter part. In the mixed dentitional period healthy girls grow from 2 to 3 inches per year, while boys grow 2 to $2\frac{1}{2}$ inches. Their respective gains in weight range from 6 to 10 and 6 to 8 pounds annually. As in the deciduous dentitional period these tend to be more uniform in children free from disturbance.

**The Head.**—The head has approximated the adult size. There is growth in the region of the lambdoid suture in the very early part of the period but little change in the latter two years.

**The Face.**—The face, however, grows materially in height with the development of the permanent dentition and the countenance becomes appreciably more mature. The maxillary and ethmoid sinuses are enlarged and the frontal sinus continues to increase in size. The capacity of the nasal spaces increases as well (Compare Figs. 232 and 233).

**The Maxillæ.**—The maxillæ grow moderately in width and materially in height with the increase in the sinus spaces and the formation of the alveolar process supporting the permanent teeth. The palate continues to descend, noticeably increasing the distance of the level of its plane to that of the inferior border of the orbit. There is relatively greater growth in height posteriorly with the development of the second and third molar teeth. Pressures seem to be exerted by the soft tissues and by the enlargement of the nasal cavity and naso-pharynx which swing the bulk of the bone downward and forward, rotating upon the axes of the frontal and zygromatic sutures. Adjustment to the gradual change is here provided by reorganization of the growing bone in response to these stresses. In this way the level of the palatal plane is changed with respect to the cranial base.

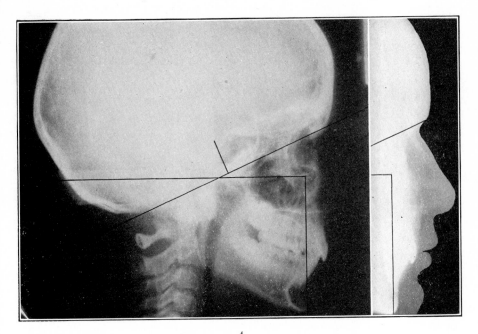

*A*

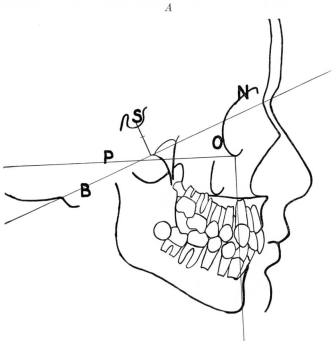

*B*

FIG. 233.—*A*, Cephalometric roentgenogram of a healthy twelve-year-old child·
(Courtesy of Dr. B. H. Broadbent, Bolton Foundation.)
*B*. Tracing of *A*.  *B*, Bolton point; *N*, nasion; *O*, orbitalis; *P*, porion; *S*, sella turcica.

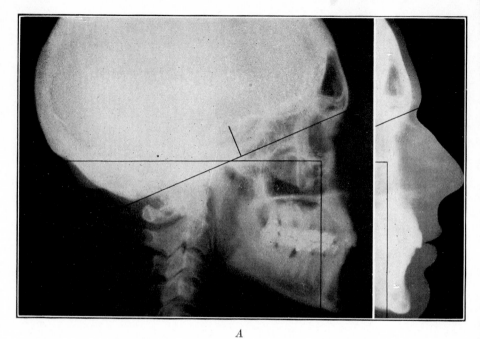

*A*

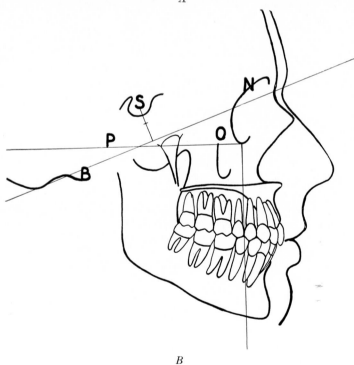

*B*

FIG. 234.—*A*, Cephalometric roentgenogram of a healthy thirty-five and a half-year-old adult.  (Courtesy of Dr. B. H. Broadbent, Bolton Foundation.)

*B*. Tracing of *A*.  *B*, Bolton point; *N*, nasion; *O*, orbitalis; *P*, porion; *S*, sella turcica.

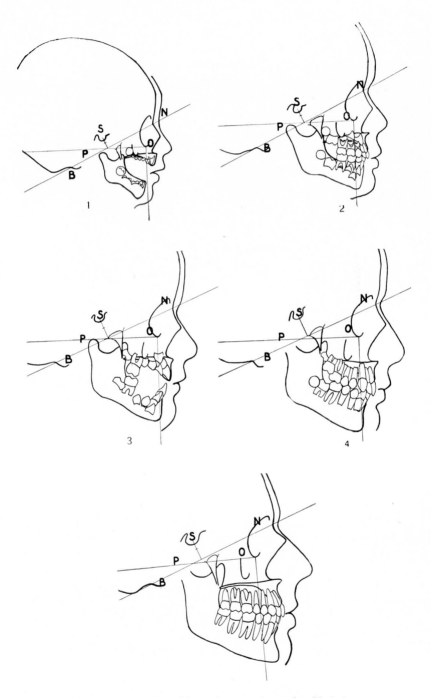

Fig. 235.—Roentgenographic tracings. 1, 3 months old; 2, 4 years old; 3, 6½ years old; 4, 12 years old; 5, adult.

These changes may readily be observed by a study of Figs. 230 to 234. By placing a pencil or straight-edge along the shadow cast by the nasal floor and comparing the angle made with the line (Bolton plane) drawn across the illustrations from the junction of frontal and nasal bones (N. Nasion) to the superior portion of the notch in the shadow cast by the occipital bone (B. Bolton point), the altered relationship is observed (Fig. 235).

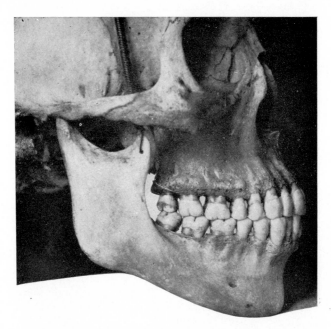

Fig. 236.—The distribution of bone in the alveolar process.

Recalling that these changes are effected by the unequal rate of growth stimulated by the essential growth forces, one gains a clearer concept of the manner through which facial type is established. Similarly the mechanism through which functional and growth disturbances may materially alter the architecture of the face is better understood. For example, disorders which retard growth in the premaxillary area may fail to lower the anterior third of the palatal plane as rapidly as the posterior portion. The plane of occlusion is in this way affected. Adjustment to this growth arrest is

LEGEND FOR PLATE XIX.

Medial View of Human Maxillæ.

Maxillæ photographed from the median line in the same relative size to show the amount and direction of growth. *A*, Two years; *B*, three years; *C*, six years; *D*, ten years; *E*, twelve years; *F*, adult.

# PLATE XIX

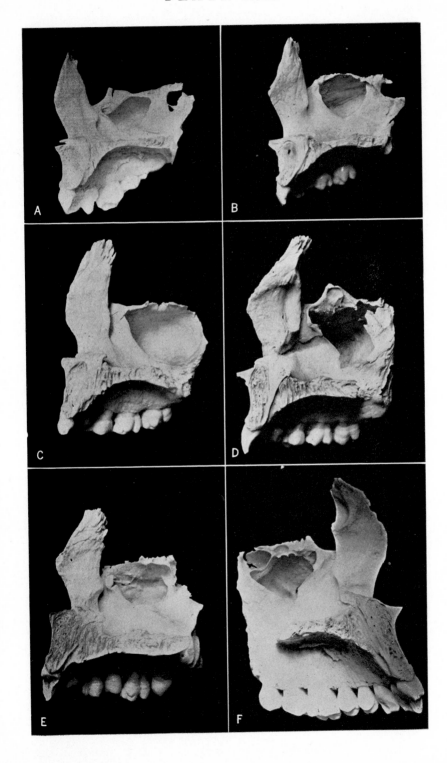

responsible for changes in tooth position and alteration in supporting structure and facial framework.

**The Mandible.**—The mandible likewise increases materially in height of the body due to the development of the alveolar process supporting the permanent teeth. The lower denture is carried forward correspondingly with the upper by increase in length of both the ramus and the body. There is at the same time a further reduction of the angle between these portions of the bone. As the body is elongated to accommodate the extension of the distal protions of the lower dental arch, the anterior border of the ramus is further resorbed and the relative antero-posterior diameter is increased by additions along the dorsal aspect. The mental eminence as well as the angle of the jaw becomes more prominent (Plate XVI and XVII, *H–L*).

It is well to remember that the condylar path of the temporomandibular joint guides rather than controls the movements of the mandible. Very satisfactory masticatory function is possible when the heads of the condyles have been removed surgically. In the mandibular movements of speech and mastication the bone is moved into position and force exerted by the coördinated action of its musculature. For this reason it is difficult if indeed possible to duplicate the movements of the mandible by a mechanical articulator. The bone of the lower jaw is moulded in response to the forces which it receives from the action of the musculature both through the muscle attachments and the pressures transmitted through the teeth and their supporting framework as the jaws are brought together. The bulk of the soft tissues adjacent to the bone including the lips, cheeks and tongue exert a positive influence.

**The Deciduous Teeth.**—The deciduous teeth are gradually shed during this interval. The dates at which they are lost are given in Table 2. The process of resorption of the roots of the deciduous teeth appears to be related to pressure from the expanding crypts or crown of the permanent tooth beneath. There are, however, other factors, for resorption of the roots of teeth of the first dentition occurs when the permanent successors are missing. However the rate of resorption is usually retarded in such cases.

Shifting of the deciduous teeth may so affect the function of the supporting tissues that changes in form are produced as a consequence. Changes in the position of the deciduous teeth do not invariably alter the position of the underlying permanent tooth or its crypt.

**The Permanent Teeth.**—The permanent teeth as they develop furnish pressures which contribute to the growth of both maxillæ and mandible. Likewise their eruption is attended by the building of their own alveolar process which furnishes increased width and height. Growth in both directions is materially aided by function, for the formation of the teeth alone does not develop a well-formed jaw.

The usual age at which the crowns and roots of the teeth are completed as well as the time of their eruption is given in Table 2. The crowns of the centrals are wider than those of the teeth shed, and they consequently exert pressure upon the mesial surfaces of the laterals, pushing them apart and carrying them occlusally and forward.

In cases where the first teeth have been lost prematurely, the permanent teeth tend to compensate by early eruption. This seems particularly true when the cause of loss has been dental caries.

*First Permanent Molar.*—About the sixth year the first permanent molars take their place distal to the temporary teeth and their cusps interlock. The importance of these teeth can scarcely be overstated. They are not only the chief means of mastication during the time in which the deciduous teeth are lost and replaced by their successors, but also maintain the relation between the jaws. The way in which these teeth lock determines the balance between the forces exerted by the action of the muscles attached in the region of the ramus and symphysis. Deviation from the normal relation of the molars will entirely change the direction of the forces, and will be manifested by a modification in the development in the bone.

*Third Molars.*—It is well to remember that in healthy children the third molars begin to calcify between nine and ten years of age. After the second molar is in place the growth of the third molar should exert sufficient force so that room is provided for it. Bone activity frequently becomes so sluggish that the growth of the third molar cannot produce the effect it should, and it remains impacted.

**The Alveolar Process.**—The alveolar process is subject to marked changes during this period. That portion which has supported the first teeth undergoes extensive resorption as they are shed. It is replaced in turn by the bony support developed about the roots of the permanent teeth as these continue to erupt and assume their position in the dental arch. Consequently the alveolar process is the site of intensive activity, bone being built and destroyed in answer to physiological necessity. The result is the building of a new alveolar process about the permanent teeth at an advanced level, further increasing the height of both maxillæ and mandible and consequently of the face as well.

**Histophysiological Remarks.**—The relative position of the teeth within the arches and the form and position of the denture as a whole is the result of the sum of the forces acting upon them. When there is a balance in the reciprocating forces, the teeth do not move. When the equilibrium is disturbed there is movement in the direction of the weaker force. If this parity of influences prevails in a denture which is harmonious with respect to type and function ,it is considered a normal occlusion. If the dynamic balance is disturbed, adjustment occurs until an equilibrium is reestablished. This may or may not be within the limits of normal occlusion. These changes are effected by the response of vital tissues to pressure stimuli. The terms balance and equilibrium are used in a relative sense, for a state of absolute balance is undoubtedly rare and of very brief duration. It is rather the cumulative effect of these varied and intermittent forces such as eruption or muscular pressure. One must consider also the character, intensity, duration, direction and frequency of repetition of each force to fully appreciate its influence. A practice such as thumb-sucking may not always cause malocclusion, and distortions of form may, through alterations in the forces to which the denture is subjected, be only transient.

The period of the mixed dentition is hazardous because of the sudden alteration of the forces to which the denture is subjected in function: the intensity of the growth forces; the frequency of disease; and the loss of resistance and contact support through the shedding of the deciduous teeth. The shifting of position of the first permanent molar with the loss of the second deciduous molar is a case in point. The latter tooth is of greater mesio-distal diameter than the second premolar which succeeds it. In the normal sequence of events the eruptive force of the premolar carries it to position before the forces of occlusion and the soft tissues posterior to the permanent molar have carried that tooth into contact. If, however, the first tooth is lost prematurely these forces may bring the six year molar mesially before the premolar has erupted sufficiently to offer resistance, causing the catastrophe so often encountered at this age. Many dentitional accidents at this and other periods may be subjected to similar analysis which if anticipated will facilitate their prevention.

## THE PERIOD OF PERMANENT DENTITION

There are three obvious divisions of the permanent dentitional period: (1) the interval prior to maturity; (2) the period of the mature dentition; and (3) senescence. While each of these subdivisions present relatively clear characteristics, the transition from one to the other may be attended by features of both and experienced at widely varied ages.

**Period Prior to Maturity.**—The period of continued occlusal growth with increasing facial height, and anterior migration of the entire denture following the eruption of the second molars (which continues with the eruption of the third molars and their adjustment to occlusion) represents the first division. Yet many adults never succeed in cutting the third molars and in some there are many features of maturity evident before these teeth appear.

**Period of Mature Dentition.**—Similarly the second division comprises the time during which the denture functions as a stable unit having attained its maximum growth and development. Yet there is never a period of absolute stability. Moreover, as soon as the maximum alveolar height is attained, there ensues a minute but steady decrease.

**Senescence.**—The third, or senescent age, is the period in which retrogressive changes appear in both dental units and supporting tissues. It does not arise suddenly, or in all teeth and areas of the alveolar process uniformly. The picture, however, of the elderly person with abraded occlusal surfaces, recession of the gingivæ and absorption of the alveolar crest and septæ, will clearly fall within this division.

**General Growth and Development.**—The early part of this period constitutes the episode of adolescence. It is a time of accelerated physical growth prior to the union of the epiphyses of the long bones, followed by

increase in length of the trunk and addition in weight. The advent of
sexual maturity with the development and accentuation of secondary sex
characteristics further emphasizes the alteration in physical appearance.
The mental adjustment, though less obvious, is fully as marked and of
perhaps even greater significance. The change is more rapid and somewhat
earlier in girls than in boys, though the age and duration is variable in both
sexes. All of these factors, including dimensional, metabolic, endocrine
and mental changes have an intimate bearing upon dental tissues and the
problems which the child of this age presents to the dentist.

There is a gradual increase in muscular power, coördination and mental
acuity following adolescence. The individual adjusts himself to his environment, and gains experience and judgment. The energy demanded by
growth is available for activity. This is a period of vigorous function, and
in health the vitality of body tissues is equal to the demands set by use and
resistance to disease. In the female these conditions may be temporarily
altered by pregnancy and menstruation.

Gradually the reactivity of body tissues is diminished. The tempo of
cellular activity is reduced. The effect of damage becomes apparent. There
is a loss of tissue turgor and slow degenerative changes become apparent.
The muscles lose tonicity, allowing the shoulders to droop and the abdomen
to protrude. The gait is slackened and body length decreases. Gradually
these changes produce the cumulative effect known as sensecence.

**The Face.**—The face passes through these progressive and retrogressive
stages from the time following adolescence when it reaches its full development through the interval when habits of facial expression develop the lines
of character. Slowly by occlusal wear and loss in alveolar height the length
of the face decreases, and this with the loss of tissue turgor accentuates the
facial lines. Changes in tissue texture and loss of the teeth eventually
produce the picture of old age.

**The Maxillæ.**—The maxillæ continue to increase in size in the first division
of the adult dentitional period, and with the eruption of the third molars,
particularly if this occurs early, assists in anterior growth of the upper
denture. There is increase in height of the alveolar process following the
eruption of the last tooth. The form of the bone is moulded by functional
stresses. The reactivity of the tissues decreases and change is effected less
readily. Resistance to stress is replaced with resorption rather than rebuilding for support (Plate XVII, $K$ to $N$).

**The Mandible.**—The mandible shares the changes of the maxillæ. The
characteristics developed in the preceding periods reach their maximum
attainment. With the diminution of function and the change of stresses
through the wear and loss of teeth, the bone again tends to resemble certain
of its infantile characteristics. The height of the body is diminished upon
resorption of the alveolar process. The symphysis, however, remains
prominent.

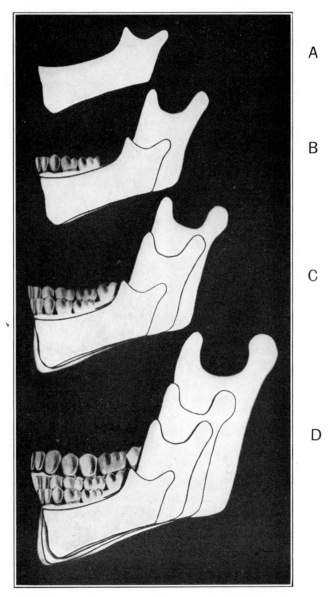

FIG. 237.—Superposition of 4 tracings of the mandible of the same individual at different age periods. *A*, 3 months; *B*, 3 years; *C*, 7 years; *D*, 18 years. (Courtesy, A. G. Brodie.)

TABLE 10.—SUMMARY OF POSTNAT..

| Developmental period. | | General growth characteristics. | Principal hazards to normal growth and development. | Head. | Face. |
|---|---|---|---|---|---|
| NEONATAL . . . . (First fourteen days of life.) | | Loss in weight. Arrest in growth. Adjustment to extra-uterine conditions. Alteration in blood vascular system. | Birth trauma. Poor neonatal adjustment. | Largest body unit. Anterior fontanelle open. Posterior fontanelle closing. Cranial sutures not united. | Relative proportion to c nium 1 to 8. Width relatively grea than height. |
| DECIDUOUS DENTITION . (Eruption of first deciduous tooth to eruption of first permanent tooth. Sixth month to sixth year.) | | Rapid in first year with trebling of birth weight. Slower thereafter with weight increase of about 5 lbs. per year and height gains 2½ to 3 in. at end of period. Development of coördination and control of musculature and mental adjustment to environment. | Detrimental habits producing abnormal pressures on rapidly growing and easily influenced tissues. Growth disturbances due to disease. | Approximation of cranial bones at suture lines. Appearance of frontal sinus. Growth at base of cranium particularly of sphenoid bone. Parietal areas and vertex raised. Angle of forehead becomes more vertical. | Increase of length in p portion to width. Growth of maxillary nuses. Appearance of ethm sinuses. Ratio of face to crani becomes 1 to 6. |
| MIXED DENTITION . . (Eruption of first permanent tooth to loss of last deciduous tooth. Sixth to twelfth year.) | | Gains in height and weight variable. Girls 2 to 3 in. and 6 to 10 lbs. Boys 2 to 2½ in. and 6 to 8 lbs. Disturbed sequence and coördination of growth due to adolescent changes in last part of period. | Childhood diseases. Changes in function due to loss of deciduous and eruption of permanent teeth. Ectopic eruption. | Increase in area of frontal sinus. Growth in lambdoidal region. Beginning closure of cranial sutures | Growth in height contin more rapidly than wid |
| PERMANENT DENTITION (From loss of last deciduous tooth to loss of last permanent tooth. Twelve years and over.) | Adolescence | Increase in height followed by increase in weight. Sexual maturity. | Lack of vigorous function. Loss of tooth substance through dental caries. | Frontal sinus developed. Approximated adult size. Growth at lambdoidal sutures. | Continued growth height. |
| | Maturity | Gains in weight, muscular power and mental stability | Dental caries. Diseases of gingivæ, dental pulp and supporting tissues. | Adult configuration. Closure of cranial sutures. | Attainment of adult p portions. Establishment of lines facial expression. |
| | Senescence | Loss of tissue tone and muscular power. Decrease in body height. Decrease in rate of cellular reactivity. Decrease in osseous mineral content. | Diseases of the periodontal tissues. | . . . . . . . . | Loss of height in low half of face. Increase in lines of fac expression |

NTAL DEVELOPMENT.

| Maxillæ. | Mandible. | Alveolar process. | Deciduous teeth. | Permanent teeth. | Soft tissues. |
|---|---|---|---|---|---|
| ntulous. ...te flat. on of premaxillary- ...axillary sutures. | Ramus short with obtuse, angle between it and body. Edentulous. | Supporting the crypts of the unerupted teeth. | Calcification of all crowns begun but none complete. Neonatal ring in enamel and dentin. | Tip of mesio-buccal cusps of first molars calcified in some cases. | Oral mucous membrane complete but easily traumatized. Tongue completely formed and active. Salivary glands formed but show little secretory activity. |
| ...ease in height and ...epth greater than ...width. ...ate lowered and extended posteriorly. ...ly carried anterior-... | Growth in height of ramus and body with decrease of angle between them. Union of lateral halves in first year. | Marked increase in height with eruption of deciduous teeth. Continued height increase after deciduous dentition is complete (entire dentition carried occlusally). | Complete calcification of crowns by first year and roots by third year. Eruption of first tooth 6 to 8 months—all teeth by 2½ years (Table 2). Use of this dentition is at first vertical and later by lateral masticatory movements. Spacing of deciduous incisor teeth. | Beginning calcification of all crowns but that of third molars. Complete calcification of first molar crowns (Table 2). | Salivary glands begin active function. Development of gingiva |
| ...tinued increase in ...eight and depth ...reater than width. ...ly moves forward. ...atal plane lowered ...nd rotated slightly ...ownward and forward with continued ...osterior extension. | Increase in length of ramus and body. Development at symphysis. Increase in height of body. | Loss of the alveolar process of deciduous dentition. Appearance of alveolar process of permanent dentition. Continued contribution to height of jaws. | Gradual resorption of roots and shedding of crowns (Table 2) | Beginning calcification of third molar crowns. Complete calcification of all other teeth. Eruption of all but second and third molars (Table 2). | Development of gingiva about permanent teeth. |
| ...tinued growth as ...bove. | Continued growth as above. | Increase in height in support of permanent teeth. | ....... | Eruption of 12-year molars. Adjustment of previously erupted teeth in occlusion. | |
| ...ainment of maximum growth. | Attainment of maximum growth. | Continued increase in height after eruption of all teeth. | ....... | Completion of roots of all but third molars. Eruption and calcification of roots of third molars. Adjustment in occlusion. | |
| ...rease in height. | Decrease in height of body | Decrease in height. Resorption of crest and septal portion. Resorption of regions where teeth have been lost. | ...... . | Attrition. Loss of teeth through diseases of soft and hard dental tissues. | |

**The Alveolar Process.**—The alveolar process attains its greatest development in the second, or adult division, of the period. Under the stimulus of vigorous function it carries each denture occlusally and forward until the maximum facial development is attained. With increasing age there is a gradual recession of the alveolar bone. In addition the loss in height in the mandible, for example, from mental foramen or inferior border is greater than that attributable to attrition. With the loss of the teeth individually or collectively, the alveolar bone slowly recedes through a process of gradual reorganization and resorption. This emphasizes the intimate relation of the alveolar to the dental units.

**The Permanent Teeth.**—The permanent teeth are normally the only dental units in the mouth throughout the three divisions of this period. The second permanent molars, which frequently have begun to appear before this time, continue to erupt and be adjusted to occlusion. The axes become more vertical and their roots completely calcified. The crowns of the third molars are calcified in the early stages of the adolescent interval, and at the end of this time break through the soft tissues. The progressive inconstancy of dental development becomes most marked with the eruption of these teeth. If their occlusal progress is retarded until the general growth impulse of the individual is expended, their opportunities for normal eruption are diminished. In such cases they mature at a time when the rate of growth in the maxillæ and mandible is diminishing, consequently the impetus for growth which they contribute is not always equal to the power of these bones to respond. Impactions and malposition are frequent.

Following the eruption of the third molars and the calcification of their roots, all of the teeth adjust themselves to the forces of occlusion, and the complex stimuli arising from the bulk and activity of the adjacent musculature. When maturity has been reached, the teeth through wear and adaptation in position have become relatively stable through the balance of the forces which act upon them. This equilibrium is easily disturbed, however, by the loss of tooth substance through dental caries or abrasion, nervous habits such as grinding the teeth, peculiarities of facial expression, disease of the supporting tissues and many other causes which may at any time change the balance, resulting in alteration in tooth position until a new equilibrium is established.

The teeth gradually decrease in size both on the occlusal surfaces from attrition and at the contact points from interproximal wear. The size of the pulp chamber decreases with the deposition of secondary dentin and the dental pulp becomes progressively more fibrotic. The retrogressive changes gradually increase until in senescence the hazards of disease to the hard and soft tissues leave few individuals with a full complement of teeth and many with edentulous mouths.

It has been the object of this chapter to suggest certain of the outstanding growth, developmental and physiological features of the oral structures. A knowledge of gross and minute anatomy is of value to the clinician in direct proportion to his understanding of structure in terms of function. In vital tissues there is so intimate a relation between form and function that comprehension of either is impossible without the other.

## BIBLIOGRAPHY.

BROADBENT, B. HOLLY: Bolton Standards and Technique in Orthodontic Practice, Angle Orthod., *7*, 209–233, 1937.

——————: The Face of the Normal Child, Angle Orthod., *7*, 183–208, 1937.

BRODIE, A. G.: On the Growth Pattern of the Human Head from the Third Month to the Eighth Year of Life, Am. Jour. Anat., *68*, 209, 1941.

——————: On the Growth of the Jaws and the Eruption of the Teeth, Angle Orthod., *2*, 109–123, 1942.

HELLMAN, M.: An Introduction to the Growth of the Human Face from Infancy to Adulthood, Int. Jour. Orthod., Oral Surg. and Radiography, *18*, 777, 1922.

The Human Face, Symposium Presented Before the Philadelphia County Dental Society, Dental Cosmos, Special Publ., 1935.

LOGAN, W. H. G., and KRONFELD, R.: Development of the Human Jaws and Surrounding Structures from Birth to the Age of Fifteen Years, Jour Am. Dent. Assn., *20*, 379, 1933.

NELSON, W. E.: Mitchell-Nelson Textbook of Pediatrics. 4th Ed. Revised. Philadelphia and London, W. B. Saunders Company, 1945.

SCHOUR, I.: The Neonatal Line in the Enamel and Dentin of the Human Deciduous Teeth and First Permanent Molar, Jour. Am. Dent. Assn., *23*, 1946, 1936.

SCHOUR, I., BRODIE, A. G., and KING, E. Q.: The Hypophysis and the Teeth. IV. A Case Report of a Hypopituitary Patient, Angle Orthod., *4*, 285, 1934.

SCHOUR, I., and KRONFELD, R.: Studies in Tooth Ring Analysis. IV. Neonatal Dental Hypoplasia, Analysis of the Teeth of an Infant With Brain Injury at Birth, Arch. Path., *26*, 471, 1938.

White House Conference on Child Health and Protection, Growth and Development of the Child, Part II, Anatomy and Physiology, New York, The Century Company, 1933.

# CHAPTER 22

# Dental Caries

**Introduction.**—While, strictly speaking, the problem of caries belongs to the field of dental pathology, the disease occupies so prominent a position in dental practice that a text which is designed to promote understanding of the dental tissues and their properties can scarcely be said to be adequate if it overlooks the intimate relationship existing between this disease and the structures it affects. Indeed, aside from a purely academic interest, the primary reason for studying the normal gross and microscopic anatomy is to obtain, maintain, or restore the normal condition to the best of our ability.

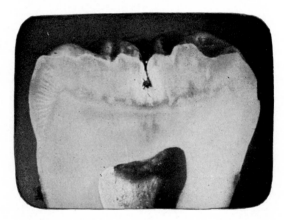

Fig. 238.—A split tooth, showing caries beginning in an occlusal groove.

For the purpose of this chapter on dental caries the disease is considered as a specific entity. It is well, however, to carry a mental reservation that as further studies improve our concept, we may eventually come to regard it as a syndrome, a clinical entity produced by more than one set of circumstances.

**Definition.**—Dental Caries is a bacterial disease of the calcified tissues of the teeth in which characteristic lesions, occurring in typical locations cause a solution of the inorganic and digestion of the organic tooth substance. The lesions progress uniformly or intermittently to the involvement of the dental pulp or become arrested spontaneously during any stage of their development.

( 342 )

## THE PROGRESS OF DENTAL CARIES

It is of the utmost importance in the recognition and treatment of caries for the dentist to clearly visualize the changes in both the enamel and dentin during the course of the disease. One who has not studied carefully the effect of caries on the structure of the enamel, so as to recognize the extent of injury to the structure of the tissue by its appearance to the naked eye, can never be considered fit to prepare cavities as a treatment for the disease. Without this knowledge he will grossly underestimate the hazard of the early lesions and the importance of basic principles in cavity preparation.

FIG. 239.—A split tooth, showing caries progressing in an occlusal groove and invading the dentin.

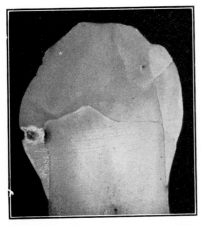

FIG. 240.—A split tooth showing caries beginning on a smooth surface.

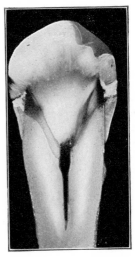

FIG. 241.—A split tooth showing the progress of caries on a smooth surface and invading the dentin.

Although for fifty years the rules of standard teaching have required the complete excavation of infected tissue and the extension of cavity walls to areas of relative immunity, a survey of average modern restorations offers startling testimony of the disregard of these fundamental principles.

As mentioned in the definition, dental caries attacks certain external surfaces of the teeth more commonly than others. These are, in the order of their importance, *pits* and *fissures, proximal surfaces* and the *gingival third* of the buccal or labial surfaces. The last two are similar in their pathological characteristics and are spoken of as *smooth surface lesions* (Fig. 240).

The progressive stages of the disease through the hard tissues of the tooth is identical for the different areas. The difference in the susceptibility of these areas is due to the opportunities they offer for the bacterial growth rather than difference in resistance of tooth substance towards invasion. The lesions themselves have a characteristic form in enamel and dentin which is determined by the structure of the tissues in the region invaded.

**Caries Beginning in Pits and Fissures.**—Over four-fifths of all cavities begin in pits and fissures. These become filled with food débris which furnish ideal culture media for acid-forming bacteria. At the opening of these recesses, the acid is washed away by the saliva as fast as it is formed, but in the deeper portions it is confined and acts upon the enamel, dissolving away the substance between the rods and following the rod direction toward the dentino-enamel junction. The form of the disintegrating enamel in such positions is always that of a cone or wedge, with the apex at the opening of the pit or groove and the base toward the dentino-enamel junction (Figs. 238 and 239). This form is determined by the direction of the enamel rods in this region.

The formation of acid under these circumstances is often so rapid and the confinement so perfect that the carious process manifests its greatest intensity here. The rods in this region are also very short; the deeper the pit or fissure, the shorter the rod and the more rapid the decay.

The action often dissolves the rods as well as the cementing substance and progresses across the rods. But even when the action follows the enamel-rod direction, the form will be broader near the dentino-enamel junction, since the rods are inclined toward the enamel surface. This region appears white by reflected light because the cementing substance has been removed from between the rods and the resulting air spaces refract the lights (Figs. 238 and 239).

The form of the disintegrating dentin is that of a cone or wedge with the apex toward the pulp and the base at the dentino-enamel junction, and thus presents an enlarged mirror image of the cone in the enamel. This process is in accordance with the direction of the dentinal tubules in this region.

**Caries Beginning on Smooth Surfaces.**—Lesions originating upon smooth surfaces which include both proximal and gingival caries, are likewise the result of the activity of acidogenic and proteolytic bacteria. As these areas are lacking the structural recesses necessary for the concentration of acid, as provided by the pits and fissures, prevention of its dilution and dissipation by the saliva must be supplied by other means. The most frequent mechanism is the *adherent bacterial plaque*. While organic or inorganic substances which furnish protection for the concentration of the acid and yet allow the acquisition of nutritive material will foster the carious lesion, the plaque is the most common and efficient agent.

Caries upon smooth surfaces of the enamel is always due to the growth of a colony of bacteria which becomes attached to the surface through the formation of a protective material. This material causes them to adhere to the surface and at the same time confines their acid products in contact with the enamel. The acid is not dissipated in the saliva and dissolves the inorganic salts of the tissue elements.

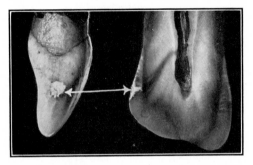

Fig. 242.—A superior central incisor, showing a white spot just to the gingival of the contact point.

Fig. 243.—A split tooth cut through such a white spot as is shown in Fig. 242.

The form of the disintegrated enamel is always that of an irregular truncated cone. In these regions, the base is on the surface of the enamel, its outline is the boundary of the colony, and the apex is toward the dentin in the direction of the enamel rods that start at the colony (Figs. 241 and 243). The inner boundary of the area is never even, but show flame-like extensions toward the dentin in the direction of the rods. This is more marked in some cases than in others, and sometimes suggests that the presence of a colony on the surface has been intermittent (Figs. 245 to 247).

The form of the disintegrated area in the dentin resembles the form in the enamel and that in the dentin of the occlusal areas under pits and fissures. The base is at the dentino-enamel junction and the apex toward the pulp (Figs. 239 and 243). The apex does not approach a point as in the occlusal areas, giving the lesion the form of a truncated cone. This fact is explained by the direction of the dentinal tubules in this region.

**Stages in the Progress of Dental Caries.**—The progress of the carious lesion through the hard tissues of the tooth may be divided into the following stages or periods:

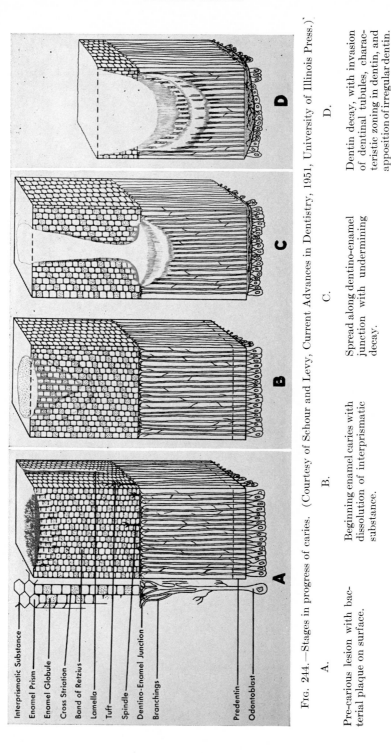

Fig. 244.—Stages in progress of caries. (Courtesy of Schour and Levy, Current Advances in Dentistry, 1951, University of Illinois Press.)

A.

Pre-carious lesion with bacterial plaque on surface.

B.

Beginning enamel caries with dissolution of interprismatic substance.

C.

Spread along dentino-enamel junction with undermining decay.

D.

Dentin decay, with invasion of dentinal tubules, characteristic zoning in dentin, and apposition of irregular dentin.

1. *Enamel Caries.*—From the lodgment of the colony until the action of the acid reaches the dentino-enamel junction (Fig. 244, A and B).

2. The spreading of the lesion along the dentino-enamel junction. (Fig. 244, C).

3. *Dentin Caries.*—The bacterial invasion of the dentin and the secondary or backward decay of the enamel (Fig. 244, D).

Fig. 245.—Carious enamel ground on the cover-glass by the shellac method. In the region *X* the cementing substance dissolved from between the rods has been replaced by shellac.

A colony of bacteria attached to the proximal surface of an incisor, just to the gingival of the contact point, will serve to illustrate the stages in the progress of caries.

**Enamel Caries.**—If a surface of a tooth can be examined during this stage, a white spot will be seen as in Fig. 242. The area appears white because the cementing substance has been removed from between the enamel rods. If a tooth is split through such a spot and viewed from the surface, the appearance will be as shown in Fig. 243. These whitened areas are often invisible unless the tissue is dried, because the saliva fills the spaces. If the surface is dried the refraction of the light by the air whitens the affected areas.

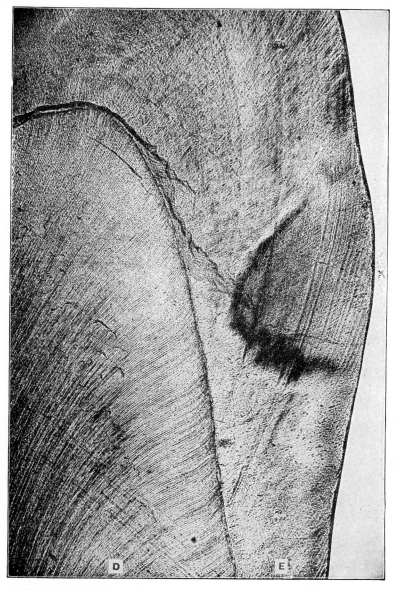

Fig. 246.—A section through a white spot in the first period of attack: *X*, disintegrated enamel; *E*, sound enamel; *D*, dentin.

A good comparison is furnished in a very familiar phenomenon. Snow is white because the air and the microscopic ice crystals are of different refracting indices, and the light is diffused by passing from air to ice crystals. If a snowball is saturated with water it losses it whiteness and becomes translucent, because the water, which is nearly of the same refracting index as ice, fills the space between the ice crystals, and the light is not diffused.

Fig. 247.—A section through a carious spot in the first period. The attack has apparently been slow and intermittent: *X*, disintegrated enamel; *E*, sound enamel; *D*, dentin.

If a section is ground through the white area of such a tooth, the enamel rods will be found entirely separated because of the solution of the inter-prismatic cementing substances, and the cross-striation will be much more apparent because the unevenness in the diameter of the rods has been increased by the action of the acid (Fig. 244, B). In such regions the inter-prismatic cementing substance is dissolved in large areas before any of the rods are dissolved or destroyed (Fig. 245). The surface of the enamel is no

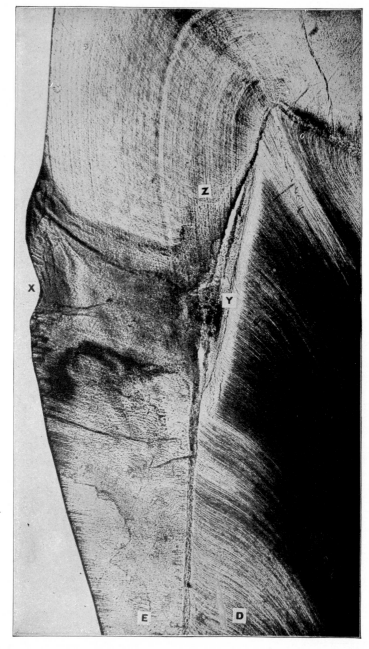

Fig. 248.—A section through a carious spot in the second period. *X*, Disintegrated area, showing swelling of the surface; *Y*, space between enamel and decalcified dentin; *Z*, secondary caries of the enamel; *E*, sound enamel; *D*, dentin.

longer smooth, but roughened. This may often be felt by passing a very fine-pointed steel explorer over the surface. If the colony be dislodged at this stage obviously it is much easier for a new one to become attached.

The boundary between the sound and the disintegrated areas in enamel is usually marked by a darker zone, the significance of which is not now understood (Fig. 245). If the disease progresses continuously, the affected tissue always appears white by reflected light, but if the progress has been intermittent, especially if there have been considerable periods in which no colony has been attached to the surface, the area darkens, becoming brownish or almost black. This is produced by organic materials derived from the oral fluids filling the space between the enamel rods and decomposing, with the probable formation of sulphides of dark color in the spaces. If immunity to caries is attained before the oral fluids have penetrated to the dentino-enamel junction, the spot changes from a white to a brownish or black color. Such spots will be found in some places on most teeth extracted from immune persons. Miller (1890) indicated that such spots are more resistant to the progress of caries than perfect enamel surfaces. At any time during the first period, therefore, the destruction may be arrested by immunity of the patient.

**Progress Along Dentino-enamel Junction.**—This stage extends from the time when the action of the acid reaches the dentino-enamel junction until the rods are destroyed or fall out (Fig. 248). As soon as the solution of the cementing substance reaches the dentino-enamel junction at the apex of the advancing cone, the solution of the inorganic salts in the dentin matrix begins. The acid formed passes through the now porous enamel and acts upon the dentin. Because of the branching of the dentinal tubules at the dentino-enamel junction, the action upon the dentin spreads along this plane.

The action of the acid follows the tubules of the dentin toward the pulp, and spreads through their branches laterally near the dentino-enamel junction so that the form of the disintegrated dentin is always that of a truncated cone with the base at the dentino-enamel junction and the apex toward the pulp chamber.

It must be remembered that the acid acting upon the dentin is formed by the microörganisms on the surface of the enamel, and filters through the spaces between the enamel rods. In this stage no microörganisms have entered the dentin, and the effect upon it is the result of the action of substances formed upon the surface.

The decalcification of the dentin may be considerable, while the surface of the enamel is still preserved. In this period a swelling of the surface is always noticeable (Fig. 248). This results in increasing the area of contact and therefore extends the limits of the colony, increasing the extent of surface attack. This is especially noticeable at the gingival level.

The decalcified dentin matrix shrinks and more or less of a space is formed under the enamel (Fig. 248). Soon, some of the loosened rods between the bottom of the defect and the dentin are either entirely dissolved, displaced or dislodged, and the microörganisms are admitted to the dentin.

The rate of progress of decay in the dentin may often become modified by the presence of a translucent zone of hypercalcified dentin. This zone was first described by Tomes and has been termed sclerosed dentin.

Fig. 249.—A drawing showing the microörganisms of caries growing through the dentinal tubules. (G. V. Black.)

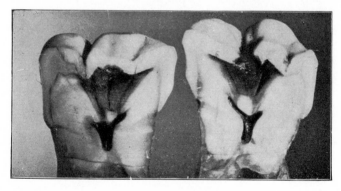

Fig. 250.—A split tooth, showing the undermining of the occlusal enamel by caries spreading at the dentino-enamel junction.

**Third Period.**—This is the period after the enamel rods have begun to fall out and an actual cavity is apparent. As soon as this occurs the surface of the tooth, at the point where the formation of the colony began, is destroyed and the protected point is lost, and the extension of surface attack ceases. The microörganisms are admitted to the dentin, where they grow through the dentinal tubules, spreading rapidly at the dentino-enamel junction (Figs. 248 and 249). The dentin is always decalcified in advance of the penetration of the microörganisms. The decalcified dentin matrix becomes food material for the bacteria, and the space produced by the destruction of tissue accommodates more decomposing foodstuffs.

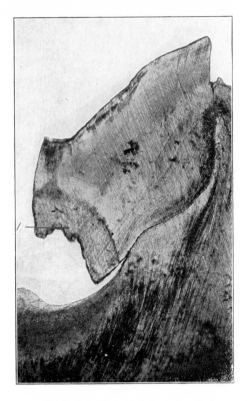

Fig. 251.—A section showing the undermining of the enamel and secondary or backward decay at *1*.

The acid formed within the cavity now attacks the enamel from within outward, producing what has been called backward or *secondary decay of enamel* (Figs. 250 and 251). The condition may progress until, as in Fig. 250, the entire occlusal enamel has been undermined and greatly weakened before the site of original attack is noticeably enlarged. This condition is shown in Fig. 251, in which the area indicated by 1 has had the cementing substance entirely removed from between the rods, and is in the same structural condition as the disintegrated areas in the first and second stages.

It is safe to say that in the past, too few cavities have been filled before the enamel has caved in. It is equally certain that in a large proportion of cases, by the time this has happened, the removal of all disintegrated tissue

23

will require a far greater loss of tooth substance than would have been required in the first period.

## BIBLIOGRAPHY.

CHASE, S. W.:   The Development, Histology, and Physiology of Enamel and Dentin—
    Their Significance to the Caries Process, Jour. Dent. Res., *27*, 87, 1948.
EASLICK, K. A. (Edited by):   Dental Caries—Mechanism and Present Technics as
    Evaluated at the University of Michigan Workshop, St. Louis, The C. V. Mosby
    Company, 1948.
KRONFELD, R., and BOYLE, P. E.:   Histopathology of the Teeth and Their Surrounding
    Structures, 3d. Ed. Revised Philadelphia, Lea & Febiger, 1949.

# CHAPTER 23

# The Relation of Histological Structure
# to Operative Dentistry

## THE RELATION OF THE STRUCTURE TO THE CUTTING OF THE ENAMEL

Two methods of cutting enamel by hand instruments are to chop or cleave it, and to shave or plane it.

**Cleaving or Chopping Enamel.**—In the cleavage of enamel the action of the instrument more nearly resembles that of splitting ice than that of splitting wood. The ax for splitting wood is strongly wedge-shaped, and the wedge pries the fibers apart. In splitting ice a small nick is made on the surface and then a sharp blow cracks the ice in the direction of the cleavage. In a similar way the chisel applied to the surface of the enamel makes a slight scratch on the surface, and the force applied at a slight angle to the direction of the rods cracks the tissue along the rod direction. The bevel of the instrument is designed to give strength and a keen edge, not to act as a wedge. In order to cleave the enamel it is always necessary that there be a break or opening in the tissue, and usually that the dentin be removed from under it. Only a small portion can be split off at a time. The edge of the chisel should be placed on the enamel 0.5 or 1 mm. from the opening, rarely more, and so piece after piece is split into the cavity. Fig. 252 shows a section of enamel. The edge of the chisel is placed with the shaft in the relation to enamel rod direction indicated; a tap of a steel mallet will split off a piece, and the chisel is moved back and a second piece is split off. Undermined enamel will split easily in this way. As soon as a point is reached where the enamel rests on sound dentin, it is recognized by the resistance it offers to the chisel.

Straight enamel can be split off from the dentin without difficulty if properly attacked with sharp hand instruments. Such enamel will split or cleave in the direction of the rods with comparative ease, and breaks down very readily when the underlying dentin is removed. It will usually cleave through its entire thickness and break away from the dentin.

If the inner portion of the enamel is gnarled, it can only be cleaved by first undermining the dentin. As cleavage is caused by the difference in strength between the rods and cementing substance, it is easy to see that gnarled enamel will not split or cleave easily when resting upon sound dentin. Such enamel will split as far as the rods are straight; but where they begin to twist they will break off, leaving a portion which is very difficult to remove by attack from the surface. If the dentin is removed from under it, the gnarled enamel will crack through in an irregular way, following the general direction of the rods.

**Planing or Shaving Enamel.**—In this manner of cutting enamel the tissue is removed without reference to the rod direction and without injury to its structure (Fig. 255). The chisel is used like the blade of a plane.

Fig. 252.—Diagrammatic position of chisel in cleaving enamel. This can be accomplished best when the enamel is undermined.

The cutting edge is placed against the surface with the shaft of the instrument almost parallel to it, and the tissue is shaved away. In this way the rods that have been cracked apart by the cleavage are removed, and the walls arranged in terms of their structural elements so as to gain the required strength of margin.

**Sharp Instruments.**—Chisels and hatchets for use in cleaving or planing enamel must be kept keenly sharp. If a dull edge is placed on the surface of the enamel it will rest across the ends of many rods, and force applied

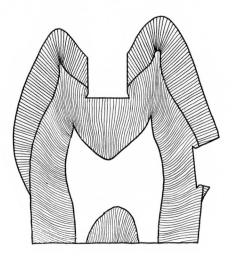

Fig. 253.—Diagram to illustrate two classes of cavities. Note that in one the enamel rods incline toward the cavity and that in the other the enamel rods incline away from the cavity.

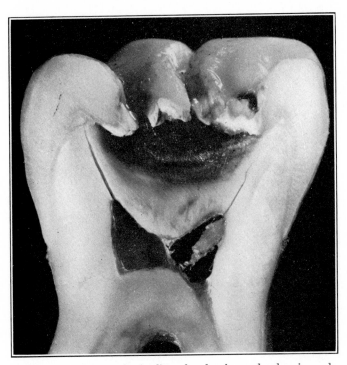

Fig. 254.—Photograph of split molar showing occlusal caries and undermining of the enamel (J. M. Spence).

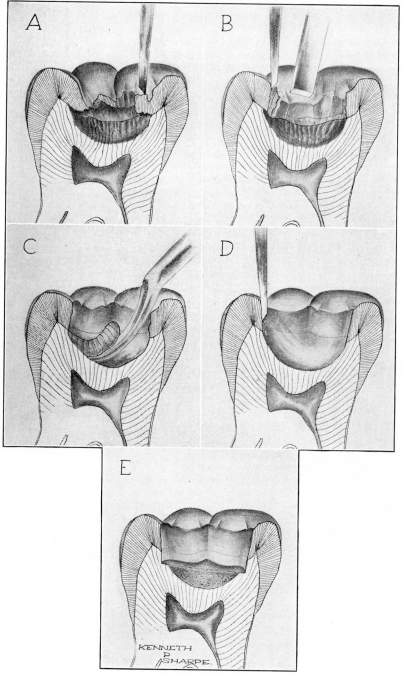

FIG. 255.—Diagrammatic drawings showing the preparation of the cavity of Fig. 255 with hand instruments. *A*, the undermined enamel is cleaved with the use of a chisel: *B*, further removing or clearing of the enamel; *C*, carious dentin is removed by a spoon; *D*, planing of the enamel walls to assure removal of unsupported enamel rods; *E*, completion of cavity showing the cement base for the protection of the vital pulp (J. M. Spence, Manual of Operative Dentistry).

will only crumble rather than split them. The edge must be keen (Fig 252), so as to engage between the rods and start the cleavage. To use hand instruments successfully in cutting enamel, the stock instruments must either be retempered or they must be ordered hard tempered. The cutting edge of the blade of an enamel instrument should be straw-colored when tempered.

The chisel and hatchets are the instruments for removing enamel. The bur is the instrument for removing hard dentin. When the bur is used on enamel it should be remembered that it is used as a revolving chisel. It is by the thoughtful use of hand instruments that knowledge of enamel rod direction is gained, and only by the use of them can the enamel walls be prepared in terms of their structural elements. In cleaving undermined enamel the edge may be used either with a pulling or a pushing motion. For instance, in opening a cavity in the occlusal surface of a molar, the buccal portion of undermined enamel is split off by placing the instrument as shown in Fig. 255*A* and *B*. The bevel of the blade is held toward the cavity and the shaft of the instrument at a slight angle to the rod direction, and the force is applied in the direction of the shaft. The lingual portion may be removed by placing the instrument as indicated in Fig. 255*B* the bevel of the blade away from the cavity and the force applied in the direction of the bevel by a pulling force in the direction of the shaft. This is the way in which force is applied on enamel cleavers. The pitch of the bevel in an enamel cleaver and its relation to the shaft of the instrument is extremely important. The efficiency of an instrument may easily be ruined by careless honing. Every time a cutting instrument is applied to the enamel it must be done with a knowledge of the relation of the cutting edge and the force to the direction of the enamel rods, until the action becomes automatic. The acquirement of this knowledge and skill will do more to increase facility and success in the preparation of cavity walls than any other manipulative factor. The preparation of enamel walls requires the continual application of the knowledge of enamel structure. Enamel is a very hard tissue, but it is composed of structural elements, and walls prepared without reference to them will prove their own weakness.

**Classes of Cavities.**—Cavities may be classified according to their operative procedure or their structural characteristics. Black has given the following clinical classification:

Class 1. Cavities beginning in pits and fissures in any parts of the teeth in which these occur.

Class 2. Cavities beginning in the proximal surfaces of the premolars and molars.

Class 3. Cavities beginning in the proximal surfaces of the incisors and canines which do not require the removal and restoration of the incisal angle.

Class 4. Cavities beginning in the proximal surfaces of the incisors which require the removal and restoration of the incisal angle.

Class 5. Cavities beginning in the gingival third—not pit or fissure cavities—of the labial, buccal or lingual surfaces of the teeth.

From a consideration of the direction of the enamel rods in the tooth crown, and the positions where caries begins on the enamel, enamel walls may be divided, according to their *structural type*, into two classes (Fig. 253).

1. Those in which the enamel rods are inclined toward the cavity, characteristic cavities on occlusal surfaces and cavities beginning in fissures and pits.

2. Those in which the enamel rods are inclined away from the cavity, characteristic of cavities on smooth surfaces.

In the first class it is comparatively easy to obtain a strong margin, and this is fortunate, for when the filling is completed the margin will be subjected to the full force of mastication. In the second it is comparatively difficult to obtain a strong margin, but only sufficient strength is required to withstand the force of condensing the filling material, as after the filling is completed it will be obliged to withstand little force from mastication.

Failures of fillings are often due to structurally imperfect walls. A study of enamel structure as related to cavity preparation will do more to improve the quality of the operation and to increase the facility of its execution than any one factor. This study is a clinical one guided by examination of the microscopic structure of the tissue. In operating at the chair one learns the detail of enamel rod direction as applied to cavity preparation. If instruments are to be properly used, a sufficient knowledge must have been acquired to permit one to think of enamel in terms of its structural elements.

## THE STRUCTURAL REQUIREMENTS FOR STRONG ENAMEL WALLS

From the consideration of the physical character of the enamel, its structural elements and their properties, it is evident that the strength of any enamel wall is dependent upon the arrangement of the rods which make up the walls, and their relation to the dentin. Certain requirements for strength, applicable to all enamel walls, can be clearly stated. They cannot always be secured with equal facility or perfection, but the wall will be strong in proportion as these principles are observed and attained. When these conditions are understood, many failures may be clearly seen to have been the result of their neglect.

1. The enamel must rest upon sound dentin.

2. The rods which form the cavosurface angle must have their inner ends resting upon sound dentin. The rods which form the cavosurface angle (the angle between the surface of the tooth and wall of the cavity) must be supported by a portion of enamel in which the inner ends of the rods rest on sound dentin and the outer ends are covered by the filling material.

3. The cavosurface angle in certain types of cavities should be trimmed or beveled so that the margin will not be liable to injury in condensing the filling material.

Each of these requirements should be considered separately.

**The Enamel Must Rest Upon Sound Dentin.**—The dentin gives strength to the tooth, a fact which should never be lost sight of in operations. Sound dentin should always be conserved to the greatest possible extent in the preparation of cavities. The enamel must therefore have the support of sound dentin, and all portions which are undermined by the removal of dentin must be cut away. When the inner ends of the enamel rods rest

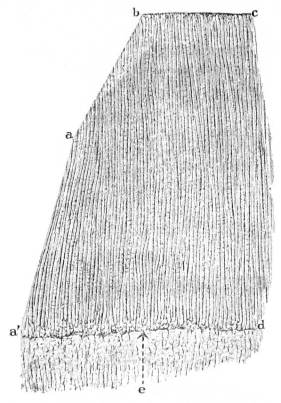

Fig. 256.—The structural requirements for a strong enamel wall: *a, b,* the bevel of the cavosurface angle. The rods forming the margin of the cavity at *b* reach the dentin at *e,* and are supported by the portion *a, b, e.*

upon sound dentin, the elasticity of the latter gives to the enamel a certain degree of elastic support. The enamel without this support is extremely brittle. A force that causes it to yield will crack it through its entire thickness. No filling material or substitute for the lost dentin can restore the original conditions. Fig. 256 illustrates these requirements. The enamel plate *a, b, c, d* rests upon sound dentin. The rods which form the cavo-surface angle at *b* run uninterruptedly to the dentin, and their inner ends rest on it at *e.* The rods *b, e* are also supported by a portion of enamel, *a, b, e*, made up of rods whose inner ends rest upon the dentin and whose outer ends are covered by the filling material, supporting the marginal rods like a buttress. The cavosurface angle is bevelled, including from one-third to one-fifth of the enamel wall, in order to remove the sharp corner which would be in danger of crumbling under an instrument. Moreover, when the dentin has been decalcified or destroyed by the action of caries, the acid which has decalcified the dentin has also acted upon the enamel. The

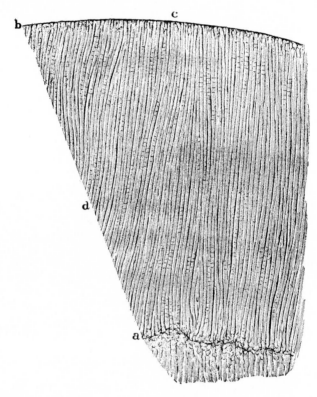

Fig. 257.—Improperly prepared enamel wall. The portion *a, b, c* has the inner ends of the rods cut off and they do not reach the dentin.

cementing substance has been dissolved from between the rods from within outward (often to a great extent) and the structure is very imperfect. Enamel that has been so weakened will not withstand the force of mastication, and will eventually crack or break away from the filling material. It should be removed and the wall formed in tissue whose structure is perfect. Occasionally cases arise where an operator decides to leave some unsupported enamel. Its weakness and the possiblity of restoration if it breaks away, without destroying the original operation, must always be considered. It is sometimes supposed that it is only necessary to have sound enamel resting on sound dentin, but by looking at Figs. 257 and 258 it will be seen that the first requirement may be present, but not the second. In these illustrations the enamel plate is resting on sound dentin, but the tissue has been cut in such a way that the inner ends of the rods have been cut off. The rods that form the cavosurface angle do not extend to the dentin, but run out on the cavity wall at *d*, and the portion *a, b, c* is held together only by the cementing substance. This is not strong enough to sustain the force necessary to condense the filling material or later to withstand the stress

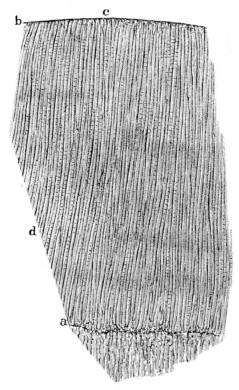

Fig. 258.—Improperly prepared enamel wall. The portion *a, b, c* is not supported by dentin.

of mastication. It will crack on the line of the cementing substance and chip out. Walls such as this account for the chipping of many margins and the failure of fillings along the gingival wall. The tissue is disintegrated in inserting the filling material, and the pieces later fall out. This often occurs in the gingival walls of compound cavities. The inclination of the entire wall must be increased to more than reach the rod direction. Such a wall as this may easily be made with a stone or a bur, but would be difficult with hand instruments.

**The Rods Forming the Cavosurface Angle Must be Supported.**—This is the key to strong enamel walls. The more perfect the support the stronger the wall. If an enamel wall is cut exactly in the direction of the rods, as in Fig. 256, the rods forming the margin are held together only by cementing substance, and a comparatively slight force on the surface in the direction toward the cavity will break off. If the same wall is trimmed, as indicated by the line, the same force would do no damage, as the rods which receive it are supported by the portion which is covered by the filling material. It is interesting to note in the wearing down of the enamel by use, that Nature provides the same support for the rods forming the angle of the worn tooth surfaces. When caries occurs on an abraded surface it starts with the rods at the dentino-enamel junction; these chip and form a protective niche for the lodgment of a colony.

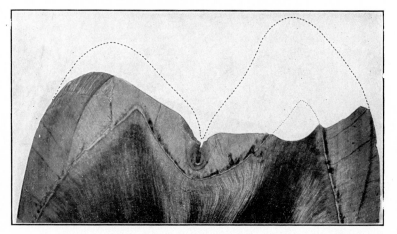

FIG. 259.—An occlusal defect in a worn tooth. The fissure is filled with coronal cementum.

**Bevel the Cavosurface Angle.**—It is not always necessary to bevel the cavosurface angle. Where the rods are inclined toward the cavity, those forming the margin are well supported and the angle need not be bevelled unless it is so sharp that it would be in danger of being injured (Fig. 255).

There are two reasons for bevelling the cavosurface angle: (1) To protect a sharp angle from injury, as in the malleting of a foil; (2) to gain support for the marginal rods. The first occurs where the enamel rods are inclined toward the cavity, the second where they are inclined away from the cavity.

## EXTENSION OF PIT AND FISSURE DECAY

The importance of pits and fissures as sites of beginning caries cannot be overestimated. They furnish ideal conditions in areas that would otherwise be immune as they are the positions in which the attacks of caries are first manifested. These occlusal grooves appear in great variety. Some are simply shallow, open grooves, in which the surface of the enamel is perfect; some are very deep and entirely empty; others are apparently filled with a granular, more or less structureless calcified material which appears to have been deposited in the groove after the enamel was completed (Figs. 259 and 261). This is probably related to cementum. It was formed after the enamel was completed, but while the tooth was enclosed in its follicle in the bony crypt. It may be compared to the coronal cementum that is characteristic of the complex grinding teeth of the ungulates and other herbivorous animals. A study of these defects furnishes the basis for the operative rule

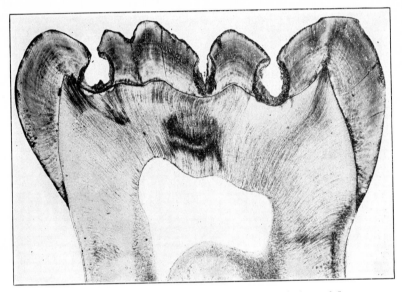

Fig. 260.—Multiple lesions originating from occlusal pits and fissures of molar. (J. M. Spence.)

that "all grooves must be cut out to the point where the margin will be on a smooth surface." If they are not, a defect will be left at the margin of the cavity to offer ideal conditions for the beginning of a new decay. When caries begins in such a defect at the margin of a filling, it progresses at the bottom of the defect until the dentino-enamel junction is reached, and then extends into the dentin and may destroy the entire crown without appearing upon the surface. The extent of these defects is much greater than would be supposed from the observation of the teeth in the mouth. Examination of such grooves with a fine-pointed explorer often reveals that the instrument may not be made to "catch" in them. The grooves have been found open two-thirds of the distance to the dentino-enamel junction, and show a beginning of caries. If caries had started in the central pit, and a small round filling had been made, open defects would be left at the margin where every groove radiated from the central cavity. These would be just as liable to recurrent decay as they were originally and, if caries occurred, it would progress in the depth of the groove, reach the dentino-enamel junction and progress in the dentin. The occlusal enamel would be so undermined that it would collapse under the force of mastication.

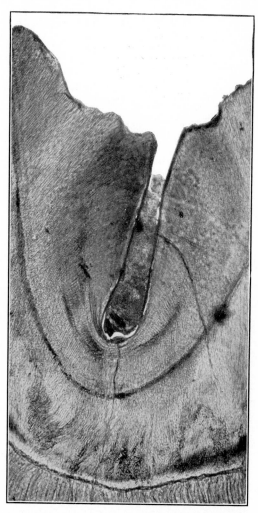

Fig. 261.—Higher magnification of Fig. 259. The fissure filled with granular calcified material. Notice the direction of the bands of Retzius around the fissure.

On the other hand, if the grooves are cut out to a point where the cavity margin will be on a smooth surface, there is no possibility of recurrent caries if the filling material is properly inserted. This one illustration, which might be duplicated countless times, is the rational basis for the rule, "All grooves must be cut out to the ends."

The condition in pits from which grooves extend, as the lingual pits of incisors and the buccal pits of molars, show the same condition as the grooves, except that the defect is both broader and deeper. Pits that are sometimes found on the tips of cusps and on smooth surfaces show an entirely different structural condition, are pathological in character and constitute hypoplastic enamel.

## SPECIAL AREAS OF WEAKNESS FOR ENAMEL MARGINS

There are certain positions of great strength in the perfect crown which, because of the peculiar structure of the tissue in these places, become areas of weakness when cavity margins are made in them. It is important to

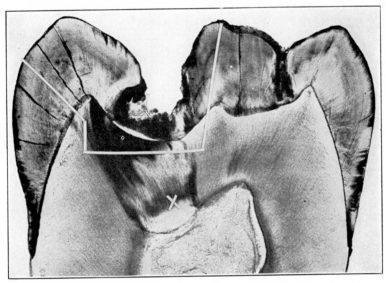

Fig. 262.—Diagrammatic outline of extension form of cavity preparation, where the cusp height is reduced in order to assure the support of enamel by sound dentin. Note the undermining of the enamel and the proximity to areas of heavy occlusal stress. It is necessary to extend the cavity preparation into areas of strength as outlined in this figure. Note the sclerotic dentin (x) in response to the carious attack. The carious lesion to the right represents an early pit cavity which calls for separate treatment so that the oblique ridge is not sacrificed. (Courtesy, J. M. Spence.)

emphasize the necessity of *not extending cavity margins into the areas of weakness*. The dangerous area should be cut away, leaving the margin in a safe position, when the area cannot be avoided.

In considering the relation of the enamel to dentin, and in studying the arrangement of the enamel-rod direction in the architecture of the tooth crown, it is seen that the dentin cusps and the dentinal marginal ridges are not directly under the corresponding points on the surface of the enamel, but are nearer to the long axis of the tooth. These areas on the surface of the enamel, from the point directly over the tip of the dentin cusp or ridge to the tip of the enamel cusps or ridges, become areas of weakness when a cavity is extended into them.

Fig. 265 shows the cavity preparation of an upper premolar. If this is filled before the destruction of dentin has extended beyond the point *A*, the lingual wall may be cut in the axial plane as indicated; but if it has reached the tip of the dentin ridge at point *B*, it must be inclined lingually, to strengthen the restoration.

The subject may be summarized by saying: the surface of the enamel from the point directly over the dentin cusp to the tip of the enamel cusp, which is an area of great strength in the perfect crown, is a region of weakness for an enamel wall. It is fully as important not to extend into this area unnecessarily as it is to form the wall properly when caries has extended to involve it. When caries of a smooth surface approaches a marginal ridge which receives the force of occlusion, the wall must be extended so that the enamel receives full support from sound dentin.

## THE STEPS IN THE PREPARATION OF AN ENAMEL WALL

1. The cleavage of the enamel until the outline form of the cavity is reached.
2. The trimming of the enamel walls.
3. The preparation of the margins.

Every enamel wall should be prepared according to these steps. The first not only removes the tissue more or less disintegrated and weakened by caries, but also places the margin of the filling in a position where it is not likely to be covered by the growth of a bacterial colony. It also determines the direction of the enamel rods so that the walls can be completed in terms of its structural elements.

The second step is accomplished by the shaving or planing process, and should always increase the inclination of the entire enamel wall slightly, in order to extend a little beyond the rod directions, and remove the portions that have been cracked or splintered by the cleavage. After cleavage the enamel wall will usually have a more or less whitish appearance produced by the cracking of the cementing substance between the rods. The light is refracted by the air in these microscopic spaces and imparts this whitish or snowy look to the tissue. These portions are removed by planing or shaving, and the tissue again obtains its bluish, translucent appearance.

The third step is also accomplished by the planing process, and should be carried out with two objects in mind: (1) to so form the cavosurface angle that the tissue will not be liable to injury in the condensation of the filling material against it, and (2) to leave rods whose outer ends will be covered by the filling material to support those which form the actual margin of the cavity. The steps in the preparation of enamel walls may be clarified by microphotographs. Fig. 262 shows a portion of enamel close

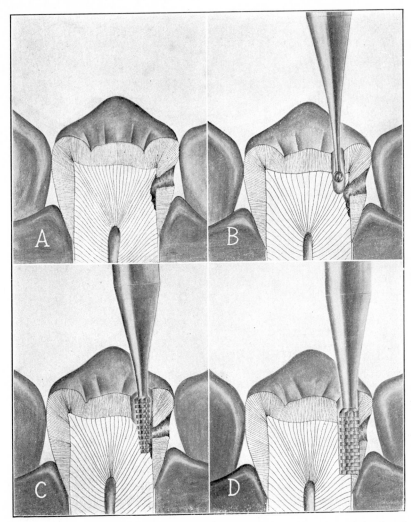

Fig. 263 (A).—Proximal carious lesion in premolar presenting the problem of cavity preparation and the challenge of avoiding injury to the papillary gingiva. This figure is based on a mesiodistal ground section prepared from a premolar of a young individual. This section does not show the pulpal horns which would be evident in a bucco-lingual section.

Fig. 263 (B).—Approach to the carious lesion is made through the enamel of the occlusal pit nearest the lesion. A ½ round bur is used to reach the dentin immediately below the dentino-enamel junction.

Fig. 263 (C).—The use of a 700 bur to remove the carious dentin and to extend the cavity gingivally and bucco-lingually. This bur is used within the dentin and at a slight distance from the dentino-enamel junction. The dentino-enamel junction is a sensitive area in cavity preparation.

Fig. 263 (D).—The use of a 557 bur, which measures approximately 1 mm. at its cutting edge, for the purpose of preparing the gingival floor of the cavity, and extending the cavity proximally. Note that this can be done for the most part without any contact with the gingiva. (J. M. Spence, Manual of Operative Dentistry.)

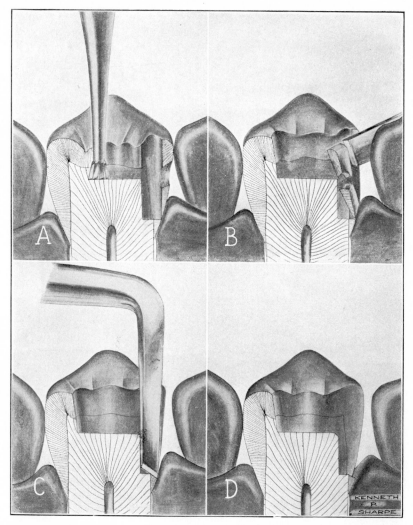

Fig. 264 (A).—Use of inverted cone bur ($33\frac{1}{2}$ or 34) for the purpose of extending the occlusal portion of the cavity. The action of the inverted cone is laterally and occlusally so as to minimize the amount of pressure and pain (J. M. Spence, Manual of Operative Dentistry).

Fig. 264 (B).—The completion of the occlusal portion of the cavity and the removal of the remaining marginal ridge by the use of hand instruments. A chisel placed in the direction parallel with that of the enamel rods will readily and painlessly remove the enamel which was previously undermined, as indicated in Figure 263(D). In addition, the chisel will give sufficient bucco-lingual extension to conform to the requirements of extension for prevention.

Fig. 264 (C).—The use of the gingival marginal trimmer to remove the gingival enamel which is not supported by dentin. This is an important step in view of the occlusal stress the tooth is called upon to bear. Unsupported enamel rods if not properly removed could fracture very readily, particularly in inlay restorations, and thus lead to open margins at the gingival floor of the cavity.

Fig. 264 (D).—The cavity is now completed. This cavity was prepared for the insertion of an inlay restoration. While modifications of cavity preparation are necessary in order to fulfill the requirements of the particular restorative materials, the same basic histologic facts must be respected.

to a carious cavity which is to be extended to the left. The chisel is placed close to the margin and the portion is split off. The wall then appears whitish since the cementing substance has cracked in several places, and in a number of areas rods have been broken across. The wall must now be planed to increase its inclination slightly. Finally, the cavosurface angle must be prepared, involving from two to three mm. of the thickness of the lingual wall to give support to the rods forming the margins. In this case the rods are straight and parallel, but they may be twisted (Fig. 67). If the dentin is removed from under gnarled enamel and the chisel placed as indicated, the portion will be split out. Not only has the tissue been splintered, but also a considerable portion is left in which the rods have been

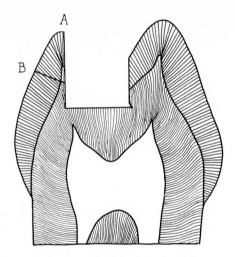

Fig. 265.—Diagram showing (*A*) extension into an area of weakness and (*B*) extension into an area of strength.

broken across. By feeling the margin with the chisel this can easily be determined, and the angle of the wall must be increased by planing to leave the wall in the position shown in Fig. 250, and finally the cavosurface angle must be bevelled when indicated.

**Preparation of Simple Occlusal Cavities for Amalgams.**—Caries often begins in the mesial and distal pits of the upper bicuspids, and in preparing the cavities for filling they must be united. In the pits and fissures the enamel width is smallest and becomes greater towards the tips of the cusps. This is another reason for beginning the cavity preparation in the pits. Fig. 266 is a bucco-lingual section through a first superior premolar. Suppose caries has reached the dentino-enamel junction in both the mesial and distal pits, and they are to be united along the groove. A small spear drill is carried into the mesial pit until the dentino-enamel junction is reached, than a small inverted cone bur is carried into the dentin just under the enamel and drawn from the dentin to the surface of the enamel.

When a narrow cut has been made from the mesial to the distal pit, a chisel placed at the edge of the opening will split out the enamel. Now the walls must be planed on both the buccal and lingual to bring them into the axial plane, and the structural requirements will have been completed (Fig. 268). Fig. 261 shows the relation of the cavity to the crown.

Fig. 266.—Occlusal fissure in an upper premolar, showing direction of rods. (About 80 ×.)

All occlusal defects should be filled before the decay has reached the dentino-enamel junction. All progress of the disease beyond that point requires sacrifice of tissue which otherwise would be saved, and the enamel wall becomes less and less strong. Fig. 262 shows a much more extensive occlusal cavity that has been neglected until the enamel has been broken, and as result of which there was much unnecessary loss of tooth structure.

The chisel is applied to the surface as indicated, and the undermined enamel removed until sound dentin is reached. On the buccal the enamel wall is cut to the axial plane and the cavosurface angle bevelled. If the decay in the dentin had reached the tip of the dentin cusp, it would be necessary to remove the tip of the enamel cusp and incline the wall about

Fig. 267.—The same section as Fig. 266, showing the position of the chisel in cleaving the enamel to open the cavity.

30 degrees buccally from the axial plane in order to obtain a strong wall. The cusp would then be replaced by filling material. On the lingual the undermined enamel is removed, and the wall inclined slightly lingually from the axial plane and the cavosurface angle slightly bevelled.

FIG. 268.—Preparation of enamel walls in occlusal fissure cavities
(the same as Figs. 266 and 267).

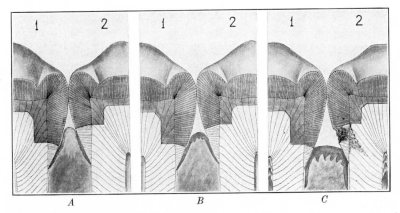

FIG. 269.—The role of gingival recession in determining in cavity preparation the gingival extension for prevention:

Restoration 1 and 2 are identical.

Figures A, B, and C represent relations existing during adolescence and young adulthood when caries incidence is relatively high.

A. Note the height of the intentional papillary gingiva in relation to the restorations I and II. Restoration 1 is correct and extends approximately 1 mm. below the crest of the gingiva. Restoration 2 shows insufficient gingival extension.

B. Gingival recession has occurred. The gingival floor is still covered with the gingiva in restoration 1, but is exposed in restoration 2.

C. With further recession, the gingival floor of restoration 1 is still at the crest. However, the gingival floor of restoration 2 has become exposed and has become more susceptible to recurrent decay (J. M. Spence, Manual of Operative Dentistry).

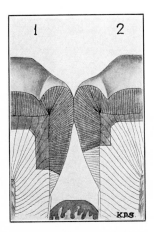

FIG. 270.—This figure shows relations that may obtain in advanced age. Restorations in 1 and 2 are correct when placed at this age and state of recession. They do not require gingival extension for prevention because the high incidence of caries has abated (J. M. Spence, Manual of Operative Dentistry).

Fig. 271.—Lines of Fracture in a ground section of a bicuspid, showing the natural lines of cleavage in a gingival third area.

**Gingival Third Cavities.**—Figure 271 is a bucco-lingual section of a superior bicuspid, showing a break in the enamel in the gingival third. The occlusal wall is cleaved to find the enamel rod direction, then planed to increase the inclination about 30 degrees occlusally from the horizontal

Fig. 272.—Diagrammatic preparation of the cavity shown in Fig. 271 for gold foil restoration.

plane. The cavosurface angle is bevelled to obtain support for the marginal rods. The gingival wall is prepared in the same way, inclined gingivally about 20 degrees from the horizontal plane, and the cavosurface angle bevelled. Fig. 272 shows the walls prepared.

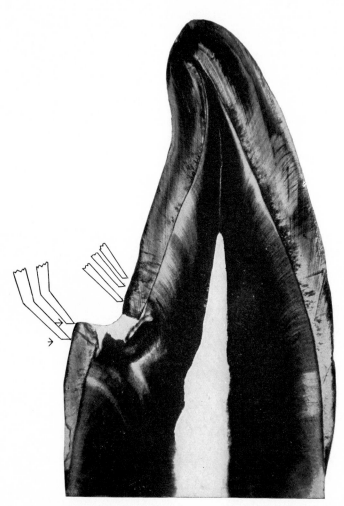

Fig. 273.—A cavity in the lingual pit of a lateral incisor showing the position of the chisel in opening the cavity.

FIG. 274.—The preparation of the gingival wall of the cavity shown in Fig. 273.

FIG. 275.—The preparation of the cavity shown in Fig. 273. Special care must be taken in this type of cavity preparation because of the close proximity to the pulp.

**Lingual Pit Cavities.**—Figure 273 shows a cavity in the lingual pit of a superior lateral incisor in which caries has undermined the enamel to a considerable extent. Placing the chisel close to the occlusal margin, as indicated, the enamel is chipped away around the entire cavity. On the lingual wall the chisel may be reversed and used, with a pulling motion, like a hoe. Thus the undermined enamel is chipped away and the tip of the marginal ridge removed. The wall is then planed horizontally and the cavosurface angle bevelled. Fig. 274 shows the structure of the gingival wall, and Fig. 275 its relation to the crown.

## BIBLIOGRAPHY.

BLACK, G. V.:   Operative Dentistry, Four Volumes, Seventh Edition, London, Medico-Dental Publishing Company, 1936.
BÖDECKER, C. F.:   Enamel Fissures, Their Development, Form and Diagnosis, Dental Digest, *33*, 73, 1927.
HYATT, T. P.:   Prophylactic Odontotomy, New York, Macmillan Company, 1933.

# CHAPTER 24

# Comparative Dental Histology

**Introduction.**—Since Darwin and Wallace advanced the theory of organic evolution the comparative method has been one of the most useful means of investigation. If all present-day life has sprung from previous forms it would naturally appear that a study of a progressive series would shed light on the paths that have been followed, and that a study of simpler forms should help to reveal the fundamental patterns of the complex forms of today.

The theory now generally accepted places evolution on the basis of chance. It is easy to realize how in a jungle existence any change in a characteristic, whether it were a keener eye or nose or a different shade of hair would make its possessor either better or worse fitted than the rest of his kind. If he were better fitted he had a better chance to survive and to transmit his characteristics than if he were not so favored by his mutations. The environment thus determined whether he survived or not, but had nothing to do with calling forth the favorable mutation.

One can easily imagine the advantage that was enjoyed by the first possessors of teeth. These organs became so indispensable that those forms which did not develop them either perished or developed special means of defense against those who had them. They have been one of the most important determinants of evolution. Indeed, they became of such importance that they gradually became unchangeable in form during the life of the animal. Once their pattern is laid down it cannot be modified, except by wear or accident. This happy condition, together with the fact that they are composed of the hardest tissues of the body and hence more likely to survive to tell their story to future generations, make them ideal as organs for the study of evolution.

## THE EVOLUTION OF TOOTH FORM TO ACCOMMODATE FUNCTION

One is apt to think of teeth as organs, the prime function of which is mastication. Actually, mastication is one of the last functions they have come to serve. Teeth should be regarded as mechanical objects designed to perform certain mechanical work. They have been brought to their present high state of efficiency by gradual mutational changes. Only those forms survived which were best fitted to their environment. The teeth constitute one of the best examples of the law of Nature that when new needs arise, they are met by the modification of parts already in existence.

Thus the various forms of the teeth have evolved to serve the demands of function, and once any given form is specialized, it is not reversible.

The following factors in design affect the efficiency and therefore the utility of the tooth:

1. The design of the crown and root.
2. The relative location of the tooth.
3. Provision for the control of movement.
4. The structural characteristics of the tooth tissues.
5. The relative distribution of these tissues.
6. The nature of the attachment.
7. Provision for wear and accident.

The teeth are not part of the osseous system, but are appendages of the skin, supported in man by a special development of the alveolar ridges of the maxillæ and mandible.

**Prehension.**—Before the migration of animal forms from the water to land, and for long ages thereafter the teeth served only for prehension of food. They were at first mere peaked scales set on the margins of the jaws. Their function was to hold the slippery objects seized in the water. This proved of tremendous advantage to their possessors and we find that the peaks became higher and sharper and more widely distributed. In some fish they invaded the mouth and are found covering the palate and the vomerine bones. In this stage of development they also changed their axes, tending to point toward the gut so that the movement of living prey is in that direction (Figs. 276 and 277).

**Combat.**—With comparatively few changes the primitive cone became a weapon of offense and defense. This persists today in the canines of the carnivora.

It was probably not until long after animal forms had left the water and taken up a land habitat that form modifications, other than those in size, began to take place. This extreme change in the mode of living set greatly increased demands on the teeth, and these organs then took different directions in their evolution. These directions were determined by the diets available and the demands set by the changes within the animal themselves. Since the teeth are the hardest structures in the animal body they have been the best preserved and constitute a very complete record of organic evolution. The gradual evolution of their form is fairly well established and is admirably discussed in Gregory's *Origin and Evolution of the Human Dentition.*

In some forms, certain teeth seem to have been developed mainly for sexual combat or for the selection of mates, and in a few the function of locomotion has been assumed by specialized teeth, as is the case in the tusk of the walrus while on land.

**Tools.**—As the source of food became more varied, much of it was not available by ordinary prehension. Certain of the animal forms developed teeth, the prime function of which was to obtain such food. Such teeth

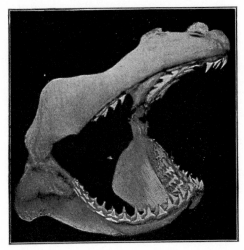

Fig. 276.—Shark's skull (Lamna cornubica), showing succession of teeth.

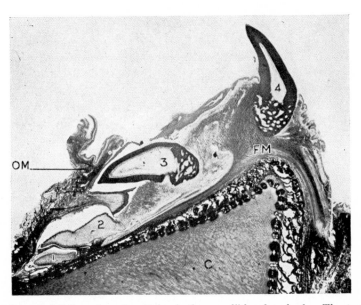

Fig. 277.—Labio-lingual section through the mandible of a shark. The teeth are attached to the jaw by a fibrous membrane, *FM*. An erupted tooth (4) stands upright on the crest of the jaw. On the lingual side there are three more unerupted, successional teeth (3, 2, 1) in successively earlier stages of development. C, cartilage of jaw; *OM*, fold of oral mucosa on the lingual side of the jaw covering the unerupted teeth. Magnification × 6. (Kronfeld, Dental Histology.)

should be looked upon as tools. They assumed many forms which ranged from the enormous plates set in the mandible of the shovel-jawed mastodon or the tusks of the modern elephant to the highly specialized incisors of the rodent.

**Mastication.**—Until the late mammalian era, digestion was largely a matter of putrefaction and the gut took care of the food regardless of the manner in which it was received, which was generally in the whole form. Since that time, however, there has been a trend toward the initial preparation of food by the teeth, and mastication has become one of the chief ends of the denture. It is in this stage that teeth show their most striking modifications. These reflect the diets that were available for the different classes of animals. Some species chose or were driven to food consisting of insects; others ate plants, roots and grasses; while still others continued on a pure animal diet. Finally there were those whose teeth enabled them to live on a mixed diet.

It is in a study of these various strikingly different forms that Nature reveals the manner of her working. Among other principles which become apparent is the fact that the function of a tooth determines its form and position. Regardless of the time at which a branch diverged from the main trunk of the evolutionary tree or how widely or thoroughly it became separated from its predecessors, a similar diet or similar function always led to a similar tooth form. Thus the rodent incisor is identical in all essential respects whether found in Australia or in the Americas, although these land masses were separated from each other long before such specialization could have taken place.

Function determines not only the form of the tooth but also its position in the jaws. Thus, the prehensile teeth, concerned with *obtaining* food are gradually restricted to the anterior part of the mouth, whether they be the digging tusks of the elephant, the gnawing chisels of the rodent or the snipping tools of the apes and of man. The teeth specialized as weapons take up their positions at the corners of the mouth where the firmest anchorage and the greatest speed are available. The teeth used for true mastication are always found in the back of the mouth, closest to the articulating joint where power is greatest.

## EVOLUTION OF STRUCTURAL ELEMENTS TO ACCOMMODATE FUNCTION

As might be expected from the above, the functional demands determined not only the anatomical form, the position and adjustment of the various teeth, but their microscopic architecture as well.

Just as in the matters of form, position and adjustment, we find that Nature has been experimenting to find the proper degrees of hardness, elasticity and strength. These experiments are of two main types, *viz.*, degree of calcification and the arrangement of the structural elements. Both of these affect the physical characteristics of teeth (Table 11).

TABLE 11.—HISTO-PHYLOGENY OF THE TEETH.*

| Tissues | Types | Characteristics | Where Found |
|---|---|---|---|
| Enamel | Tubular | Tubular, relatively soft and probably of ectodermal and mesodermal origins. | Fish and some marsupials. |
| | Prismatic (True) | Very hard Prisms cemented together. Ectodermal in origin and separated from dentin. | All high mammals |
| Dentin | Osteo-dentin | Non-tubular. Calcified Trabeculæ giving appearance of cancellous bone. No Pulp Chamber. Relatively very soft. | Fish |
| | Vaso-dentin | Non-tubular. Pink because of vascular inclusions in dentin. True pulp cavity present. Harder than Osteo-dentin. | Bony fish |
| | Plici-dentin | Tubular. Multiple foldings in walls of pulp cavity. Harder than Vaso-dentin. | Highly specialized fish. |
| | Ortho-dentin | Finely tubular. Avascular. Hardest type. | Mammals |
| Pulp | Varies with type of Dentin. | Remains of Dentin Organ. | |
| Attachment Apparatus | Fibrous Attachment | Attachment by fibrous tissue to skin or dermal plate. Root and periodontal tissues absent. | Fish |
| | Hinge-joint | Fibrous attachment of *Cementum* of tooth on one side of dental papilla to special bone of attachment of jaw. | Reptiles |
| | Ankylosis | Union of tooth to special bone of attachment of jaw. Ossification of pulp (Osteo-dentin). | Fish |
| | Acrodont | Teeth set atop alveolar ridge. Held by fibrous membrane. | Amphibia and soem reptiles. |
| | Pleurodont | Teeth set against lingual side of alveolar ridge. Held by fibrous membrane. | Reptiles |
| | Gomphosis (Thecodont) | Teeth set within alveolus in jaw and held by periodontal membrane. | Mammals |

*From Schour, Chapter I in Gordon, S. M., Editor, Dental Science and Dental Arts, Lea & Febiger, Philadelphia, 1938.

25

The study of the tooth structures of different forms and species shows that all teeth, from the simplest to the most complex, arise from identical tissues and are composed of enamel, dentin, and pulp.

The teeth may thus be defined as mucomembranous organs which are characterized by dentin derived from a connective tissue papilla and by

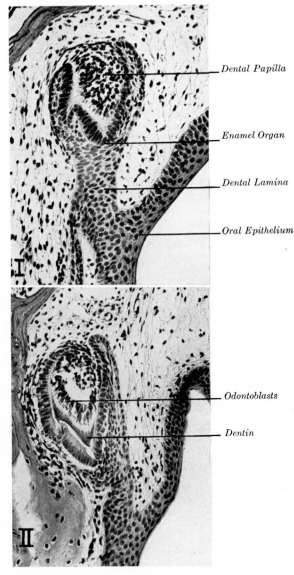

FIG. 278.—Early stages in the development of a maxillary tooth of the frog, showing features typical of the vertebrates: I. Epithelial enamel organ arises from dental lamina and incloses mesenchymatous dental papilla. II. Odontoblasts differentiate and begin formation of dentin. (From Gillette, Am. J. Anat. Vol. 96.)

enamel derived from the cuticular secretion of epithelium. All teeth are maintained in position and rendered functional by certain supporting tissues.

It is true that considerable differences exist in the microscopic structure of the tissues in the teeth of different animals, but the typical characteristics persist throughout (Figs. 278 and 279).

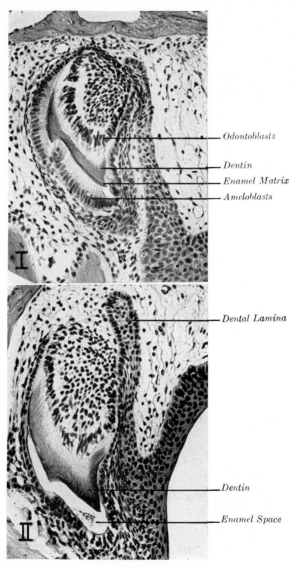

Odontoblasts

Dentin

Enamel Matrix

Ameloblasts

Dental Lamina

Dentin

Enamel Space

FIG. 279.—Later stages in development of frog's tooth: I. Tall columnar amelo-blasts differentiate from enamel organ and deposit a layer of enamel matrix exterior to the dentin. The dental lamina persists and gives rise to the succeeding generations of teeth. II. Enamel matures and dissolves out in tissue preparation, leaving an "enamel space." (From Gillette, Am. J. Anat., Vol. 96.)

**Enamel.**—The very wide distribution of this tissue is not surprising since the occurrence of an enamel organ in the early development of teeth is universal. The enamel is always associated with the cutting edge of a tooth but varies in its major characteristic hardness according to the function it is to serve. Thus the enamel of the beaver, used for felling trees, is the hardest known in the animal kingdom, and this hardness is obtained largely by the interlacing of the enamel rods. The hardness of the enamel of the grazing animals, on the other hand, only slightly exceeds that of the dentin of the same animal. Enamel also varies in amount and in structure. Sometimes it forms a complete or partial covering, sometimes a fine spear point to give a sharp tip to the tooth, and again, in some species it is completely absent.

In some animals enamel appears to be almost without structure, as in the small enamel caps of some fishes. Tomes believes that this absence of structure is merely a question of degree of calcification. If calcification goes far enough, all structural elements might become masked.

**Tubular Enamel.**—Enamel which is normally penetrated by tubules from the dentin is described as tubular enamel. This type is found in some of the fishes, marsupials, rodentia and insectivora. Animals which possess tubular enamel usually show a comparatively small amount of dentin. This type may be looked upon as a primitive form—one of Nature's early trials.

The most common type of enamel found in mammals is histologically like human enamel. Its main differential characteristic is its prismatic structure. Mummery described the processes which connect the rods as the intercolumnar bridges of v. Ebner. These can be easily studied in the molar of the elephant.

**Enamel of Rodents.**—The enamel of the rodents is divided into an outer and inner portion in which the single rods are continuous from the dentin to the surface, but bend sharply incisally at an angle of 45 to 50 degrees at the junction of the two portions.

In teeth of limited growth, like those of man, the enamel usually terminates at the neck of the tooth. In teeth of continuous growth the enamel usually covers the tooth completely on one surface.

**Dentin.**—Dentin shows a much greater variety of forms than does enamel. Tomes classifies the following types of dentin:

1. Osteo-dentin.　　　　　3. Plici-dentin.
2. Vaso-dentin.·　　　　　4. Ortho-dentin.·

1. **Osteo-dentin.**—This type of dentin is unlike the three other types in that it resembles cancellous bone in structure and no pulp chamber exists. It contains no dentinal tubules but consists of calcified trabeculæ extending through the pulp (Fig. 280), so that the pulp cannot be extirpated as can be done in the other forms. The channels are irregular, multi-shaped and of various sizes. It is often difficult to distinguish osteo-dentin from bone. There is, however, an outer wall of tubular dentin which is unique in itself. The tubules, though parallel to one another for quite a distance, become

joined as they pass inward into fewer and larger tubules, which in turn originate from the irregular shaped and sized channels in the interior of the tooth (Fig. 280). The tooth of the pike offers a good example of this type of dentin.

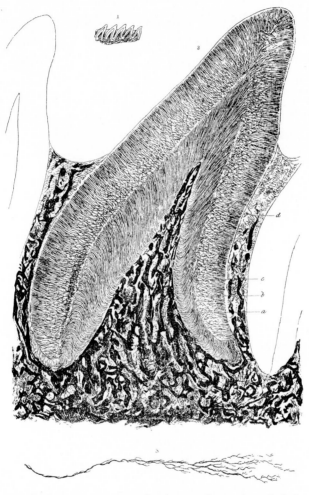

Fig. 280.—Tooth of *Scarus muricatus*, showing attachment by ankylosis: *1*, vertical section of five pharyngeal teeth of Scarus muricatus; *2*, section of a single tooth magnified; *a*, osteodentin; *b*, dentin; *c*, enamel; *d*, cementum; *3*, termination of a single dentinal tubule. (Owen.)

2. **Vaso-dentin.**—Capillaries penetrate this type of dentin serving as nutritive channels, the tubules are still absent. The outer appearance of a tooth composed of vaso-dentin is quite pink. The vascular canals branch and supply most parts of the dentin. In some forms such as the conical teeth of the flounder, there exists a combination of fine tubed ortho-dentin in the cusp region and vaso-dentin lower down (Fig. 282).

3. **Plici-dentin.**—This is a hard dentin in which tubules are present and radiate from a pulpal wall which is made complex by multiple foldings or invaginations (Fig. 283). This type is found in the teeth of the monitor lizard, in some lower forms of fish, insectivora and reptilia.

4. **Ortho-dentin.**—This dentin is hard and avascular. Nutrition is provided by the penetration of protoplasmic processes, the dentinal fibrils. This type is observed in human and other mammals and the lower forms, as has already been discussed.

Fig. 281.—Saggittal section through the mandible of a small lizard. The erupted teeth (1, 2, 3, 4) are firmly united with the alveolar bone (AB) by ankylosis. The successional teeth (5, 6, 7) form beneath the erupted ones and cause resorption of the latter; 8, unerupted tooth which has not yet developed a bony attachment; M, lower border of the mandible. Magnification × 36. (Kronfeld, Dental Histology.)

**The Attachment of Teeth.**—The mode of attachment of teeth seems to have been a steady progression from a mere surface fastening to the gradual development of a root and the grasping of this root by bone which grows up around it. This latter type of attachment was at first only a fibrous attachment of tooth to bone, but ultimately became a fibrous suspension between tooth on the one hand and bone on the other (gomphosis). Alveolar bone is the servant of the teeth and phylogenetically and ontogenetically its presence depends upon the presence of the teeth.

Tomes has given a very good classification of the methods of attachment of teeth:

1. By fibrous membrane.  3. By ankylosis.
2. By hinge joint.  4. By gomphosis.

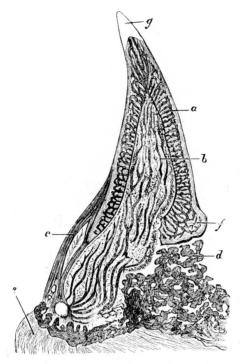

FIG. 282.—Tooth of a hake, showing attachment by hinge joint: *a*, vaso-dentin; *b*, pulp; *c*, elastic hinge; *d*, buttress to receive *f*, formed out of bone of attachment; *e*, bone of jaw; *f*, thickened base of tooth; *g*, enamel tip. (Tomes.)

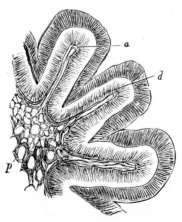

FIG. 283.—Section of plici-dentin with the pulp *in situ* (Lepidosteus): *a*, prolongation of the pulp; *p*, connective tissue framework of pulp; *d*, dentin. (Tomes' Dental Anatomy, courtesy of J. A. Churchill, Ltd.)

These various forms will be considered and the evolution of the more complicated from the simpler forms will be shown.

**Attachment by Fibrous Membrane.**—This form of attachment is most rudimentary and is found in the simplest teeth and the dermal scales as seen in the shark (Fig. 276). There is no development or modification of the arch of the jaw, and the teeth have no direct attachment to the bone; in fact the jaws themselves are chiefly cartilage. A fibrinous membrane attaches the base of the tooth to the cartilage (Fig. 277).

**Attachment by Hinge Joint.**—The formation of the hinge attachment as illustrated in many of the fishes (Fig. 282), may be understood as a modification of the attachment in a fibrous membrane in a more highly specialized creature. These hinged teeth are found in many fishes and in the poison fangs of snakes. The jaws are calcified, and the basal plate or cementum may be considered as confined to one side of the dentin papilla, which is also more highly developed, especially in snakes. This cementum is built and calcified around the fibers which pass directly to the bone of the jaw at any given point. This bone is to be regarded as an addition to the jaw specially developed for each tooth. Thus, there is not only a modification in the arrangement of the cementum, but also a development of bone for attachment of the tooth. The blood-vessels pass through the fibers of the hinge to the pulp, and are not affected by the motion of the tooth on the hinge; in fact, the pulp seems to be joined to the hinge. There are many complications of this method of attachment, but this may be taken as the type. The distinction, in this form of attachment, from the dermal scale consists in a modification of the arrangement of the cementum of the basal plate and a development of bone from the jaw to attach fibers which pass directly from cementum to bone. There are developments in the hinge teeth also related to the third form of attachment (ankylosis) which cannot be understood until this form is studied.

**Attachment by Ankylosis.**—The third form of attachment is an ankylosis (Fig. 280), or direct calcified union of tooth with the bone of the jaw. In the body of the dental papilla of many fishes there occurs the formation of spicules of calcified tissue which resemble neither dentin or typical bone. They are analogous to the first formation of endomembranous bone in the body of the human jaw. These calcifications contain lacunæ, and have tubules or canalicules running through them and, as Tomes says, are intermediate between dentin and bone. They divide the pulp into irregular spaces and interdigitate, or perhaps actually join, the dentin which has been progressing from the surface of the pulp. These spicules run down into the bone of the jaw, forming an actual calcified attachment for the tooth with the jaw. It is to be regarded as a formation and calcification of bone in the pulp papilla interlocking with the dentin. In some fishes, as in Scarus, there is at the same time formed the remains of the cementum of the basal plate on the outside of the dentin around the base of the cone. Ankylosis is confined to the teeth of many fishes, and may be considered a modification of the dermal scale, resulting in the reduction or loss of the basal plate and an ossification of the pulp continuing through the connective tissue at the base of the pulp to the body of the jaw.

**Gomphosis (Attachment by Implantation in Socket).**—The development of the fourth form of attachment, by implantation in a socket, seems to be an evolution starting from the same point as above but proceeding in a different direction (Fig. 284). It is associated with a very great increase in the size of the teeth and consequent necessity for a stronger attachment. The evolution of this is illustrated in the teeth of reptiles. Weidersheim classifies the teeth of reptiles as (1) resting upon a ledge on the lingual side of the jaw—pleurodont dentition; (2) resting on a slight ridge around them —acrodont dentition; (3) lodged in permanent alveoli, as in the crocodile— thecodont dentition. These three classes illustrate three stages in the development of the socket method of attachemnt.

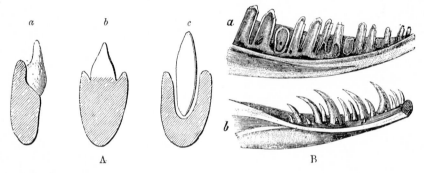

Fig. 284.—*A*, Diagrams of transverse sections through the jaws of reptiles showing pleurodont (*a*), acrodont (*b*), and thecodont (*c*) dentitions. *B*, *a*, Lower jaw of Zoötoca vivipara; *b*, anguis fragilis. (After Leydig.) (Weidersheim, Comparative Anatomy of Vertebrates.)

In the simplest form there is a cone-shaped tooth, attached to the bone around its base by the fibers built into the cementum and bone. There is little modification of the rudimentary form, and little development of bone for tooth attachment. In the higher forms the tooth has become long or peg-shaped, and the bone has grown up around a portion of it for support. It is attached to the bone by connective tissue fibers, being built into the cementum on the surface of the tooth and into the bone for attachment on the jaw. The development of the peg-formed tooth from the cone may be understood as a continuation of the development of odontoblasts, and the formation of dentin (which always begins at the apex of the cone) farther and farther down the sides of the dental papillæ. Following this, is the formation of the cementum, which begins around the base of the cone and continues down on the outside of the calcified dentin, covering its outer surface, and building the connective tissue fibers into the tooth. The development of bone follows that of the tooth, building the other ends of these fibers into the bone developed to support the tooth.·

**Summary**.—To review the subject matter, all teeth have been evolved from the simple placoid scale. In the simplest forms, as in the teeth of the shark, there is no relation to the bone whatever, but the fibers of the subcutaneous tissue are built into the basal plate of cementum. As the tooth becomes larger and demands more support, there is added to the bone of the jaw that which Tomes has called "bone of attachment." The osteoblasts build up additions to the jaw which surround and embed the fibers, so that those which we·e orig'nally in the subcutaneous tissue are fastened to the bone at one end and to the cementum at the other. The evolutions of attachment by hinge joint and by gomphosis are therefore direct evolutions from the simple attachment in membrane. The form of ankylosis is also evolved from the simplest type, but in this case the bone of attachment is associated with the pulp, and the formation of bone and dentin become interlocked and united.

## METHODS OF ACCOMMODATING FOR ABRASIVE WEAR AND ACCIDENT

Since teeth are of vital importance to an animal we find that there is always present a mechanism to adjust for wear or accident.

**By Continuous Succession**.—This is the earliest mechanism which is found in the placoid scale when, upon the loss of one scale, another takes its place. This method has been retained and refined until today it is found in such widely diverging animal forms as the teeth of fish, the poison fangs of snakes and the molars of the elephant.

**By Continuous Growth and Eruption**.—Teeth that serve extreme abrasive functions such as felling trees (beaver), gnawing through hard shells (squirrel, rat) or spading up ground (elephant, boar) are subject to rapid wear. Such teeth grow at their bases and erupt as rapidly as they are worn down at their functioning ends.

**By Continuous Eruption**.—The grinding teeth of those animals living on a vegetable or grass diet require the maintenance of a rough corrugated surface, which is subject to extreme wear. Such animals have teeth which, although completely formed early in life, continue to erupt during the life of the animal.

In some animals we find two such systems working on teeth having different functions. Thus in the elephant the incisors are of continuous growth, while the molars are of continuous succession. The rodent always has incisors of continuous growth, but his buccal teeth are specialized for his diet. The beaver has cheek teeth strongly resembling those of the grazing animals, while the rat has molars quite similar to those of man.

Even in those dentures where the teeth are of limited growth and are restricted to two sets, there is a mechanism of adjustment for wear located in the periodontal membrane. In man the teeth slowly erupt to take care of occlusal wear and drift toward the midline to adjust for interproximal wear (physiological occlusal and mesial drift).

## SPECIALIZED FORMS OF TEETH

If the teeth of various animals are studied comparatively, many modifications will be found in the relative amount and distribution of the dental tissues and adaptations of the tooth to perform special functions. A study of these modified or specialized teeth will give a better understanding of the *functions* of the tissues of the tooth.

**Dermal Scales.**—The work of Oscar Hertwig, published in 1874, established very clearly the homology that exists, both as to similarity of structure and development, between the teeth and the dermal or placoid scales of the ganoid, silurioid and dipnoan fishes. All teeth arise from a simple

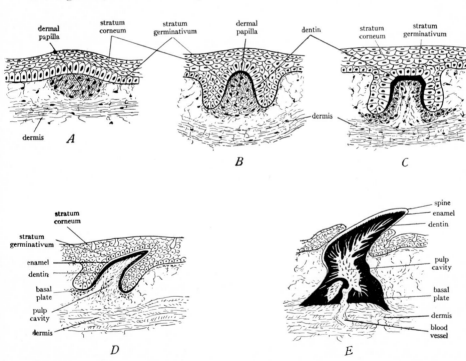

FIG. 285.—Five successive stages in the development of the placoid scale of the dog-fish. *A*, Gathering of the cells of the dermis to form the dermal papilla; *B*, evagination of the dermal papilla and secretion of the dentin (colored black) by the outer cells of the papilla; *C*, continued secretion of dentin, thinning of the interior of the papilla to form the pulp; *D*, beginning secretion of the basal plate and formation of the enamel (left white) by the under surface of the stratum germinativum. *E*, eruption of the spine through the epidermis, completion of the basal plate and pulp. (From Goodrich, in Part IX of Lankester's *Treatise on Zoology,* courtesy of the Macmillan Company and A. C. Black, London.)

conical form and the great differences seen between this and the highly complicated architecture of specialized teeth have been brought about by slight mutational changes in the growth pattern of this cone. The dermal scales are composed of a conical cap of calcified tissue developed from within outward by an epithelial organ, and corresponding in structure to the enamel. This cap rests upon a conical papilla of calcified tissue of mesodermal origin formed from without inward, and corresponding to dentin. The latter contains a vascular core or pulp (Fig. 285). In the outer dentin layer the arrangement of the fine tubules through the calcified matrix corresponds very closely to human dentin, but in the inner portions the formation of the dentin appears to progress irregularly over the surface of the pulp and maintain a special relationship to the proximity of the blood-vessels. Irregular projections of dentin are thus found on its inner surface which form around and embed the blood-vessels in the calcified tissue, producing what has been called vaso or vascular dentin. The formation is still from the surface of the pulp until the latter is obliterated, except for the parts remaining in the larger canals. The odontoblasts are much smaller than the human odontoblasts and resemble very closely simple spindle-shaped connective tissue cells.

The dermal scale is surrounded by a basal plate of a cementum-like tissue into which the fibers of the derma are embedded. Only the tips of these scales are to be regarded as a part of the outside surface of the body which has been enclosed by the development of neighboring parts. The dermal scales, or rudimentary teeth, which are found in the skin covering the arches forming the jaws, have undergone special development for the purpose of seizing food. In the simplest forms, there is only a development in the size and shape of the scales, which are supported by the underlying connective tissue. These teeth are easily torn off in the attempt to hold a resisting prey, and in the shark they are continually being replaced. In the more highly developed forms the bone of the jaw grows upward around the bases of these scale-like teeth to support them more firmly and render them more permanent.

**Teeth That Serve as Tools.**—Teeth that are subjected to extreme stresses are often made up entirely of dentin, the enamel being lost very early in life. In the tusks of elephants during the adult period, the dentin is not covered by enamel. However, when the tusk first erupted there was a slight enamel cap, which was at once broken or worn off. If the tusks of the elephant consisted entirely of enamel, they would fracture the first time they were locked in the branches of a tree or driven into the ground. But, fortunately for the elephant, the elastic dentin yields and bends and will stand great stress. The teeth of many animals who use their tusks in fighting are constructed on the same plan. In many instances the enamel is apparently absent, consequently it has sometimes been called the most inconstant of the dental tissues. In every case, however, in which the development of the tooth has been studied, an enamel organ has been found.

**The Rodent Incisor.**—The incisors of rodents (such as rats, mice, squirrels and beavers) present an interesting modification of the tooth for a special function. These teeth are used as chisels for cutting hard substances such as wood or the shells of nuts. Here both strength and hardness are required. The upper and lower incisors are separate segments of the same logarithmic spiral and thus take the form of arcs of spirals of different diameters (Fig. 286). In their functional capacity they wear away, and in order to continue their work these teeth grow throughout the life of the animal.

Teeth of rapid and persistent growth, such as the rodent incisors, have no roots but consist of a powerful crown that may be divided longitudinally into two parts, the labial or convex half covered with enamel and the lingua or concave with cementum (Fig. 287). These teeth grow in length by the constant apposition of tissue at their bases. The enamel, dentin and cementum form at the same time and grow at a rapid rate to keep pace with the great functional demand produced by the wearing of the incisal edges. This rate of eruption can be readily measured by marking the enamel surface, and in the mature rat is approximately 2.2 mm. per week for the upper and 2.8 mm. for the lower incisor.

The aternate backward and forward movement of the jaws in gnawing produces a much more rapid wearing of the cementum and dentin on the lingual slide than on the enamel of the labial surface, so that a sharp chisel-shaped edge is formed. There is also a modification of the temporo-mandibular articulation, allowing the lower jaw to move forward and backward as well as up and down, so that the lower incisors can be closed either lingually or labially to the upper. In this manner both the upper and the lower incisors sharpen each other through use.

In the adult rat, the rate of wear equals the rate of eruption, consequently the tooth remains of constant size. The failure of an incisor to occlude normally with its antagonist results in an elongation unchecked by wearing which may kill the animal by starvation.

## TEETH SPECIALIZED FOR GRINDING

The teeth of the ruminants offer a striking example of extreme specialization for a very exacting masticatory function. In these animals every resource seems to have been used to give efficiency to function. The cusps are extremely high, over one-half the height of the entire tooth in some forms, and are of many shapes depending on the species. In some they are finger-like, in others flattened, resembling marginal ridges which assume various curvatures. The enamel is thin and evenly distributed and cementum covers not only the root but the entire crown as well and fills in the interstices between the cusps. The tooth appears to be a solid block.

When such a tooth is subjected to wear the surface cementum is quickly ground away, revealing the cusps or ridges of enamel. As wear continues these tips are ground off and now each field of enamel shows a gradually expanding center field of dentin surrounded by enamel. The surface of the tooth presents these enamel-enclosed areas of dentin in a field of cementum and since the three tissues have different indices of hardness they wear at different rates of speed and always present an extremely harsh and rough surface that is ideal for the handling of a fibrous diet. Such teeth, as noted previously, continue to erupt as wear takes place.

The guinea-pig molar is another example of a tooth specialized for grinding (Fig. 291). It will be described in detail in the following chapter on Experimental Dental Histology.

## BIBLIOGRAPHY

BRODIE, A. G.: The Significance of Tooth Form, Angle Orthod., *4*, No. 4, 1934, *5*, No. 1, 1935.

GILLETTE, ROY: The Dynamics of Continuous Succession of Teeth in the Frog (Rana Pipiens)., Am. J. of Anatomy, *96*, (1), 1–36, January, 1955.

GREGORY, W. K.: The Origin and Evolution of the Human Dentition, Baltimore, Williams & Wilkins Company, 1922.

JORDAN, H. E.: The Comparative Histology of the Enamel Organ of the Mammalian Tooth, With Special Reference to Its Blood Supply, Am. Jour. Anat., *29*, 379, 1921.

MUMMERY, J. H.: The Microscopic and General Anatomy of the Teeth, Human and Comparative, Second Edition, Oxford University Press, 1924.

OWEN, R.: Odontography, London, Baillière, Tyndall & Cox, vols. *1* and *2*, 1840–1845.

SIMKINS, C. S.: History of the Human Teeth; An Introduction to Comparative Dental Anatomy, P. Blakiston's Son & Co., Inc., 1937.

TOMES, C. S.: A Manual of Dental Anatomy, Human and Comparative, Eighth Edition, New York, The Macmillan Company, 1923.

# CHAPTER 25

# Experimental Dental Histology

**Introduction.** — The preceding chapter on comparative dental histology has considered the many dental experiments that nature has conducted during the evolution from lower to higher forms.

In relatively recent years man himself has learned to conduct experiments in order to elucidate further facts regarding the biologic mechanisms involved in structure and function.

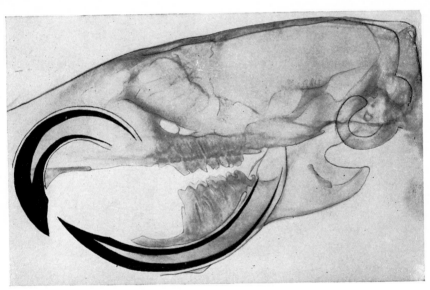

FIG. 286.—Radiograph of the head of a normal rat. Note the relation of the molars to the incisors in the upper and lower jaws. The calcified portions of the upper and lower incisors are traced in black. (Schour, courtesy of Angle Orthod.)

## THE RAT INCISOR

A considerable impetus to our knowledge of normal oral histology and embryology has come about through experimentation. This approach permits an exaggeration of the normal processes so that normal structure and function can be more easily understood. Particularly for a better understanding of the processes in tooth development, the continuously growing rat incisor is significant and affords decided advantages in experimental studies.

( 399 )

It may be regarded as one of the special gifts of nature to dental research. It is a tooth of persistent growth, and permits a study, in a single adult of any age, of the structural changes which the dental cells and tissues undergo from their early development to their maturity and final state (Figs. 286 and 287).

**The Formative Epithelium.**—The rat incisor develops primarily from an epithelial base which is structurally and functionally different on its labial and lingual aspects. On the labial, and slightly overlapping onto the lateral surfaces, this base resembles in structure and function the enamel organ

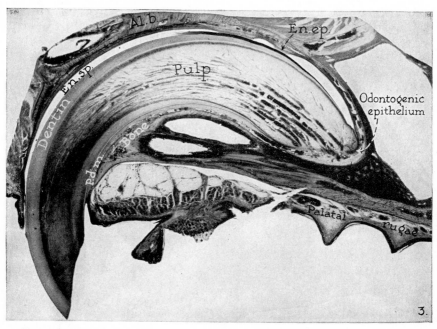

Fig. 287.—Photomicrograph of a midsagittal section of an upper incisor of a normal rat sixty-five days old. ($\times$ 8.2.) Note the extension of the pulp to the distal edge and the greater labio-lingual width in the proximal than in the distal portion. *Al.b.*, Alveolar bone; *En.ep.*, enamel epithelium; *En.sp.*, space formerly occupied by enamel lost in decalcification; *P.d.m.*, periodontal membrane. (Schour, Anatomical Record.)

of the human tooth. On the greater part of the lateral surfaces and on the lingual it resembles Hertwig's epithelial sheath. On the labial aspect this epithelial base is situated more proximally and inferiorly than on the lingual. The various portions of this epithelial anlage differentiate into ameloblasts or stimulate the formation of dentin and possibly that of cementum. The term "odontogenic epithelium" may therefore be used to denote this germinal tissue (Fig. 287).

The proximal epithelial base of the incisor in cross section approximates an elliptical outline. The connective tissue, which is surrounded by the epithelial cells is comparable to the dental papilla of the human tooth germ and represents the future pulp. The boundary between the epithelium and the connective tissue represents the future dentino-enamel and dentino-cemental junctions.

Cellular activity of the epithelial base is more rapid on the labial than on the lingual surface, therefore the incisor becomes curved.

**The Dentin Pattern.**—The peripheral cells of the connective tissue filling the curved epithelial tube become odontoblasts. They migrate toward the distal end of the tooth and at the same time recede centrally, *i. e.*, toward the pulp. The dentin thus increases in width anteriorly, with a corresponding reduction in size of the enclosed richly vascular pulp (Figs. 287 and 288).

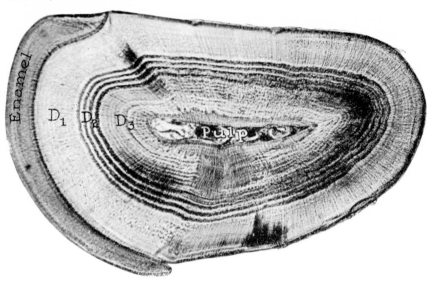

Fig. 288.—Photomicrograph of a transverse ground section of lower incisor of a rat which was given four injections of 2.5 per cent sodium fluoride forty-eight hours apart and killed fourteen days later. (× 45.) To the left, the enamel covers the normal dentin, $D_2$, was formed during the experiment and consists of four pairs of light and dark layers, each pair 32 mircons in width. Note the dentin, $D_3$, formed during the fourteen days that intervened between the last injection and death. This zone, $D_3$, is characterized by a stratification consisting of fourteen pairs of light and dark increments, each pair 16 microns in width. This illustration is taken from University of Arizona Technical Bulletin No. 52 (Schour and Smith, 1934).

The pulpal recession of a given odontoblast is in direct proportion to the amount of dentin that is laid down. Experimental studies have shown that dentin is laid down at the rate of 16 microns in twenty-four hours. The forward movement of the odontoblasts is in direct proportion to the rate of eruption. This rate is about 2 mm. a week in the upper incisor.

Thus in a mature rat, an odontoblast five days old has moved approxi-

26

mately 80 microns (5 × 16 microns) centrally to position i 5 (Fig. 289) and about 1500 microns anteriorly.

**The Daily 16 Micron Rhythm in the Normal Incremental Stratification.**—A histological study of the dentin and enamel of the incisor of the rat reveals an incremental stratification in form of a succession of pairs of dark (well calcified) and light (less calcified) layers. The width of each pair approximates 16 microns very closely (Fig. 288).

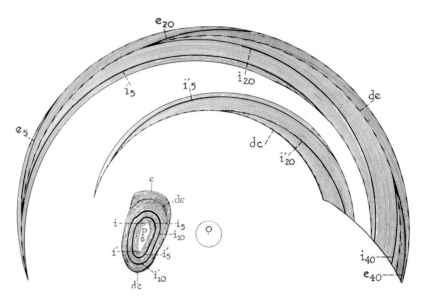

Fig. 289.—Geometric construction of the incremental pattern of the hard tissues of the upper incisor of the rat. The drawing of the longitudinal view employs a single center, o. *dc*, Dentino-cemental junction; *de*, dentino-enamel junction; *e*, enamel; *i*, incremental lines in labial dentin; *i¹*, incremental lines in lingual dentin; *ps*, pulpal slit. (Schour and Steadman, courtesy of Anatomical Record.)

The significance of this constant calcification rhythm lies in the fact that it is quantitatively identical with the amount of dentin or enamel apposed in twenty-four hours. It appears, therefore, that the 16 micron stratification rhythm is a constant, twenty-four hour formation and calcification phenomenon.·

The uniformly rhythmic process of growth and the coördinated migration of dentin and enamel yield an accurate chronological record which facilitates histological analysis. Thus in sagittal sections of the incisor of a rat killed at a given time, a given layer of dentin is situated next to the pulp or midway in the dentin substance, or near the dentino-enamel or dentino-cemental junction, depending on whether this dentin stripe was laid down approximately 5 (i5), 20 (i20) or 40 (i40) days before the death of the animal (Fig. 289). The extent of the record in any given tooth is limited insofar

# PLATE XX

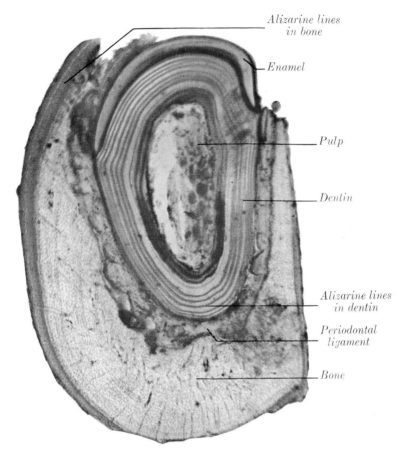

Alizarine lines
in bone

Enamel

Pulp

Dentin

Alizarine lines
in dentin

Periodontal
ligament

Bone

Transverse ground section of lower mandible of white rat which was given multiple intraperitoneal injections of Alizarine Red S. Each vital injection produced a red ring in the particular dentin increment that was calcifying at the time of each injection. The rings are distinct and separate in the dentin which is apposed at the rate of 16 $\mu$ per 24 hours. The bone shows a fusion of the incremental rings because its rate of opposition is much slower than that of the dentin. ( $\times$ 37.)

as the incisor of the adult rat erupts and wears off as fast as it grows, thus renewing itself about every forty to fifty days. Similarly in transverse sections, the dentin shows stratification in form of concentric rings, i 5 and i 10, at various distances from the pulp. This process may be observed more clearly in material obtained by vital staining with alizarine or by injections of sodium fluoride (Fig. 288). The width between two successive experimental rings indicates the amount of dentin laid down during the interval between two successive injections. (Plate XX)

**The Pulpal Cavity.**—The continuous apposition of dentin in the form of layers which move both distally and centrally (pulpally) would naturally result in an increasing approximation of the pulpal surfaces of the dentin in the distal portion of the tooth. The distal end actually tends to become entirely solid. But the activity of the odontoblasts stops in the most distal portion of the tooth so that normally the pulp assumes the shape of a narrow slit at the incisal edge where it is degenerated and is seen with the naked eye as a dark line.

**Enamel Organ.**—The enamel organ which arises from the odontogenic epithelium is not transitory as in man. In the mature animal, it is rudimentary at the base of the concave surface but persists throughout life both structurally and functionally on the convex surface up to the gingival margin. At the basal end of the tooth (Fig. 277) where there is a constant renewal and growth of cells, the enamel organ has fundamentally the same four layers as seen in man. The inner layer consists of distinct tall columnar ameloblasts, the stratum intermedium of two or three layers of flattened cells and the stellate reticulum of loosely arranged cells. The outer layer, however, consists of a single row of cuboidal cells which sends out papilla-like buds into the connective tissue so that the numerous blood-vessels of the latter occupy the depressions between the epithelial elevations. Toward the middle portion of the labial surface of the tooth where the enamel organ reaches its highest functional development, the ameloblasts are taller (40 microns), their nuclei are at the proximal ends, and the stratum intermedium consists of one or two rows of cuboidal cells. The stellate reticulum loses its characteristic appearance and seems to be replaced by the outer enamel epithelium which is now in contact with the stratum intermedium and forms papillæ which are more prominent and considerably higher than at the basal end. They are surrounded by an abundant capillary blood supply and present an increased surface area for the absorption that may take place through the blood stream. The enamel organ finally undergoes regressive changes, and a transition occurs toward the stratified squamous epithelium of the gingival margin. The layers of the enamel organ lose their former arrangement; the ameloblasts become shorter and cuboidal; and the formerly highly specialized organ shows a gradual and final transition toward the stratified squamous epithelium of the gingival margin.

**The Enamel Pattern.**—In a manner somewhat similar to that displayed by the odontoblasts, the ameloblasts move forward at a rate equal to that of eruption and recede labially with the apposition of organic enamel matrix. The apposition of the latter proceeds similarly to that of the dentin matrix at the rate of 16 microns per twenty-four hours. The enamel epithelïum begins its recession later than the odontoblasts because the organic matrix begins to form only after the first dentin is laid down. Furthermore, the recession of the enamel epithelium stops when the enamel matrix has reached its full and limited thickness, approximately 128 microns. The growth pattern in the enamel thus follows the same rate as that in the dentin but is of more limited extent.

The enamel starts at the base and increases in thickness and becomes more fully calcified as it extends toward the anterior region. Here it is absent in decalcified sections (Fig. 287). Normally it follows the convex curvature of the tooth in the form of a logarithmic spiral, and slightly over laps the lateral surfaces near the labial side. The adult enamel consists of an outer thin fibrous layer and an inner thick plexiform layer. The rods are parallel in the outer portion but alternating layers decussate in the inner portion. Longitudinally they incline toward the cutting edge as they run from the dentino-enamel junction to the surface of the enamel. The individual rods are strongly cross striated so that they sometimes resemble rouleaux.

**Pigment.**—The yellow or orange pigment is located in the superficial portion of the outer enamel layer. In thin ground sections under low magnification the pigment appears as an orange band at the outer surface of the enamel. This pigment is easily scraped off the young newly formed enamel, and may also be seen within the ameloblasts studied in fresh condition.

**Cementum.**—The cementum covers the lingual dentin and is very thin, especially when compared to the periodontal membrane which has a rich blood supply. It is laid down along the lingual, mesial and distal surfaces at an apparently very slow rate, since normally it gradually increases in thickness to 3 to 4 microns toward the incisal end.

**Incremental Pattern of Enamel and Dentin.**—Figure 289 is a diagrammatic sketch of a midsaggital section of an entire tooth. It shows the forty daily incremental lines that are found in the dentin in an incisor forty days of age. This diagram consists of lines which were drawn from a single center, $o$. The dentino-enamel and dentino-cemental junctions and the boundaries of the pulpal slit are arcs of circles drawn from this center. In addition, the incremental lines representing the daily deposition of enamel and dentin are logarithmic spirals employing this same center, $o$, as an axis. Because of the more technical and mathematical aspects involved, a detailed description of the construction of Fig. 289 is not given here. It may be pointed out, however, that a logarithmic spiral is one which increases (or decreases) its radius vector at a constantly increasing rate. In the rat incisor the gradient of the rate is extremely small so that the daily rate of apposition of enamel and dentin is 16 microns. The radius vector rotates about its fixed axis at a constant rate of eruption which in the upper incisor of the rat is about 2 mm. per week. The size and shape of an individual incisor at a given age is the arc of the same logarithmic spiral at different levels.

In interpreting histologically the teeth of rats used for experimental purposes, one must keep in mind the normal range of variation, which may be surprisingly wide. Even with the so-called adequate diet there is a certain range of imperfect calcification, and in the molars there may be an incidence of caries which may be seriously misleading if considerable control tissue is not studied with the same diligence as the experimental material.

## THE RAT MOLARS

A short discussion on the anatomy and histology of the rat molars is given at this point because of the interesting possibilities which these teeth offer in experimental investigations and because of the striking structural similarities which they have to the human molars.

The influence of the different vitamins or endocrines upon the rat dentition is so characteristic that in a number of instances it is possible by histologic examination of the teeth to diagnose the experimental condition (Plate XXI).

The rat is a monophyodont with a dental formula of $1 \frac{1}{1} M \frac{3}{3}$ (Fig. 286). The molars are of limited growth and similar to those of the human except for the enamel-free areas at the cusps. The study of two types of teeth (those of persistent and of limited growth) may thus be carried on in the rat.

When the experimental condition permits, the study of animals before the time of eruption of the third molar, which occurs about the thirty-fifth day, offers the advantage of showing early developmental processes in the molars as well as in the incisors.

There are three upper and three lower molars present on each side of the mouth. In the mandible, the limits of the anterior surface of the first molar and the posterior surface of the third molar lie within the posterior third of the arch of the lower incisor. In the maxilla the anterior limits of the first molar lie posterior to the odontogenic base of the upper incisor (Fig. 286).

According to Addison and Appleton, the enamel organ of the first molar is fully present in the eighteen day fetus. Vascularization begins in the twenty day fetus. The rat is born on the twenty-first day of gestation, and in the new-born the deposition of dentin has begun when the first indications of enamel are present. On the third day following birth a definite layer of enamel and dentin is seen on the developing cusps. The enamel, however, is seen to be present only on the inclines of the cusps and absent on the tips, though the enamel organ may have been overlying the tips (Fig. 290).

It has recently been shown that the enamel and the corresponding coronal dentin in the lower first molar is complete in its formation and calcification on the tenth day of postnatal life and that the dentin of the root is still being deposited up to the hundredth day.

PLATE XXI

## TOP ROW

*Normal.*—The characteristic histologic structure of the periodontal tissues of the rat molar.

*Vitamin-D Deficiency.*—The bone and cementum are *under-calcified* and hyperplastic, with resulting ankylosis.

*Hypervitaminosis D.*—The bone and cementum are *over-calcified* and hyperplastic, with resulting ankylosis.

*Hyperparathyroidism.*.—The alveolar bone (red) shows marked resorption and osteoclasis with replacement by fibrous tissue. Note the absence of resorption of dentin.

## BOTTOM ROW

*Normal.*—The characteristic histologic structure of the growing dentin of the rat incisor.

*Vitamin-D Deficiency.*—The dentin is undercalcified. Note the wide predentin and the markedly interglobular dentin.

*Hypervitaminosis D (or Hyperparathyroidism).*—Note the primary *hypocalcified* and secondary *hypercalcified* zone in the dentin.

*Parathyroidectomy.*—The dentin is poorly calcified. Note the alternate stratification of over- and under-calcified layers and the vascular inclusion in the dentin.

PLATE XXI

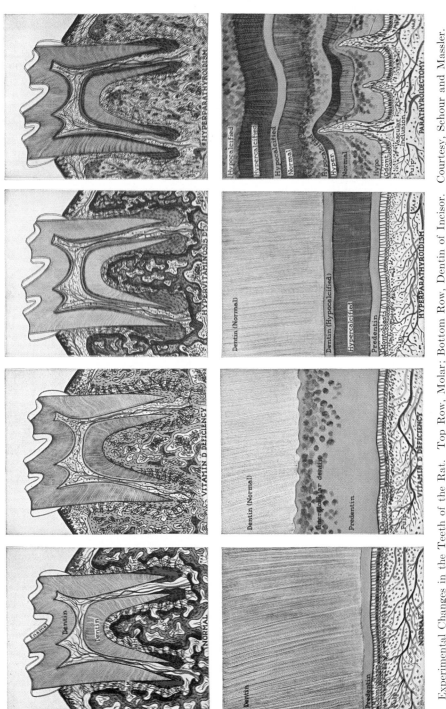

Experimental Changes in the Teeth of the Rat. Top Row, Molar; Bottom Row, Dentin of Incisor. Courtesy, Schour and Massler. The Teeth in Farris and Griffith, The Rat in Laboratory Investigation, courtesy of the J. B. Lippincott Company, Philadelphia, 1949.

*(See opposite page for explanation.)*

The rate of dentin apposition is demonstrated by injections of Alizarine Red S. The rate ranges from 16 microns per twenty-four hours to 2 microns per twenty-four hours, according to gradient vectors from the dentino-enamel and dentino-cemental junctions toward the pulp and from the tips of the cusps to the apices of the roots. The fastest rates are found during the earliest periods of formation and the slowest rates toward the later stages of formation (Fig. 290).

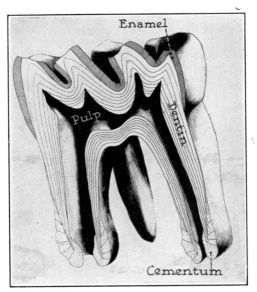

Fig. 290.—Diagrammatic representation of a rat's molar showing the incremental pattern of the dentin. (Hoffman and Schour.)

The first molars make their initial appearance in the oral cavity about the 19th to the 21st days. The processes of formation, calcification and eruption of the second and third molars, respectively, follow the first molar within a few days to a week.

## THE MOLAR OF THE GUINEA PIG

In the guinea pig the incisor and molars are of continuous growth. Its molar has proved to be especially valuable in the investigation of the dental alterations in experimental Vitamin C deficiency. (Scurvy). The molar consists of three prisms or plates which are joined into one whole. The basal portion contains a large common pulp chamber which extends into horn-like projections with each plate (Fig. 291). At the proximal base of the molar, new dentin and enamel are developed by the odontoblasts which are differentiating from the indifferent cells of the dental papilla and by the ameloblasts which differentiate from the enamel organ (the odontogenic epithelium). These cells continue to deposit dentin and enamel as they migrate occlusally, so that their thickness becomes correspondingly increased. The ameloblasts cease enamel formation before they reach the occlusal level. The odontoblasts continue to form dentin for a longer time, but reach senility and show degenerative changes near the biting edge of the tooth. At this level the pulp is obliterated and filled with secondary dentin, or what Fish has termed calcific scar tissue.

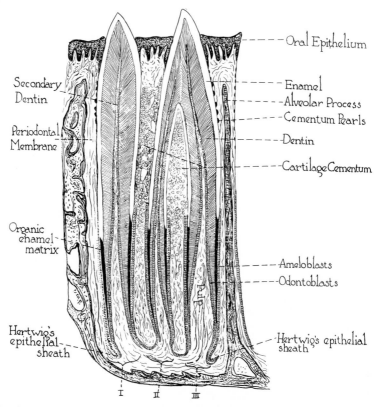

FIG. 291.—Schematic representation of a longitudinal decalcified section through a guinea-pig molar. Each molar consists of three prisms (I, II and III). (After Kotanyi.)

Fish has summarized the three-fold growth history of the molar of the guinea-pig in the following manner: "The tooth is elongating and being pushed up to compensate for the wear on its biting surface, the pulp chamber at any given point is becoming narrower by the deposition of fresh dentin on its walls, and the total diameter of the tooth is increasing at the growing end, where active enamel formation is in progress, by the deposition of enamel on the outer surface of that already formed. The cheek teeth of a normal guinea-pig take about forty days to complete one cycle of their growth from growing and to biting edge."

The guinea-pig molar possesses a coronal cementum which is not of the bone type but is a modified form of calcified cartilage. The latter, according to von Brunn (1891), is distinguished from hayline cartilage by the small amount of intercellular substance and the dense cellular arrangement, thus resembling embryonal cellular cartilage. This cementum consists of a honeycomb framework of fine fibrillar ground substance in the spaces of which lie cells that are of common connective tissue type at the periphery but show typical regressive changes in the center. According to Gottlieb and Greiner (1923) this special structural modification of more primitive type is developed in response to the need of the rapidly growing and erupting tooth for a rapidly forming coronal cementum. A second type of cementum in the form of isolated circumscribed deposits called pearls is found exclusively on the surface of the enamel.

## BIBLIOGRAPHY.

Addison, W. H. F., and Applefon, Jr., J. L.: The Structure and Growth of the Incisor Teeth of the Albino Rat, Jour. Morph., *26*, 43, 1915.

————: On the Development of the Ameloblasts of the Molars of the Albino Rat With Special Reference to the Enamel Free Areas, Anat. Rec., *21*, 43, 1921.

Erdheim, J.: Rachitis und Epithelkörpschen Densch r. den Math. Naturw. Klass der Kais. Akad. der Wissenschaften, Wien, *90*, 363, 1914.

Fish, E. W., and Harris, L. J.: The Effects of Vitamin C Deficiency on Tooth Structures in Guinea-pigs, Brit. Dent. Jour., *58*, 3, 1935.

Hoffman, M. M., and Schour, I.: Rate and Gradients of Growth in the Rat Molar Demonstrated by Injection Effects of Alizraine Red S. Jour. Dent. Res., *17*, 307, 1938.

Hojer, J. A.: Scurvy. Acta Pediatrica III (Supplement), p. 39, 1924.

Hunt, A. M.: A Description of the Molar Teeth and Investing Tissues of Normal Guinea Pigs, Jour. Dent. Res., *38*, No. 2, 216–231, 1959.

Marshall, J. H.: An Experimental Study With Certain Vital Dyes of the Persistent Teeth of the Albino Rat, Jour. Dent. Res., vol. *2*, 1920.

Schour, I.: Endocrines and Teeth, Jour. Am. Dent. Assn., *21*, 322, 1934.

————: The Growth Pattern, Growth Rhythm and Ring Analysis of the Tooth, Anat. Rec., *67*, No. 4, Suppl. *3*, 45, 1937.

————: Chapter on Experimental Dental Histophysiology in Gordon, S. M.: Dental Science and Dental Art, Lea & Febiger, 1938.

Schour, I., Chandler, S. B., and Tweedy, W. R.: Changes in the Teeth Following Parathyroidectomy. I. The Effects of Different Periods of Survival, Fasting, and Repeated Pregnancies and Lactations on the Incisor of the Rat, Am. Jour. Path., *13*, No. 6, 945, November, 1937.

Schour, I., and Ham, A. W.: The Action of Vitamin D and of the Parathyroid Hormone on the Calcium Metabolism as Interpreted by Studying the Effect of Single Doses on the Calcification of Dentin, Arch. Path., *17*, 22, 1934.

Schour, I., and Hoffman, M. M.: The 16 Microns Daily Rhythm in the Rat Incisor Demonstrated by Alizarine, Jour. Dent. Res., *16*, 349, 1937.

Schour, I., and Massler, M.: Chapter on The Teeth in:
The Rat in Laboratory Investigation, edited by Griffith and Farris, Philadelphia, J. B. Lippincott Company, Second Edition, 1949.

Schour, I., and Smith, M. C.: Mottled Teeth: An Experiment and Histologic Analysis, Jour. Am. Dent. Assn., *22*, 796, 1935.

Schour, I., and Steadman, S. R.: The Growth Pattern and Daily Rhythm of the Incisor of the Rat, Anat. Rec., *63*, 325, 1935.

SCHOUR, I., TWEEDY, W. R., and McJUNKIN, F. A.:   The Effect of Single and Multiple Doses of the Parathyroid Hormone on the Calcification of the Dentin of the Rat Incisor, Am. Jour. Path., *10*, 321, 1934.

SCHOUR, I., and VAN DYKE, H. B.:   Changes in the Teeth Following Hypophysectomy. I. Changes in the Incisor of the White Rat, Am. Jour. Anat., *50*, 397, 1932.

————: Changes in Teeth Following Hypophysectomy.   II. Changes in the Molar of the White Rat, Jour. Dent. Res., *14*, 69, 1934.

WOLBACH, S. B., and HOWE, P. R.:   The Incisor Teeth of Albino Rats and Guinea Pigs in Vitamin A Deficiency and Repair, Am. Jour. Path., *9*, 275, 1933.

# CHAPTER 26

# Laboratory Exercises

(TWELVE PERIODS IN THE LABORATORY.)

THIS chapter presents selected laboratory exercises that permit the students to learn selected aspects of oral histology from personal experience with readily obtainable material.

It is assumed in this work that the student has studied general histology (including laboratory work), that he is familiar with the technique of handling the microscope, and that he is able to recognize at once the elementary tissues. The same material is required as for general histology, including microscope, slides and blank labels for them, cover-glasses, lens paper, a 1-ounce reagent bottle containing xylol, a box for the slides, a notebook, a hard and a soft drawing pencil, a good eraser, and a piece of clean soft linen for wiping slides and cover-glasses.

The student should take the attitude of an original investigator and study the material for himself as far as possible, remembering that he has a far better opportunity than the man who worked out the details of the structures. He must constantly attempt to visualize the structure in three dimensions.

*Drawings.*—Microscopic drawings are done to make the student's observations more accurate and detailed and to fix the impressions of structure more perfectly in his mind. Many students excuse themselves for slovenly work by saying that they are not artists. Anyone with no knowledge of the principles of art can in a very short time become proficient. A few principles of procedure will help greatly. The first is that a light line can always be made darker, therefore the drawing should always be kept light until the later stage.

After selecting a field, draw the outline of the principal masses first, the smaller ones second. In this way the proportion of objects in the field and their relation to each other can be maintained. Draw detail such as individual cells, nuclei, etc., when all of the outlines are completed. The outlines are by far the most important stage in the drawings.

Each outfit should contain a 4 H and an H–B pencil and a good eraser which must be kept clean. The pencils should be kept sharp and always used with a light touch upon the paper. The beginner always tends to start his drawing by making a circle. This should be avoided, for it is objects that are being studied, not fields, and in many cases the object cannot be bounded by a circle  There is also a tendency to represent the object smaller on the paper than it appears in the field.

The drawings should be labeled carefully and completely. Full labeling makes the drawing more valuable for study and review and facilitates its correction when indicated.

The prime requisites in a microscopic drawing are *accuracy* and *correctness of detail*. The drawings are made to show all the detail of structure that can be observed. It often happens that a drawing that looks very well shows very little knowledge of the structure of the tissue which it represents.

## HUMAN MATERIAL

These exercises are suggested for the training of the student in the preparation of simple ground sections and their study as a background for the examination of special clinical cases. Extracted teeth and bone materials are available to students while in school.

## PERIOD I

### TOOTH MORPHOLOGY

**Teeth for Grinding.**—The student should bring to the laboratory a number of suitable teeth from which a selection can be made for the grinding of microscopic sections. Old, dry teeth are absolutely useless for the purpose, however, perfect their structure may have been. When a tooth has been extracted for some time the tissues give up water and consequently shrink. The shrinkage of dentin and enamel is unequal; the result is a cracking of the tissue. Besides the macroscopic cracks the tissue is full of microscopic ones. In grinding sections from such teeth, enamel will break and pieces will be lost before the section is reduced to sufficient thinness for microscopic observations. A tooth that is to be used for grinding must be placed in a solution as soon as it is extracted, *and never at any stage of the process be allowed to dry,* until ready for mounting. Any solution that will prevent decomposition will suffice. I have found 4 per cent formaldehyde in 50 per cent alcohol to be best This may be roughly prepared as follows:

| | |
|---|---|
| Alcohol (95 per cent) . . . . . . . . . . . . | 45 cc. |
| Water . . . . . . . . . . . . . . . . | 45 cc. |
| Formalin . . . . . . . . . . . . . . . . | 9 cc. |

This solution not only prevents the drying, but also has a hardening action (which facilitates the grinding) on the organic matter. Teeth may be preserved in this indefinitely. A solution of lysol may also be used.

From his collection the student should select for grinding an incisor or canine, a premolar, and a molar. The teeth should be free from caries and their crowns as perfect as possible. If caries is to be studied the teeth should have small occlusal or small proximal carious lesions which involve only one side of the tooth. Normal as well as pathologic structure can then be studied on the same slide.

**The Relation of the Section to the Crown.**—The practical value of the study of ground sections depends upon obtaining a knowledge of enamel-rod directions in relation to the tooth crown as well as the section. In operating, the teeth are observed from their outside surface, but the operator must see in the enamel not simply a hard and extremely dense tissue but a tissue made up of minute rods whose general direction he knows beforehand. If a tooth is selected and a section cut from a known position, and the relation of the section to the crown remembered, the direction of enamel rods can be placed in relation to the entire crown as well as to the section. This is one of the objects to be sought in the making of the outline drawings An-other advantage in studying the sections enables the student to become acquainted with the relative depth of the enamel, dentin and cementum, and the relative position of the pulp.

Having selected the teeth for grinding, the next step is to locate the position and direction of the section. This must be so placed as to cut the ena-mel rods through their length. The section from the incisor or canine should be ground labiolingually, but the section from the molar and pre-molar may be ground either buccolingually, mesiodistally, or diagonally to include carious lesion if present. The surface of the tooth should be con-sidered, and the section placed in an area in which the student desires to discover the enamel-rod directions and the structure of the tissue The line of the section should now be marked on the tooth with India ink and a fine pen.

**The Drawings of the Teeth.**—After marking the position of the section the tooth should be carefully and accurately drawn, showing the position of the section as seen from the axial and occlusal surfaces. The drawings should be from five to ten times natural size, and accurately to scale (Fig. 292). Measure the length and breadth of the tooth and lay out a rectangle about eight times these dimensions, to serve as a guide. If the tooth is marked for a bucco-lingual section, stick the apex of the root on a bit of wax and place the tooth on the table with the buccal surface toward you. *Do not change its position until the drawing is completed* for to do so would change lights and shadows After getting the outline accurately, work in the shadows to give the drawing roundness. When the drawings are com-pleted the section is ready for grinding.

## PERIOD II

### Preparation of Ground Sections of the Teeth

The advantage of having the student grind his own sections, particularly up to the position marked, lies in the fact that the student while grinding can at the same time reconstruct in his own mind the three-dimensional relationship of the various dental tissues. The student is thus in a certain sense able to study the anatomy of the teeth as if cut in serial sections,

Considering the fact that the dentist applies so much of his effort in treating and operating on teeth, the additional time spent in preparing these ground sections is worth while. For this work the student should have two large corundum stones not less than 4 inches in diameter, one of "C" and one of "E" grit. Corundum is very much better than carborundum for this purpose. In grinding the stone should be kept revolving slowly and moistened with a stream of water. Holding the tooth against the flat side of the coarse stone with the fingers, the tissues should be rapidly ground away until the position marked for the section is reached, when the fine stone should be substituted and the grinding continued just enough to remove the scratches. The surface should now be polished on the Arkansas stone until a very perfect surface has been obtained.

The tissues may be rapidly ground until the section is about as thin as a calling card, when the fine stone should be substituted and the section reduced to the required thinness. It should not be more than 20 microns thick. In the final stages progress of the grinding may be followed with a hand magnifying glass. Finally the second surface should be polished on an Arkansas stone. Further directions are given later.

**The Preparation of Transverse Sections of the Root.**—For this purpose one of the flattened roots furnishes the best material, as, for instance, the mesial root of a lower molar, the root of a lower premolar, or of an upper second premolar. Holding the root in a vise by the remains of the crown, with a metal saw or carborundum disc, remove the tip of the root $\frac{1}{8}$ inch or less. Then saw off as thin a slice as possible. In the same way saw out at least two other sections, one from the gingival and one from the middle third of the root. These should be dropped into a bottle of formalin-alchohol until the grinding is completed. The grinding is easily accomplished on the flat side of the corundum stone, holding the section on the finger or under a cork. The last grinding should be done on the fine Arkansas stone.

Transverse sections of the root are easily ground and can be made very thin.

## Etching and Mounting of Ground Sections.

The ground sections are to be mounted on slides. The following procedure has been found effective:

1. In a small dish carefully wash the section in water to remove the débris of grinding. A clean camel's-hair brush is suggested.

2. With the root part held between the fingers one side of the crown is covered with vaseline. The latter should be wiped from the center toward the edges to prevent running over to the other side of the crown.

3. Dip the *crown* into 1 per cent hydrochloric acid until minute bubbles form on its surface.

4. Immediately remove from the acid and place into dilute ammonia for one minute.

5. Remove the vaseline carefully with absolute alcohol or ether and place the entire section into 95 per cent alcohol.

6. Carefully clean a slide and cover glass.

7. Place on the center of the slide a drop of balsam as long as the section and heat gently over a flame to spread the balsam.

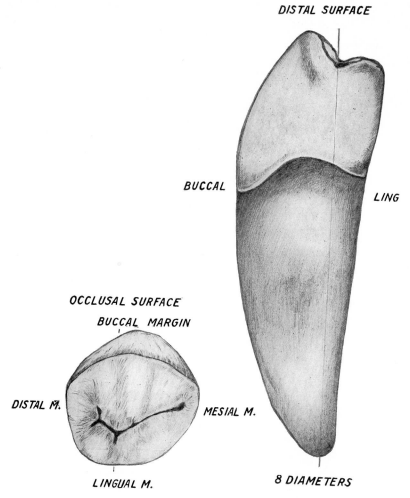

FIG. 292.—Drawing of occlusal and axial surfaces of a tooth to show the relation of the section to the tooth. (Drawn by W. A. Offiil, 1910.)

8. Allow the slide to cool and then test the balsam. If properly done the balsam will take the imprint of a finger nail but will not be sticky. If it is sticky it must be reheated, but if it is brittle enough to chip then the original process must be repeated.

9. Now prepare a balsam film on the cover-glass.

10. Wipe the section with filter paper and dry in air for several minutes.

11. Place the section, *etched side up*, on the balsam on the slide and place the cover-glass, *balsam side down*, and gently warm the slide while pressing the cover-glass down.

12. All excess balsam should be squeezed out to the edge of the cover-glass.

13. Protect the cover-glass with blotting paper and adjust a spring clip to keep the parts together while the balsam dries.

14. When entirely hard the excess balsam may be gently removed by scraping with a knife blade and wiping with xylol.

Label with classification of tooth, direction and position of section, your name and the date.

Hard balsam improves the value of a section by filling with air the dentinal tubules and cementum lacunæ and thus facilitating study. Soft balsam is used for very thin or broken sections.

## PERIOD III

### Outline Drawings From Ground Sections.

The outline drawing has as its object the study of the dental tissues, their distribution and relation to each other and their more gross structure. To be of value they must be made large and accurately to scale. Measure the tooth with a Boley gauge and multiply this result by eight or ten times. Use this constant factor throughout the drawing. A rectangle may be drawn to mark the greatest length and width of the section. Measure a number of points on the tooth and mark these on the paper in their proper scale and relationships. In this manner the outlines of the entire section, the dentino-enamel junction, the pulp chamber and the cementum may be constructed (Fig. 293). Low-power observation of the cemento-enamel function is important at this stage. Why?

Portions of the section lost in grinding or by abrasion may be added by dotted lines.

Make such drawings for incisor or canine, premolar and molar to illustrate each tooth class. Insert in these drawings measurements of the widths of the hard structures at the grooves, middle and gingiva thirds of crown and middle of root. How far is it from the tip of the growth center to the pulpal horn?

## PERIOD IV

### Minute Study of Enamel and Dentin.

Using the low-power objective observe the structures which follow. Fill in the outline drawings only in part to show the essential features. Select three representative portions of enamel and dentin (Fig. 293).

1. *Bands of Retzius.*—Indicate their direction. Note the pigmentation. Are the bands parallel?

2. *Enamel Rod Direction.*—Begin at the gingival line at one side and follow it around the crown to the other side. In a portion at the incisal

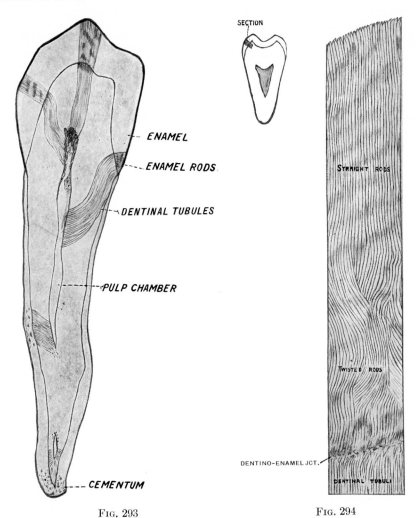

FIG. 293                                   FIG. 294

FIG. 293.—Outline drawing of longitudinal section, made as a study of the dental hard tissues. (Drawn by E. J. Schmidt.)

FIG. 294.—High-power drawing of the enamel. (Drawn by A. B. Hopper, 1902–03.)

edge, or on the occlusal surface, indicate the rod directions and in the same way show them in a portion near the center of the axial surface on one side and near the gingival line (Fig. 293). Where would you expect to find gnarled enamel?

27

3. *Bands of Schreger.*—This appearance can be seen with reflected light.

4. *Dentino-enamel Junction.*—Note the characteristic contour in each class.

5. *Dentinal-tubule Direction.*—Follow the *dentinal tubules* which end next to the portions of enamel which have been filled in to the point where they open into the pulp chamber.

6. Mantle dentin.

7. Submantle interglobular zone.

8. Contour lines of Owen.

9. Contour lines of deviated growth.

10. Granular Layer of Tomes.

11. Pulpal outline and secondary dentin.

**High Power.**—Select a field from one of the ground sections where the specimen is very thin, and, if possible, where the entire thickness of the enamel plate can be seen in one field. To select this field all of the enamel in the three sections should be again carefully stud'ed with the low power and the one chosen in which the rods can be best seen and most easily drawn. Having selected the field, study the enamel with the high power, beginning at the dentino-enamel junction (Fig. 294).

Using both the low and the high power, draw as accurately as possible the enamel from the surface to the dentino-enamel junction, showing all the details of structure that can be distinguished. Include just enough of the dentin to show the dentino-enamel junction and the character of the dentin at that point.

### Study.

1. Enamel rods and their *cross-striations.* Estimate the diameter of the enamel rods and dentinal tubules and the distance between cross-striation, using a red blood corpuscle as a standard of measurement.

2. *Interprismatic substance.*

3. *Enamel lamellæ and enamel tufts.*

4. *Enamel spindles.*

5. *Dentino-enamel Junction.*—Note the scalloped appearance and the relation of the enamel and dentin at this junction.

6. *Dentinal Tubules.*—Observe the forking and the anastomosis of the tubules as they approach the enamel, and follow then as far as possible. Note the amount of matrix that separates the tubules.

7. *Interglobular dentin.*

**Isolated Enamel Rods.**—Obtain a fragment of enamel broken in the direction of the rods and moisten the broken end with a drop of water. Scrape the moistened end with a sharp chisel and dip the scrapings into a drop of distilled water on a clean slide. Place a cover-glass over this and examine under high power with the light cut down. Note the diameter of the rods and their cross-markings. Draw.

Repeat the procedure on enamel previously placed in 1 per cent hydrochloric acid for several hours. Compare the appearance of the rods with those seen above. Draw.

Remove the softened dentin from a carious tooth and avoid touching the enamel if possible. Lightly scrape the whitened inner enamel surface next to the cavity and mount the scrapings. Compare the appearance of these rods isolated by the action of caries with those previously etched by acid. What changes are seen in the cross-markings and the expansions and constrictions of the rods? Draw.

## PERIOD V

### Outline Drawings From Transverse Section of the Root.

Following the usual procedure in outline drawings make a sketch to scale of sections through several roots. Fill in one half of each section.

1. Direction of *dentinal tubules.*
2. *Granular Layer of Tomes.*—Note its position and character.
3. *Cementum.*—Indicate primary and secondary cementum, lamellæ, lacunæ and cementum corpuscles.
4. *Pulpal Outline.*—Note the reduction of the pulp toward the apex in the several sections. Is secondary dentin present? If so, note the direction and character of the dentinal tubules.

Insert measurements of hard structure as was done in Period III.

### Cementum.

Study ground longitudinal and cross-sections of roots. Locate the cementum and observe its features (Fig. 295).

1. Note the relation of the cementum to the dentin surface and the *Granular Layer of Tomes.*
2. *Primary Cementum.*—Where is it thinnest and where thickest?
3. *Secondary Cementum.*—Where is it thickest? Is this the tooth of a young or elderly person? Were the forces of mastication heavy?
4. *Cementum Corpuscles, Lacunæ and Lamellæ.*
5. *Embedded Periodontal Ligament Fibers.*—Find these fibers in longitudinal and cross-section.
6. Find some areas of resorption and rebuilding.

Make one drawing each of a resorption area; lacunæ and their canalicules; and gingival, middle and apical cementum in longitudinal and three cross-sections.

## PERIOD VI

### Deciduous Teeth.

Examine a longitudinal ground section, prepared as outlined above, of a deciduous incisor and molar.

1. Note the differences as compared to the sections of permanent teeth previously studied. Make a drawing to scale to illustrate differences in

size, shape and direction of enamel prisms and dentinal tubules in the two types of teeth.

2. What is the contour of the dentino-enamel junction?

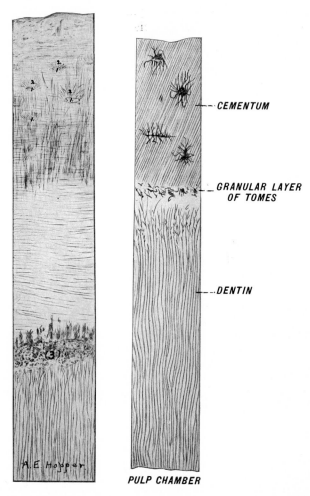

CEMENTUM

GRANULAR LAYER
OF TOMES

DENTIN

PULP CHAMBER

Fig. 295.—Cementum and dentin. (Drawn by H. J. Lund and A. E. Hopper.)

3. Hold the section up to the light and with the 10× eyepiece note the thickness of the enamel and dentin. Compare with that of the permanent tooth. Make a sketch superposing a deciduous tooth outline onto that of a permanent.

4. What is the significance of the neo-natal line? Mark its position into the drawing previously made. In addition to this, also denote the position of other striæ of Retzius in the enamel.

5. Observe the degree of calcification of the deciduous dentin and enamel as compared to that in the permanent teeth. Which are more highly calcified? Compare the calcification of prenatal and postnatal portions of the tooth.

6. Note the distance along the dentino-enamel junction from growth center to cervical line. Compare enamel rod direction at the same distances from growth centers in deciduous and permanent teeth.

7. Using the neonatal line as a reference plane, compare the amount of prenatal enamel and dentin laid down in the deciduous incisor and deciduous molar.

## PERIOD VII

### CARIES.

Examine grossly, with the 10× eyepiece, a bucco-lingual section through a molar having a pit of fissure cavity.

1. Note the direction and outline of the progress of caries through enamel and dentin. Show this process by an outline drawing.

Trace the progress of decay in respect to the direction of the enamel rods, the modification of the course of decay at the dentino-enamel junction and the extension along the dentinal tubules. Do you find evidence of decalcification? Of what value are these various factors as aids in cavity preparation?

2. Repeat this procedure for caries on a smooth surface in a mesio-distal section (proximal cavity). Compare the outline of the carious process with a roentgenogram of a similar condition. What is the value of the knowledge of dental anatomy and histology in roentgenographic interpretation?

3. Under low-power study and draw the progress of the disease shown in the above slides. Shade lightly the carious areas and indicate by a solid line the original tooth outline.

4. By the use of dotted lines show the position and contour of the dentinal tubules and enamel prisms as they existed before the existence of caries.

5. Indicate on these drawings the probable cause of the caries if it had had an opportunity to proceed further.

6. By gross examination find on one of your sections a white spot on the enamel. What is the significance of such spots? Draw such a place under low magnification.

## PERIOD VIII

### OPERATIVE DENTISTRY.

From the sections used in the previous period, make outline drawings of the teeth showing the carious areas (shaded) and the original tooth contours. Add to these one field through a cavity in the gingival third.

1. Superpose upon these the outlines of proper cavity preparations. Remember that the first consideration in cavity preparation is the removal

of caries. From the histological standpoint this must be followed by the removal of enamel unsupported by dentin. Why?

2. Add to the drawings several lines indicating enamel rod direction at the cavity margins, both before and after the removal of undermined enamel. Consider carefully the relationship between the bevel at your cavity margin and the direction of the rods. On what margins is a bevel necessary? Why?

3. Indicate on the drawings the direction of force used in applying a chisel to remove undermined enamel as well as to bevel the cavity margins. What is meant by "lines of cleavage"?

At this time refer to the drawings and charts made in Periods III and V.

Why is the depth of a cavity an important consideration? How far would cavities have to progress from an occlusal groove before the pulp would be exposed? How far in the gingival third? On a proximal surface at the level of the contact point?

Prepare a chart showing the thickness of the enamel and of the dentin at the following places: the gingival third, the occlusal surface, and the middle of a proximal surface. Indicate the distance between the pulpal horns and the tip of the cusps. What variations in thickness of enamel and dentin may be expected between the incisor and the molars?

Analyze the progressive size of the pulp at varying ages and indicate in the drawing the general pulp outline in proportion to tooth outline.

Draw the tooth as it is seen under the microscope, including secondary dentin. Insert in another color, the hypothetical pulp outline at varying ages. Why is this incremental growth-pattern significant in cavity preparation?

## PERIOD IX

### APPLICATION OF ORAL HISTOLOGY
### TO AGE DETERMINATION

This exercise is based on a method published in: Gustafson, G.: Age Determination on Teeth, Jour. Am. Dent. Assn., *41*, 45, 1950.

The student is supplied with a tooth in order to estimate the age of the patient from whom the tooth was removed. The information on the actual age of the patient which is kept in the instructor's records is not made available to the student until after he has determined the age on the basis of the following procedures.

A. *Gross Examination of Tooth.* Record the general characteristics of the tooth as an aid to later study of the section. Good clues may be obtained from a gross study of stain, calculus, caries, periodontal recession, closure of apical foramen (root formation), transparency of root, attrition, developmental defects and any other individual features.

B. Prepare *central* bucco-lingual or labio-lingual ground section of tooth for microscopic study (through growth centers, pulp horns and pulp canal if possible).

C. Examine the mounted ground section with the naked eye, then with the inverted eye piece (10×) and finally with low power (100×).

D. *Microscopic Examination of Tooth.* Evaluate and record each of the following characteristics:

1. *Attrition:* O (no attrition) ——— 1 (within enamel) ——— 2 (within the dentin) ——— 3 (reaching primary pulp) ———
2. *Periodontal recession:* 0 (no recession) ——— 1 (just begun) ——— 2 (one-third of root) ——— 3 (two-thirds of root) ———
3. *Secondary dentin:* 0 (none visible) ——— 1 (just begun) ——— 2 (pulp half-filled) ——— 3 (nearly filled) ———
4. *Cementum apposition:* 0 (normal layer) ——— 1 (slightly greater) ——— 2 (great layer) ——— 3 (heavy layer) ———
5. *Root resorption:* 0 (none visible) ——— 1 (small isolated spots) ——— 2 (greater loss of substance) ——— 3 (great areas of both cementum and dentin) ———
6. *Transparency of the root:* 0 (not present) ——— 1 (noticeable) — ——— 2 (apical third of root) ——— 3 (apical two-thirds of the root) ———

E. Sum the points assigned to each of the six characteristics listed under D and use the following table for estimating age:

| Point Values | Age Estimates (years) | Point Values | Age Estimates (years) |
|---|---|---|---|
| 0 | 11 | 8 | 48 |
| 1 | 16 | 9 | 52 |
| 2 | 21 | 10 | 57 |
| 3 | 25 | 11 | 62 |
| 4 | 30 | 12 | 66 |
| 5 | 34 | 13 | 71 |
| 6 | 39 | 14 | 75 |
| 7 | 43 | 15 | 80 |

F. Check your estimate with the actual age of the patient as listed in the original records kept by the instructor.

## PERIOD X

### BONE—GROUND SECTIONS.

Cut from the shaft of a human long bone a disc about $\frac{1}{4}$ inch thick. From this cross- and longitudinal sections should be cut, ground, mounted in balsam and labeled with the essential facts.

Study the transverse section and note:

1. Arrangement of *lamellæ*, resting lines, reversal lines, etc.
2. Distribution of *subperiosteal* and *Haversian system* bone.

An inch wide and page long drawing will be made showing the bone from its surface to the marrow cavity.

In the longitudinal section find Haversian canals cut lengthwise, transversely and in other directions.  Draw one of each.

**Decalcified Bone.**

Examine longitudinal and transverse sections.

1. Note the *bone corpuscles, marrow* and *Haversian canals.*

### ALVEOLAR PROCESS.

Examine under low magnification a labio-lingual ground section of a maxilla and mandible cut through the center of a tooth (Figs. 142 and 143).

1. Are you able to separate histologically the alveolar processes from the body of the jaw bone?  Study the *cortical plate* and make a drawing to show the variations in its subperiosteal and Haversian parts.  Note that the plate is thicker on the lingual than on labial or buccal.

2. Study the *cribriform plate* and make a drawing to show its structural characteristics.  Locate places in the tooth socket which show *bundle bone* and *lamellated bone.*  In which parts of the socket would you expect to find these varieties of bone?  When drawing these it is important to keep in mind their physiological significance.

3. Draw fields through the maxillæ and mandible to show variations between their *cancellous* portions (the spongiosa).

What is the significance of the position of the bone spicules?

### EXPERIMENTAL MATERIAL (RAT)

The white rat is a common and inexpensive laboratory animal which is suitable for the following experiments.

### PERIOD XI

### RATES OF ERUPTION.

1. The rate of eruption in the rat incisor is very readily demonstrated by notching the tooth at the gingival line and noting at intervals of several days the position of the mark.  Keep this animal under observation for several weeks and note the eruption rate about one a week.  In how many days is the mark worn off?

2. The lower incisors of a rat will be cut off at the gingival line.  Check eruption rates of these incisors against normal readings.  Watch the growth and the position taken by the upper incisors.  How do you account for their lingual movement?  Do the teeth elongate?  Why?  Of what clinical significance are these observations?

### PERIOD XII

### VITAL STAINING.

An intraperitoneal injection of a saturated solution (2%) of alizarine Red S at a dosage of 50–100 mg. per kg. produces a sharp red line in the dentin and bone calcifying at the time. This method permits the measurement of the rate of growth of calcifying structures in normal and experimental animals (Plate XX).

1. A young adult white rat injected with alizarine Red S, fourteen and seven days previously will be sacrificed and one of its incisors ground for histological examination. For each injection there is an experimentally accentuated incremental line. In the constantly erupting incisor of the rat such lines are visible in the dentin for about forty days, at which time the tooth has been completely worn off and replaced. Knowing the times of injection, the rate of growth per day may be calculated by measuring the distance between the lines and dividing that figure by the number of days between injections.

2. The above procedure may be repeated using .3 cc. of a 2.5 per cent solution of sodium fluoride. What differences are seen in the fluorine lines as compared to the alizarine lines? Why?

What is mottled enamel and what produces it?

**Vital Staining of Bone.**—A young rat will be injected with alizarine Red S and sacrificed in several days. The skull will be macerated and alizarine will be seen in the bones. More will be found at the alveolar crest than at any other place in the jaw. Why?

## TEXTBOOKS CONSULTED

BLACK, G. V.: Operative Dentistry, Four Volumes, Seventh Edition, The London Medico-Dental Publishing Company, 1936.

CHURCHILL, HERMAN R.: Editor, Meyer's Normal Histology and Histogenesis of the Human Teeth and Associated Parts. Philadelphia, J. B. Lippincott Company, 1935.

EBNER, V.: Histologie der Zähne mit Einschluss der Histogenese, in Handbuch der Zahnheilkunde, ed. by Dr. J. Scheff, 4 Aufl., Wien, Alfred Hölder, 1922.

EIDMANN, H.: Die Entwicklungsgeschicte der Zähne des Menschen, Berlin, Verlag von H. Meusser, 1923.

ERAUSQUIN, JORGE: Histologia Dentaria Humana, Buenos Aires, Progrental, 1953.

GREEP, ROY O.:Histology, New York, The Blakiston Company, Inc., 1954.

HOPEWELL-SMITH, A.: Normal and Pathological Histology of the Mouth, Philadelphia, P. Blakiston's Son & Company, 1918.

KRONFELD, R.:* Dental Histology and Comparative Dental Anatomy, Philadelphia, Lea & Febiger, 1937.

KRONFELD, R., and BOYLE, P. E.: Histopathology of the Teeth and Their Surrounding Structures, Philadelphia, Lea & Febiger, 1949.

LEHNER, J., and PLENK, H.: Die Zähne, in Mollendorff Handbuch der mikroscopischen Anatomie des Menschen, Berlin, Julius Springer, 5, Pt. 3, 449, 1936.

MUMMERY, I. H.: The Microscopic and General Anatomy of the Teeth, Second Edition, Oxford, Milford, 1924.

ORBAN, B.:* Oral Histology and Embryology, 4th ed. St. Louis, C. V. Mosby Co., 1957.

SCHOUR, I.:* The Teeth, in Special Cytology, edited by E. V. Cowdry, Second Edition, New York, Paul B. Hoeber, Inc., 1, Sec. III, 69, 1932.

SICHER, H.:* Oral Anatomy, St. Louis, C. V. Mosby Company, 1952.

SOGNNAES, R. E.: Ch. 19 "Oral Cavity" in *Histology*, Greep, Roy O., New York, The Blakiston Company, Inc., 1954.

TOMES, C. S.:* A Manual of Dental Anatomy, Human and Comparative, Eighth Edition, by H. W. N. Tims and C. B. Henry, London, J. and A. Churchill, 1923.

* Recommended to the student for supplementary reading.

# Index

Important references are indicated by bold-face type.

( 427 )